TRIPLE CONQUEST OF EVEREST, *earth's
mightiest mountain, marked the Society's
75th anniversary in 1963. The National
Geographic-sponsored American Mount Everest
Expedition put three teams on top, pioneered
a West Ridge route, achieved the first traverse
of the summit. Here a support party packs
supplies across the grim face of Lhotse.*

BARRY C. BISHOP, NATIONAL GEOGRAPHIC STAFF

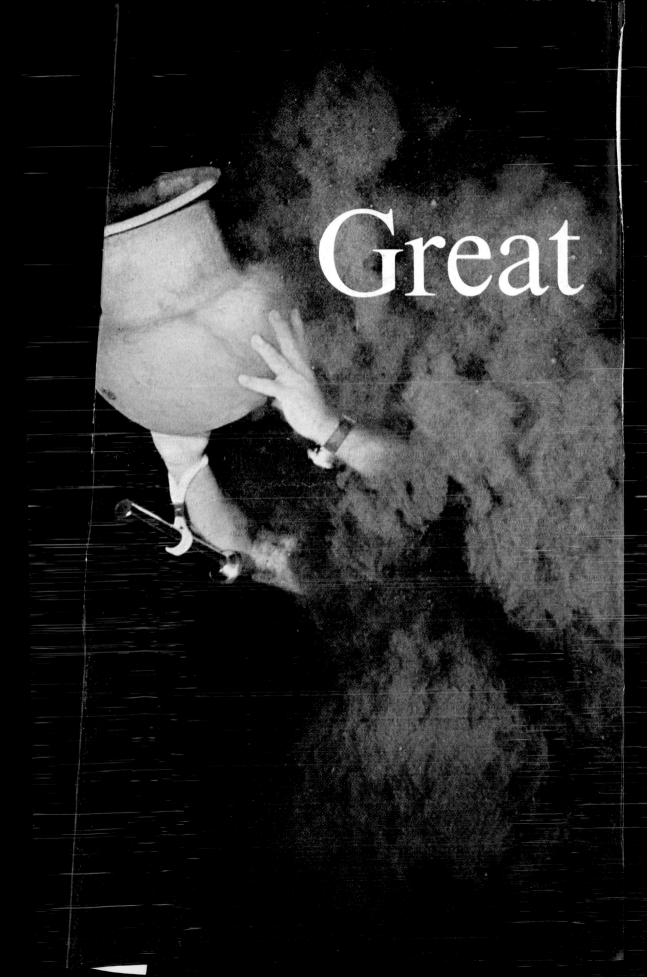

Great

NATIONAL
GEOGRAPHIC
SOCIETY

Great Adven

with

NATIO
GEOGRA

Adventures

with

NATIONAL GEOGRAPHIC

Exploring Land, Sea, and Sky

NATIONAL GEOGRAPHIC SOCIETY
WASHINGTON, D.C.

A volume in the STORY OF MAN LIBRARY, *prepared by* NATIONAL GEOGRAPHIC BOOK SERVICE

583 illustrations
356 in full color, 19 maps

Staff for this book

MELVILLE BELL GROSVENOR
Editor-in-chief

MERLE SEVERY
Editor and Art Director

EDWARDS PARK
Associate Editor

WAYNE BARRETT, JOSEPH A. CALLANAN, JAMES A. COX, SEYMOUR L. FISHBEIN, JOHN J. PUTMAN, *Editor-writers;* ROSS BENNETT, EDWARD C. SHEPHERD *Researcher-writers*

ANNE DIRKES KOBOR
Picture research

JOHN M. LAVERY
Layout and production

WILLIAM W. SMITH, JOE M. BARLETT, *Engravings and printing*

DOROTHY M. CORSON *(Index)*
KARL GUDENBERG *(Maps)*
HOWARD E. PAINE *(Design consultant),* ANDREW POGGENPOHL *(Paintings),* MARY ANNA BROOKE CONSTANCE CALLAWAY, SARA LOUISE DANIS, JOYCE A. McKEAN JUDITH S. STARK *(Assistants)*

Composed by National Geographic's Phototypographic Division
HERMAN J.A.C. ARENS, *Director*
ROBERT C. ELLIS, JR., *Manager*
Printed, bound by R. R. Donnelley and Sons Co., Chicago
First printing 200,000 copies

NATIONAL GEOGRAPHIC'S BARRY BISHOP (RIGHT) CARRIES THE SOCIETY FLAG TO THE TOP OF "UNCLIMBABLE" AMA DABLAM, PRELUDE TO HIS EVEREST TRIUMPH; WALTER ROMANES
OVERLEAF: FROM THE DEPTHS OF A CENOTE AT DZIBILCHALTUN, IN YUCATÁN, AN EXPEDITION DIVER BRINGS UP AN ANCIENT MAYA JAR; LUIS MARDEN, NATIONAL GEOGRAPHIC STAFF

Introduction

By MELVILLE BELL GROSVENOR
President and Editor
National Geographic Society

"THEY'VE MADE IT! They're atop Everest!" The news came to Society headquarters from halfway around the globe, and I couldn't suppress a shout: "Wonderful, just wonderful!"

Like millions throughout the world, I had followed each step of the American Mount Everest Expedition as it tackled mountaineering's greatest challenge. Like all Americans, I was thrilled that Old Glory waved from earth's summit.

But the triumph held special significance for me—the National Geographic Society was the principal sponsor for this 1963 expedition. And when our own staff man Barry Bishop unfurled National Geographic's blue, brown, and green banner beside our nation's flag atop Everest, it seemed a fitting capstone to all the great adventures that have marked the Society's 75 years of exploring land, sea, and sky.

Yet adventure is only part of the Everest story. This was a scientific quest for secrets of glaciers, climate, and the effects of high altitude on men—secrets that can be explored only on the frigid reaches of earth's highest peaks.

Great scientists, great explorers—such were the imaginative men who created the National Geographic Society. John Wesley Powell had explored the raging Colorado River through the Grand Canyon. Adolphus W. Greely had led a polar expedition that set a record for "Farthest North"—83° 24'. George Kennan had crossed Arctic Siberia by dog sled.

These and 30 other men of action and of science met in the Cosmos Club in Washington, D. C., on the evening of January 13, 1888, to consider "the advisability of organizing a society for the increase and diffusion of geographical knowledge." Though the night was chill and foggy, the project kindled warm enthusiasm.

The Society was born, and its first President, Gardiner Greene Hubbard, my great-grandfather, grasped the magnitude of the challenge as they embarked "on the great ocean of discovery."

Two years later the Society's first expedition set out for the unknown—the Mount St. Elias region in Alaska. The explorer-scientists mapped 600 square miles of wilderness, discovered 19,850-foot Mount Logan, North America's second highest peak, and reported their findings in the Society's studious little journal.

The transformation of that journal with its terra-cotta cover into today's brilliantly illustrated *National Geographic* was no dramatic caterpillar-to-butterfly change. Alexander Graham Bell, inventor of the telephone and second President of the Society, envisioned a magazine of broad appeal—geography in human terms—and set about finding an editor. He hired my father, Gilbert H. Grosvenor—and gained a son-in-law in the bargain.

In the 55 years that my father guided and developed the magazine, changing Dr. Bell's "bright vision into fact," he moved with the tide of exploration that swept into earth's farthest corners.

In 1906 President Theodore Roosevelt awarded the National Geographic Society's first Hubbard Medal to a stubborn, red-headed naval officer for reaching a new "Farthest North"—87° 06'. And when this explorer, Robert E. Peary, set out two years later for his cruel trek over the ice to the North Pole—a feat never accomplished before, or since—his expedition went with a supporting grant, the largest our Society had made to that time.

I recall first seeing Peary (and learning that his name was pronounced "Peer-y") when he was a luncheon guest at my father's house. Just 11, I was allowed to peep through the curtains at the distinguished guests. And, as boys will, I found myself looking instead at the ice cream being served. Suddenly, Admiral Peary

Meeting in Washington, D. C. — the 33 eminent men

RESPONDING to an invitation to organize "a society for the increase and diffusion of geographical knowledge," the men gathered at the Cosmos Club on January 13, 1888. Within its first year, the Society gave birth to the *National Geographic Magazine*. Artist Stanley Meltzoff based his depiction of the historic meeting on individual photographs.

Key identifies: (1) Charles J. Bell, banker; (2) Israel C. Russell, geologist; (3) Commodore George W. Melville; (4) Frank Baker, anatomist; (5) W. B. Powell, educator; (6) Brig. Gen. A. W. Greely, polar explorer; (7) Grove Karl Gilbert, geologist and a future Society President; (8) John Wesley Powell, geologist, explorer of the Colorado River; (9) Gardiner Greene Hubbard, lawyer and first President of the Society, who helped finance the telephone experiments of

who founded the National Geographic Society

Alexander Graham Bell; (10) Henry Gannett, geographer and a future Society President; (11) William H. Dall, naturalist; (12) Edward E. Hayden, meteorologist; (13) Herbert G. Ogden, topographer; (14) Arthur P. Davis, engineer; (15) Gilbert Thompson, topographer; (16) Marcus Baker, cartographer; (17) George Kennan, explorer of Arctic Siberia; (18) James Howard Gore, educator; (19) O. H. Tittmann, geodesist and a future Society President; (20) Henry W. Henshaw, naturalist; (21) George Brown Goode, naturalist; (22) Cleveland Abbe, meteorologist; (23) Comdr. John R. Bartlett; (24) Henry Mitchell, engineer; (25) Robert Muldrow II, geologist; (26) Comdr. Winfield S. Schley; (27) Capt. C. E. Dutton; (28) W. D. Johnson, topographer; (29) James C. Welling, educator; (30) C. Hart Merriam, Chief, U. S. Biological Survey; (31) Capt. Rogers Birnie, Jr.; (32) A. H. Thompson, geographer; (33) Samuel S. Gannett, geographer,

7

noticed me and called me in, insisting that I share the dessert. He presented me to Roald Amundsen – Mr. North Pole introduced me to Mr. South Pole!

Ever since, I've always thought that if it took a great man to reach the North Pole, it also took a good one to see that a youngster got a serving of ice cream.

As I helped shape this book, and later read the proofs, scores of such memories flooded back. I remember the day a young naval officer – straight as a jack staff, handsome, forthright – called at National Geographic headquarters. My father and his associate editor, John Oliver La Gorce – "Uncle Jack" to me until I joined the staff – were not free at the moment. I was asked to welcome the officer.

His name was Richard E. Byrd, and he had come to win backing in a new kind of exploration: by airplane over the frozen Arctic. A bold idea, but sound; and Byrd's enthusiasm captured us all. We backed him. And today we honor him as "Admiral of the Ends of the Earth," conqueror of both Poles by air, guiding genius of seven assaults on Antarctica.

Those early days of flight were glorious days! We knew the Wright brothers, the Lindberghs, Amelia Earhart. I remember the thrill of gazing up at the majestic silver *Shenandoah* as she soared over the nation's capital on her record-breaking transcontinental flight. I rode dirigibles myself, to take, with bulky Finlay process plates, the first successful natural color photographs from the air.

Among our treasured mementos is the Society flag that balloonists Stevens and Anderson carried to the stratosphere in 1935; the tiny National Geographic flag that Astronaut John Glenn sent me with a note informing me it had orbited the earth with him in 1962 – and now the very flag that Barry Bishop carried to the top of Everest (page 334).

What travels the National Geographic flag has had since my mother, Elsie May Bell Grosvenor, designed it just after the turn of the century!

William Beebe took it to the depths of the ocean in his bathysphere; Robert Griggs flew it amid the fumeroles in the Valley of Ten Thousand Smokes in Alaska;

AMERICA'S FIRST SPACEMAN, ALAN B. SHEPARD, JR., STRIDES TO ADVENTURE AT CAPE CANAVERAL, FLORIDA, MAY 5, 1961. NATIONAL GEOGRAPHIC HAS CHRONICLED THE PROGRESS OF FLIGHT IN MORE THAN 150 ARTICLES. WILLIAM TAUB, NASA

Joseph Rock carried it into the mystery mountains of western China.

When Rock returned to Society headquarters, he brought a Nashi tribesman who had served on the expedition. We projected motion pictures of Rock's journey and there were scenes of the guide's family. With a cry of joy, the tribesman dashed to the screen and covered it with kisses! This moment often comes to mind when I witness spontaneous and warmhearted gestures among the many peoples I meet as I travel this fascinating globe.

I remember another explorer who came into the Society's offices, like Byrd, seeking support. He was a little-known Frenchman named Jacques-Yves Cousteau, co-inventor of a device he called the Aqua-Lung. His descriptions of the new "silent world" beneath the sea so excited the Society's Research Committee that we immediately agreed to back his work. We were his first United States sponsors; we continue to participate in his revolutionary underwater research.

How typical of this explorer who has risked his life so often for science to remark when studying a bold new device: "I think it will work and perhaps bring valuable information, but will it be fun?"

CREATING THIS BOOK has been both exciting and fun. I'm sure you will find it exciting and fun too. When we first considered publishing a book to mark the Society's diamond jubilee, we wondered what kind of a book it should be.

I asked, "What more precious gift can we share than the great adventures that have thrilled *National Geographic* readers over the past 75 years?" Not a book about explorers, but a book *by* explorers — narratives in their own words, illustrated by photographs they took.

Here is a book spanning the great age of exploration from Peary to John Glenn. A book to stir warm memories in old friends, to answer the requests of newer members who want to learn more about the epic deeds of an earlier day.

How wonderful, I thought, if our younger readers could climb the Andes to discover an Inca city with Hiram Bingham; fly halfway around the world in an open

DR. GROSVENOR SURVEYS RUINED ANGKOR WAT, CAMBODIA, ATOP ITS HIGHEST TOWER; W. ROBERT MOORE, NATIONAL GEOGRAPHIC STAFF

cockpit with Ross Smith; explore Brazil's River of Doubt in a dugout with Theodore Roosevelt; face bandits in the Gobi with Roy Chapman Andrews. Here are adventures too thrilling — achievements too important — to be forgotten.

But what a task of selection! The 200 and more expeditions of the Society present a monumental chronicle of exploration. Each issue of *National Geographic* — and there are more than 800 — is packed with memorable stories. Lecture transcripts preserve the words great explorers spoke before Washington members.

From this vast treasure, gifted editor Merle Severy and his expert Book Service staff have distilled the essence of adventure. From more than 75,000 photographs published in the *Geographic*, and thousands preserved in our archives, we have gleaned the greatest. New paintings capture the drama of unphotographed moments. Maps by the Society's cartographers show routes to discovery.

Our safari is ready. Let's begin *Great Adventures with National Geographic.*

Melville Bell Grosvenor

CONTENTS

EXPLORING LANDS OF EXOTIC LIFE

SCOUTING THE WILD SKY

NATIONAL GEOGRAPHIC EXPEDITION LEADER E. THOMAS GILLIARD
ENCOUNTERED THIS ARAWE WARRIOR ON NEW BRITAIN

"X" MARKS THE SPOT *that Peary (below) called "the object of my every effort." In 1909 he sledged to it in 37 days; 44 years later National Geographic President Gilbert Grosvenor flew over Peary's route in 3½ hours, dropped a Society flag, and made this photograph, first to pinpoint the North Pole.*

Conquering the Polar Frontiers

"AMERICA REFUSES to be left in the rear. Already her explorers are in every land and on every sea. Already she has contributed her quota of martyrs in the frozen north. . . ." The frozen north! In his very first address to the infant National Geographic Society in 1888, President Gardiner Greene Hubbard stirred a 300-year-old dream and a grim memory of what men had already paid in the attempt to fulfill it. The memory was especially vivid to one of Hubbard's Vice Presidents, Brig. Gen. Adolphus W. Greely.

Six years earlier, Greely had pushed his American expedition farther north than man had ever before ventured. But his trail was harsh. Sixteen men starved, one drowned, one was shot for stealing food. Greely and six others were more dead than alive when a search party found them.

And so America's "quota of martyrs" joined the ranks of Scandinavian, Dutch, Russian, and British explorers who had perished in the Arctic. But that spot of 90° latitude known as the North Pole remained a taunt and a challenge as the 19th century drew to a close. The growing Society watched the onslaughts upon it and logged their progress.

In 1893 Norway's Fridtjof Nansen steered his little *Fram* northward. Three

ANTARCTIC PIONEER *Shackleton (with Gilbert Grosvenor at left) was awarded the National Geographic Society's coveted Hubbard Medal for his 1909 push to within 111 miles of the South Pole.*

Scott's doomed party (below) made it to the Pole in January, 1912. Too late: A month before, Amundsen (right) had claimed it. He was given the Society's Gold Medal by Peary.

PAUL POPPER, LTD.

years later he staggered back to civilization – a "weird figure... with straggling hair and beard and garments covered with grease and blood," reported *National Geographic*. He had sledged to 86° 14' – closest yet.

Then came Robert E. Peary. The Society had invited him to lecture when it was but a few months old, had voted $400 to help bring him home from Greenland in 1896, and in 1906 struck the first Hubbard Medal to honor him for his new "Farthest North" – 87° 06'. Accepting the award from President Theodore Roosevelt, Peary spoke of "the final and complete solution of the Polar mystery ... the thing that I must do." In 1909 he did it.

Now the South Pole beckoned with new urgency. Already Britain's Robert Falcon Scott had led an expedition to within 534 miles of that magic point in the bitter heart of Antarctica. Already Ernest H. Shackleton had toiled to within 111 miles; until, as he said in *National Geographic*, "there was no food remaining. . . . The entire party was prostrated by dysentery."

In 1911 a desperate race began. Scott and Roald Amundsen, conqueror of the Northwest Passage, both headed for Antarctica. Amundsen landed at the Bay of Whales and sledged straight south. On December 14 he won the Pole.

13

SUN COMPASS *guided Byrd to both Poles. Its inventor, Albert H. Bumstead, the Society's first Chief Cartographer, presents it on the eve of Byrd's first Arctic flights in 1925.*

U. S. NAVY PLANE *makes first South Pole landing in 1956, 21 years after Lincoln Ellsworth (left) flew across Antarctica. The Society backed his explorations.*

Scott fought across 900 miles of white hell—to find the Norwegian's flag fluttering over his goal. "Great God!" he wrote in his diary. "This is an awful place and terrible enough for us to have laboured to it without the reward of priority." Starvation stalked the return. Only 11 miles from a supply cache Scott penciled his last entry. "We are getting weaker ... the end cannot be far." Months later his body was found. "Had we lived," his diary read, "I should have had a tale to tell of the hardihood, endurance, and courage of my companions which would have stirred the heart of every Englishman."

"The dog sledge must give way to aircraft; the old school has passed." Lt. Comdr. Richard E. Byrd, fresh from his flight over the North Pole, spoke those words to a National Geographic audience in 1926. He then proceeded to prove his point at the other end of the earth, winging over the South Pole in 1929.

Byrd's vision was uncanny. In the mid-20's he predicted that "within thirty years ... regular flights will be made over the Polar Regions." This dream moved a step closer to reality in 1935 when Lincoln Ellsworth piloted his single-engine *Polar Star* across Antarctica, a feat that won him the Society's Hubbard Medal. In 1957, when Byrd was Officer in Charge of United States Antarctic Programs,

SCIENTIFIC EXPLORER *bites a core from*
Antarctica's frigid heart. Dust and pollen
locked in ice tell secrets of past weather.
From the dog sled era to the Atomic Age,
National Geographic *has brought to the world*
the great adventures of Antarctic exploration.

"ADMIRAL OF THE ENDS OF THE EARTH,"
Richard Evelyn Byrd receives the National
Geographic Society's Special Medal of Honor from
President Herbert Hoover in 1930 for "distinguished
contributions to knowledge of Antarctica."

he saw airplanes establish and regularly supply the first scientific station at
the South Pole. Scientific leader of that station through the long polar night
was Paul A. Siple, who had first come to the ice-mantled continent with Byrd as
the representative of America's Boy Scouts. On January 19, 1958, the men of
the South Pole station welcomed Sir Vivian Fuchs on his historic mechanized
trek from sea to sea across Antarctica.

Fourteen months later the nuclear submarine *Skate* surfaced at the North
Pole, heralding a new mode of Arctic exploration. Fifty years before, an arm-
chair adviser suggested that Peary try a submarine. "He did not explain how
we were to get up through the ice after we had traveled to the Pole beneath it,"
observed Peary. But *Skate* got up, piercing a "skylight" in a lead. Comdr. James
F. Calvert and his crew became the first men since Peary to stand at the Pole.
It was, he told *Geographic* readers, "a wild and forbidding scene."

What drove Greely, Nansen, Amundsen, Scott, Byrd, and others of this proud
band? Perhaps Peary said it best at a National Geographic Society banquet:
"The true explorer does his work not for any hope of rewards or honor, but
because the thing he has set himself to do is a part of his very being."

15

Dash to the Pole

Robert E. Peary capped centuries of dreams in 1909
when he became the first man to reach the top of the world.
This is his own story of bitter hardship and final triumph.

THE STEAMER *Roosevelt* rounded the northeastern tip of Ellesmere Island in early September, 1908 — two months after her departure from New York. She had paused in the Cape York area of Greenland to pick up supplies and recruits for the North Polar Expedition.

With expedition members and Eskimo families packed aboard, and 246 howling dogs on her deck, the little black ship had fought through the ice and fog of Robeson Channel. Twice she had been forced aground by heavy ice. Her port rail had been smashed, a bulwark stove in. But now we were in a patch of open water slightly beyond Cape Sheridan.

I put the *Roosevelt* into an opening in the ice and made her snug for the winter in shoal water. We rushed to unload her, sledding supplies to shore and building a village of packing boxes, each house covered with sails and fitted with a stove.

As winter neared we began transporting supplies to Cape Columbia, farthest north point of Ellesmere Island and jumping-off place for the spring sledge journey toward the Pole. Ross G. Marvin, my secretary and assistant, set off first with two men who were new to the Far North — Dr. J. W. Goodsell, expedition surgeon, and George Borup, a recent graduate of Yale where he was prominent in athletics. They took a party of Eskimos, 16 sledges of supplies, and about 200 dogs. "Captain Bob" Bartlett, master of the *Roosevelt*, soon followed. Matthew A. Henson, my

CONQUERING OPEN LEAD AND PRESSURE RIDGE, PEARY PRESSES ON TO HIS PRIZE — THE NORTH POLE. PAINTING BY TOM LOVELL FOR TRUE MAGAZINE

Negro assistant who has been with me since 1887, led a hunting party to find meat. Donald B. MacMillan, who had left an instructor's job at Worcester Academy in Massachusetts to join me, had the grippe but went to Cape Columbia in November to make tidal observations.

Hunting and scientific work continued through the December and January moons. On February 15 Bartlett left once more for Cape Columbia. Goodsell, Borup, MacMillan, and Henson followed on successive days with their sledge divisions. Then Marvin and I left. By February 27 all necessary supplies had been brought to Cape Columbia, the dogs rested and double-rationed, the sledges overhauled. The final work was to begin.

On February 28 Bartlett and Borup, with six Eskimos and seven sledges, got away due north. After four months of northerly winds I expected a great deal of rough ice, and I was prepared to hew a trail for the first hundred miles or so. Bartlett was to pioneer the road, keeping a day ahead of the main party. Borup was to serve as Bartlett's support for three marches, then cache his loads, hurry back to Cape Columbia in one march, reload, and overtake the main party.

On March 1 the main party set out on Bartlett's trail, my division in the rear. In an hour I crossed the glacial fringe. At last all 7 expedition members, 17 Eskimos, 133 dogs, and 19 sledges were on the ice of the Arctic Ocean. Due north—413 nautical miles—lay the Pole.

RAMMING AND BLASTING *through the ice, the 186-foot* Roosevelt *bore Peary as far north as he could get by ship—Cape Sheridan—then was frozen in for the winter (top). Crammed with sled dogs, walrus blubber, and 70 tons of whale meat, the ship wore a "choking stench" that skipper Bartlett never forgot.*

PEARY'S HISTORIC PHOTOGRAPHS, SOME PUBLISHED HERE FOR THE FIRST TIME, WERE PRESENTED TO THE NATIONAL GEOGRAPHIC SOCIETY BY HIS WIDOW, JOSEPHINE D. PEARY.

FROM AN IGLOO CAMP *at Cape Columbia which Peary named Crane City (left), the route to the Pole lay across 413 miles of white hell. Peary's plan: "Work the supporting parties to the limit," then send them back with the weakest dogs and sledges as supplies dwindle.*

From latitude 87° 48', with Henson, four Eskimos, and 40 iron-hard huskies, Peary made his sprint to the Pole. Thus he climaxed a trek covering 4,500 miles since the party left New York the year before with a "Godspeed" from President Theodore Roosevelt.

On the way north, Peary's ship Roosevelt *called at Cape York, now a landmark for Thule Air Force Base. Northeastward, under the icecap so hostile to Arctic explorers, lies the U. S. Army's Camp Century, world's first nuclear-powered community. On Ellesmere, weathermen keep vigil at stations Alert and Eureka.*

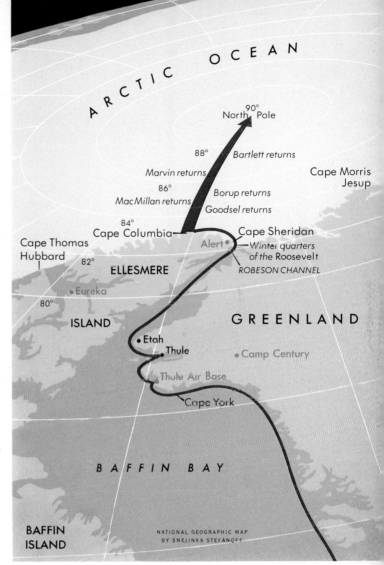

NATIONAL GEOGRAPHIC MAP
BY SNEJINKA STEFANOFF

A strong easterly wind whistled wildly about us, but we were all in new and perfectly dry fur clothes and could bid defiance to it. The ice was very rough and two sledges were smashed beyond repair.

We camped ten miles out, using igloos that Bartlett and Borup had built, and building more ourselves. The temperature was so low that the alcohol in Henson's stove failed to vaporize. It could not be lit until we dropped in lighted paper to warm the fuel.

On our second march we saw a dark cloud on the northern horizon and knew it meant open water. Fog always forms near a lead. Sure enough, I soon sighted black spots in the distance — my divisions held up by a lane of open water about a quarter mile wide. The wind had wrenched the floes apart after Bartlett passed.

We camped beside the lead, and before daylight heard the ice grind together. Hurrying across, we picked up Bartlett's trail which the shifting ice had moved about a mile and a half. We saw by the tracks that Borup had started back as planned, but missed his way owing to this same faulting of the trail. I sent Marvin back, too, for more fuel. The wind continued. Leads formed all about us.

At the end of the fourth march we came upon Bartlett. He had been stopped by

BORUP

BARTLETT

PEARY

MACMILLAN

MARVIN

Peary's men of iron

THE ARCTIC *"brings a man face to face with himself,"* said Peary. *"If he is a man, the man comes out; and if he is a cur, the cur shows as quickly."* Peary had all Spartans.

Capt. Bob Bartlett, *"true as the compass,"* won the National Geographic Society's Hubbard Medal for reaching nearly 88°. He sailed back to the Arctic many times. Matthew Henson, who stood with Peary at the Pole, had been at his side on six earlier expeditions. Ross Marvin of Cornell had joined Peary in 1906. His death was *"a bitter flavor in the cup of our success."*

Dr. Goodsell, Donald MacMillan, and young George Borup were Peary's Arctic tenderfeet. After 1909, MacMillan returned north again and again; in 1925 he led a National Geographic expedition. His friend Borup drowned, ironically, while canoeing in Connecticut in 1912.

a wide lake of open water extending east and west as far as we could see. There was nothing for it but to camp and wait for the ice to close.

At noon of March 5 the red sun, shaped like a football by refraction, raised itself just above the horizon for a few minutes and then disappeared. It was the first time I had seen it since October 1.

My pleasure in this and the fine weather, with temperatures ranging from 5° to 32° below zero F., was mitigated by growing anxiety over Marvin and Borup. Day after day went by and they failed to show up with their indispensable cargo of fuel.

On March 11, after a week's delay, the big lead finally closed. Leaving a note for Marvin and Borup to push along after us by forced marches, we proceeded north. During this day's march, an easy one, we crossed the 84th parallel and traversed many leads on newly formed ice.

On the 14th we got free of these leads at last and came on decent going in distinctly crisp weather: 59° below. While we were making camp, one of Borup's Eskimos arrived with a note from Marvin. He and

GOODSELL

HENSON

Borup were coming fast and would catch us the next day.

The following morning I sent Henson with his division to pioneer a trail for five marches. Goodsell, according to the program, started back for good. His place was at the ship. That night Marvin and Borup came spinning in, their men and dogs steaming in the bitter air like a squadron of battleships. Many times before I had been glad to see Ross Marvin, never more so than this time. His arrival relieved me of all anxiety as to our fuel supply.

THEN I DISCOVERED that MacMillan had a badly frostbitten foot. The mishap had occurred two or three days before, and MacMillan, typically, had said nothing in the hope that it would somehow come out all right. The only thing to do was send him back at once. The arrival of Marvin and Borup allowed me to spare enough Eskimos and dogs to go with him.

I was disappointed to lose MacMillan. He had driven a sledge all the way from Cape Columbia. Added to his enthusiasm, he had the powers and physique of a trained athlete, and I had been sure he could make at least the 86th parallel. But now there was no alternative.

We weeded out badly damaged sledges and unfit dogs, brought the loads up to standard, and set out with 16 men, 14 sledges, and 100 dogs.

Using one of the two wooden reels fitted with piano wire and a 14-pound lead weight, Marvin got a sounding of 825 fathoms. This substantiated my belief that we had crossed the continental shelf.

Late that afternoon we heard and felt pronounced movements in the ice, and soon an active lead cut across our path. We found some large floating ice cakes and got across by bridging them. As Borup was jumping his dogs from one piece to another, the animals slipped and took a bath. Borup leapt forward, checked the sledge so that it would not follow the dogs into the water with its 500-pound load of precious supplies, and hauled his team out. We heaved a sigh of relief.

At the end of two short marches we came up with Henson's division in camp mending sledges. We followed suit, breaking up damaged ones for material. I put

BARTLETT AND ESKIMOS *rest after an Ellesmere*

Marvin in the lead on March 19 with instructions to make two forced marches to bring up our average. He gave us a good 17 miles, thanks to level going.

At the end of the next march at latitude 85° 23', Borup turned back with his division, his job done. I was sorry to lose him. Young and plucky, he had taken a heavy sledge over the floes in a way that commanded everyone's admiration and would have made his father's eyes glisten. But he lacked experience, and like MacMillan, had frosted one of his heels.

We were left with 12 men, 10 sledges,

Island hunt. The explorers discarded heavy tents on the polar drive, built igloos instead.

and 70 dogs. I put Bartlett ahead to pioneer, sending Henson with him.

Daylight was now continuous, so I made a change in the schedule. Bartlett and Henson would make their march and turn in. Marvin and I would follow 12 hours later. When we caught up, the pioneers would break camp and start again. This contact between the two parties every 24 hours reduced the likelihood of their being separated by leads.

The going gradually improved, and we covered good distances. When a lead delayed us, we ferried across on ice cakes.

On March 25 Bartlett let himself out as though trying for a record, and reeled off a plump 20 miles. After this march Marvin got a good sight on the low sun that gave our position as 86° 38'. We had covered 59 minutes of latitude in three marches. Here I sent Marvin back. My last words to him were: "Be careful of the leads, my boy." So we shook hands and parted.

I continued with eight men, seven sledges, and 60 dogs. There seemed to be an unbroken expanse of level ice in every direction, but I was not deceived by the favorable outlook. Good conditions never continue for any distance or last any length of time in the Arctic.

Speeding north, we struck for the first time the hazy atmosphere that frequently occurs over ice fields. The light was equal everywhere. All relief was destroyed, and it was impossible for us to see very far. This melancholy light on the day of parting from Marvin gave me an indescribably uneasy feeling. Yet the trail was straight and level, except for one deflection around an open lead.

Next day, March 27, we met heavy, deep snow — a smothering mantle lying in the depressions of rubble ice. I came upon Bartlett and his party, fagged out and temporarily discouraged by the heart-racking work of making a road. I knew what the matter was — they were simply spoiled by the good going we had been enjoying. I rallied them a bit, lightened their sledges, and sent them on.

During the next march we fought a biting wind from the northeast and came upon Bartlett camped beside an open lead with water in three directions. We built our igloos 100 yards away so we would not wake him.

I was dropping off to sleep on my bed of deerskins when a movement of the ice and a shout brought me to my feet. Through the peephole of the igloo I saw a rapidly widening strip of black water between our igloos and Bartlett's. One of my dog teams had barely escaped being dragged in; another had just avoided being crushed by the ice blocks that were jamming up over them. Bartlett's igloo

"**HUK! HUK!**" *Hoarse shouts and cracking whips urge dogs over a chaos of ridged sea ice.*

was drifting east on an ice raft. Kicking out my door, I called to the captain's men to get ready for a quick dash.

At last their ice sheet crunched against ours, and we got Bartlett's party onto the floe with us. For the rest of the night and during the next day the ice suffered torments of the damned, surging together, opening out, groaning and grinding while the open water belched its dark mist like a prairie fire. Then the motion ceased, the open water closed, the atmosphere to the north cleared, and we hurried on before the lead should open again.

A day later Bartlett made his last run. He let himself out as we crossed a series of large old floes covered with hard snow, and he set such a fast pace that if I stopped for an instant I had to jump on a sledge or run to catch up. During the last few miles I walked beside him. He was very solemn and anxious to go farther, but the program was for him to turn back from here. There were no supplies for an addition to the final party.

We met a high wind that day, dead in our faces, bitter and insistent. I had no reason to complain; it was better than an easterly or southerly wind, which would have opened new leads. This was closing them behind us. Yet it was also pressing southward the ice over which we were traveling, and so robbing us of mileage.

We concluded we were on or near the 88th parallel when we made camp. In the morning Bartlett walked five or six miles to the north to make sure of reaching the 88th. But when he took an observation

Scaling ramparts, men heave at the sledges until muscles seem to tear loose.   27

PEARY'S TECHNIQUE: *Live like the Eskimos. Main party builds two igloos, uses two left by the pioneer division, off on another 12-hour trailblazing stint. At mealtime Eskimos slice off a "bite" with knives. Men eat ship's biscuit and fresh meat or pemmican, made of dried meat and suet; dogs eat pemmican. If necessary, both men and dogs eat dog.*

Arctic ingenuity (below) makes one good sledge of two wrecks. These Peary sledges, 12 to 13 feet long, could haul up to 1,200 pounds on level stretches and outlast shorter Eskimo vehicles.

after returning he found we were at 87° 48'. The continuous north wind had cheated Bartlett of his goal.

I felt keen regret as Bartlett's broad shoulders grew smaller in the distance and then disappeared from view on the southbound trail. Bartlett is just Bartlett —tireless, sleepless, enthusiastic, whether on the bridge of his ship, or in the crow's nest, or at the head of a sledge division. He had been invaluable to me. Circumstances had thrust the brunt of pioneering upon him instead of dividing it among several as I had planned. And he had cheerfully stood between me and many trifling annoyances during the course of the expedition. For these reasons I had given him the post of honor in command of my fourth and last supporting party.

Now was no time for reverie. I turned to the problem for which I had conserved my energy on the upward trip, trained myself as for a race, lived the simple life—for which I had worked for 23 of my 52 years. In spite of my age I felt fit for the demands of the coming days, eager to be on the trail. My five remaining men were as responsive to my will as the fingers of my right hand.

Henson, with his years of experience, was almost as skillful at handling dogs and sledges as the Eskimos themselves. He and Ootah had stood with me at my farthest north, three years before. Two other Eskimos, Egingwah and Seegloo, had been with that expedition and were willing to go anywhere with me.

The fourth Eskimo, young Ooqueah, had never before served in an expedition. Yet he was, if possible, even more eager than the others because of the gifts I had promised to those Eskimos who reached the Pole with me—boat, rifle, shotgun, ammunition, knives. Such riches would enable him to wrest from a stubborn father the girl whose image stirred his hot young heart.

My 40 remaining dogs were the pick of the 133 which had left Cape Columbia. Almost all were powerful males, hard as iron, in good spirits. My last five sledges, fully repaired, were ready to go. I had supplies for 40 days. By eating the dogs themselves, we could last 50.

Pacing back and forth beside the igloos, I settled on my program. We were now 133 nautical miles from the Pole. I decided to strain every nerve and sinew to make five marches of 25 miles each, crowding them in such a way that the fifth march would end long enough before noon to allow an observation for latitude.

Weather and leads permitting, I believed I could do this. If my proposed distances were cut down, I could either make the last march a forced one, stopping only to brew tea, or at the end of the fifth march I could continue with a single light sledge and one or two of the party, leaving the rest in camp. Underlying all calculations was the knowledge that a 24-hour gale would open leads, knock my plans into a cocked hat, and put us all in peril.

I hit the trail a little past midnight on April 2, leaving the others to break camp and follow. As I climbed the pressure ridge back of our igloos I set another hole in my belt, the third since I started. Every man of us was lean and flat-bellied as a board, and as hard.

It was a fine morning. The wind had subsided and the going was the best I had hit—large, clear floes surrounded by stupendous pressure ridges, all of which were easily negotiated. In a few hours the others caught up with me.

The years seemed to drop from me, and I felt as I had when I led my party across the great Greenland icecap, leaving 20, 25 miles behind my snowshoes day after day, sometimes stretching it to 30 or 40.

Remembering, I set a good pace for about ten hours. A short sleep, and we were off again. The going was practically horizontal, and we could travel as long as we pleased. The weather remained fine. At the end of ten hours we were halfway to the 89th parallel.

Again, a few hours' sleep. We hit the trail before midnight. The weather and going were even better. We marched something over ten hours, the dogs often on the trot. Once we rushed across a frozen lead 100 yards wide which buckled under our sledges and broke as the last sledge left it. We stopped near the 89th parallel, in temperature of 40° below.

Scant sleep, and on our way once more. We ran on smooth young ice, and the dogs sometimes broke into a gallop. Bitter air, keen as frozen steel, burned our faces until they cracked. Even the Eskimos

complained. We needed more sleep this time, and took it. Then on again. Up to now our fears of an impossible lead had increased. At every rise I had found myself hurrying forward breathlessly, fearing it would mark a lead. At the summit I would catch my breath in relief—only to hurry on. Now this fear fell away.

Before turning in after that march, I took an observation which gave our position as 89° 25'. A dense, lifeless pall hung overhead. The horizon was black, the ice beneath a ghastly shell white. I strained my eyes across it, trying to imagine myself already at the Pole.

On the fifth march a rise in temperature to 15° below reduced the friction of the sledges. The dogs seemed to catch our spirit. They tossed their heads and yelped as they ran with tight-curled tails.

I had now made my five marches and on April 6 was in time for a hasty noon observation: 89° 57'. Three nautical miles from the magic 90°. With the Pole practically in sight, I was suddenly too weary to take the last few steps. I turned in for a nap, then pushed on with two Eskimos and a light sledge for another ten miles and made another observation.

I was now beyond the Pole.

"THE POLE AT LAST! The prize of three centuries," I wrote in my diary that day. "I cannot bring myself to realize it. It all seems so simple. . . ."

We spent 30 hours in side trips, taking observations and photographs, planting flags, depositing records. The weather was flawless: minimum temperature 33°

ICE CAKE FERRIES A SLEDGE *across one of Peary's "ever present nightmares," a lead opened by the wind. Biggest of these channels in the ice marked the edge of the continental shelf. To plumb the depths at leads, Peary hauled 103 pounds of reels, piano wire, and weights. When the weights broke off he used pickaxes. Near the Pole he chopped through a crack, let out 9,000 feet of wire without finding bottom. In 1958 the atomic submarine U.S.S. Nautilus found it at 13,410 feet.*

PEARY'S PATCHED FLAG
*documents his epic quest.
Corner pieces, placed at
Cape Morris Jesup in 1900,
were found by MacMillan,
May, 1909, and left there.
Triangle was put in the
ice at 87° 06', April, 1906,
and never found.
Rectangle at left was
planted at Cape Columbia,
June, 1906, and found by
Canadian scientists, 1953.
Piece at top center marked
Cape Thomas Hubbard,
June, 1906; MacMillan
found it in 1914.
The diagonal band that
Peary deposited at the
North Pole has vanished
in the shifting ice.*

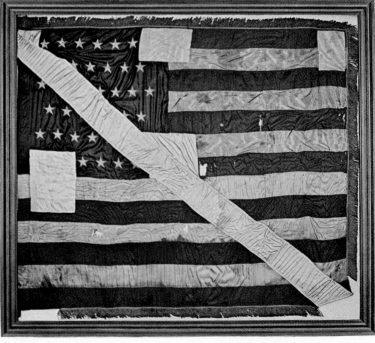

The Pole at last!!! The prize of 3 centuries, my dream & ambition for 23 years. Mine at last. I cannot bring myself to realize it. It all seems so simple & commonplace, as Bartlett said "just like every day".

APRIL 6, 1909: *Words of triumph head a page in Peary's journal. Sun shots showed him only three miles from the Pole. He walked beyond it, returned, posed Ooqueah, Ootah, Henson, Egingwah, and Seegloo before a pressure ridge (left). Next day they headed south. An era had ended.*

Peary's campaign spanned 23 years. Twice he trekked across Greenland, proving it was an island, not a continent leading to the Pole. A broken leg and the loss of eight toes failed to daunt him as he drove on.

Always with him was the "constant aid and inspiration" of his wife Josephine. In 1898 she made him a flag. He carried it wrapped around his body and left fragments at successive objectives. He had deposited five by the time he reached the Pole, and the 45-star flag was "somewhat worn and discolored," he noted. But he cut off a diagonal strip and placed it in a bottle with a note: "90 N. Lat., North Pole, April 6, 1909. I have today hoisted the National Ensign of the United States of America at this place which my observations indicate to be the North Polar axis of the earth...."

In 1954 Mrs. Peary presented the flag to the National Geographic Society where it is on display (left) in the Society's new Explorers Hall on 17th Street in Washington, D. C.

below, maximum 12° below. On the afternoon of April 7 we double-fed the dogs, repaired the sledges for the last time, discarded spare clothing, and started back.

Five miles out a narrow crack offered a chance for a sounding, which had not been feasible at the Pole because of the thick ice. I let out all my remaining wire —1,500 fathoms, which we had saved for "farthest north"—but there was no bottom. Then the wire parted. The reel thus became useless and was thrown away, lightening one sledge by 18 pounds.

Three marches took us to where Bartlett had turned back. Another 13 marches without meeting a single lead that delayed us more than a couple of hours, and on April 23 our sledges reached the glacial fringe a little west of Cape Columbia. When the last sledge was brought up I thought my Eskimos had gone crazy. They yelled and danced themselves helpless. Ootah remarked, "The devil is asleep or having trouble with his wife, or we should never have come back so easily."

NEVER SHALL I FORGET the two days of sleep at Cape Columbia. It was sleep, sleep, then turn over and sleep again. Cold water to a parched throat is nothing compared with sleep to a numbed, fatigued brain and body.

Then for the ship. We reached it in two marches. Bartlett went over the rail and came out along the ice to meet me. There was something in his face.

"Have you heard about Marvin?"

"No," I answered.

Quickly he told me the staggering news. Marvin had drowned in the big lead coming back to Cape Columbia. His Eskimos were too far behind to hear his calls when he broke through. In that water the end must have come quickly.

The rest of the story is speedily told. MacMillan and Borup, off making tidal observations, were informed by courier and returned to the *Roosevelt* in May. On July 18 the ship left her winter berth and began her battle southward. In early September we wired from Labrador: "Stars and Stripes nailed to North Pole."

This was the news that the world had been waiting to hear for 300 years—the discovery of the top of the earth.

Wings Over the Poles

Richard E. Byrd's explorations by air won him two Geographic medals and fame as "Admiral of the Ends of the Earth"

"THAT MOTOR will stop." Floyd Bennett's terse message confirmed my fears. The starboard engine of our Fokker trimotor plane was leaking oil! Calculations put us about an hour from the North Pole. Bennett, at the controls while I navigated, suggested that we set down to fix the leak. But I had seen too many expeditions fail by landing. I decided to press on, with only our remaining engines if necessary.

We had planned this flight the summer before, in 1925, on Donald MacMillan's Arctic expedition sponsored jointly by the National Geographic Society and the U. S. Navy. I had charge of the Navy unit of three amphibians, and we made one of the first aerial explorations of the Arctic,

flying from our base at Etah, Greenland.

This year we had set out to explore toward the Pole, selecting Spitsbergen as our base of operations.

We packed our plane *Josephine Ford* on a steamer and arrived there to find the Amundsen-Ellsworth-Nobile Expedition also preparing for a transpolar flight, in the dirigible *Norge*.

The little harbor at Kings Bay was choked with ice, but skillful handling got us within 300 yards of shore. We propped the awkward plane on planks laid across our whaleboats and ferried it safely to the beach through a lane we had opened among the ice cakes.

Our first attempt to take off for a trial flight ended with a broken ski in a snow-drift. Things looked black, but a repair gang worked all night installing new skis strengthened with old oars. Others bent to the task of leveling the mile-long runway. Then Bennett took the wheel and gave her the gas. She rose gracefully. That two-hour flight showed low gas consumption. We realized that we could probably visit the Pole, 663 nautical miles away, in a nonstop flight.

On May 8 Bennett and I climbed aboard and roared off. We passed the end of the runway at terrific speed and began jolting over snow hummocks. Our load was too great; again we plowed into a snow-drift. Men ran up, weary, heartsick, speechless. Apprehension turned to relief, however, when I waded through the snow

GROUND CREW CHEERS AS BYRD AND BENNETT TAKE OFF FROM SPITSBERGEN FOR THE POLE, MAY 9, 1926; FROM RICHARD E. BYRD

and examined the landing gear. It had withstood the terrible pounding!

We dug the plane out, lightened the load, and lengthened the runway. A few handclasps shortly after midnight and we were off on our great adventure.

Within an hour we passed the glacier-laden land and looked ahead at the ice pack gleaming in the midnight sun. For the first time men could gaze upon its charms and discover its secrets out of reach of those sharp claws.

Perhaps. A forced landing might mean disaster. Up to that time no one had ever navigated an aircraft with accuracy to a distant point in the polar sea. There are no landmarks on the ice, and magnetic and gyroscopic compasses are unreliable at this latitude. Yet we had to hit the Pole, for we could not fly back to Spitsbergen from an unknown position.

So we depended on a sun compass invented for us by Albert H. Bumstead, Chief Cartographer of the National Geographic Society (page 14). The sun's shadow indicates north on this 24-hour clock — the reverse of a sundial.

From time to time I relieved Bennett so he could stretch his legs. I then went back to my incessant navigating. Every hour we were opening 10,000 square miles of unexplored regions.

FIRST TO FLY OVER THE NORTH POLE!

In polar bear trousers Lt. Comdr. Byrd, 37, and (at right) enlisted pilot Floyd Bennett, 35, board their Fokker for the flight that thrilled the world.

At Spitsbergen the plane was rafted into ice-choked Kings Bay (below).

Then, through the cabin window, I saw the oil leak. When I took the wheel again I kept my eyes glued on the oil gauge. No doubt the pressure would drop any moment. But now the prize was actually in sight. We could not turn back.

At 9:02 A.M. Bennett and I looked down on the Pole. The dream of a lifetime had at last been realized. We circled, saluted the gallant spirit of Peary, and verified his report: cakes of ice were jammed together, indicating constant movement and the absence of land.

At 9:15 we streaked for Spitsbergen. To our astonishment that engine never stopped. A rivet had jarred out, and when the oil reached the level of the hole it stopped leaking.

Nearly 16 hours after takeoff we set down at Kings Bay. Our comrades carried us with wild delight down the snow runway they had worked so hard to make.

AND SO AVIATION conquered the Arctic. Now we were set to try for the Antarctic, which in 1928 remained one of the world's great mysteries. Was it a continent? How far did its mountains extend? How thick was its icecap? Did it have coal beds, fossils? What a challenge!

On August 25 the *City of New York*, an aged 512-ton bark with reinforced sides,

Airship Norge *soars over top of the world*

THE FAT *gray dirigible droned steadily over the frozen polar sea. Her radio was dead. Inside the 348-foot* Norge, *16 weary men suddenly stiffened. Bits of ice, falling from guy wires, were being batted into the hull by the propellers!*

On the morning of May 11, 1926, just two days after Byrd flew to the North Pole and back, Pilot Umberto Nobile of the Italian Air Force had nosed the Norge *away from her roofless hangar at Kings Bay, Spitsbergen (above). With him rode South Pole conqueror Roald Amundsen and American explorer Lincoln Ellsworth. Their goal: Nome, Alaska, 3,300 miles away.*

They traced Byrd's route to the Pole and pushed on. Fatigue tightened its grip; ice bullets continued their grim tattoo. "If any punctured the gas chamber there would be hardly a chance of a safe return," Nobile recalled in National Geographic. *Then, after 46 hours: "Land!" They followed the Alaskan coast south. Mountains lunged at them out of the fog. Blown almost to Siberia, they fought back on course.*

"Time and again only a miracle saved us from crashing," reported Nobile. Battling a headwind that nearly stood the Norge *on her nose, he landed safely at Teller, an Eskimo village 60 miles north of Nome. One boy, believing the ship a huge seal, begged his father to shoot it!*

sailed for New Zealand. Dunedin, southern outpost of civilization, was our last chance for preparation; when the winter night set in, the combined merchant marines and navies of the world would not be able to reach us in Antarctica. So planes and yelping dogs and crates of supplies poured aboard – pressing the ship below the load line.

Casting off December 8, we plowed south into gale and snowstorm, dodged icebergs, battled through the ice pack around the Ross Sea. On Christmas Day we were at Ross Ice Shelf, its sheer cliffs towering above our masts. We cruised along it, and on December 28 reached the Bay of Whales. On the ice barrier we put up tents and radio towers. Little America was founded (map, page 52).

For days men and dogs struggled over the bay ice, hauling tons of supplies to the base. When the trail was good and the dogs were in condition, the teams made 30 miles in two round trips a day. But the ice softened, and men and sleds often broke through. Then our dock began to crack up. We shifted position.

When the supply ship *Eleanor Bolling* arrived we tied her up to the barrier with the *New York* lashed outboard. Day and night the unloading went on.

On January 31, I was sitting in my cabin when suddenly I heard a frightful crash. I knew what had happened – the edge of the barrier had broken. I saw the bottom of the reeling *Bolling*. Why she did not capsize I do not know. On her deck rocked a chunk of the barrier.

Men were yelling; one was in the water clinging to an ice cake that spun round and round. He shouted that he could not swim and could barely hold on. I went in after him but found myself almost helpless in the frigid water. Anxious moments passed until he was rescued.

In spite of mishaps we unloaded the

LITTLE AMERICA, *"loneliest city in the world," harbored 42 men and gave wings and wireless to Antarctic exploration. Here money was useless, so the men played "ciggy ante" poker. Byrd won 30,000 bridge points in one night – but the night lasted four months.*

Bolling in five and a half days, and on February 2, 1929, she started back to New Zealand.

We set to work finishing construction. Light, strong, weathertight buildings took shape as headquarters, bunkhouses, mess hall, and machine shop. Walls and roofs were painted orange so they could be seen from planes. Doctor's storeroom, gymnasium, and weather station were carved out of the snow. Gradually Little America became a self-sufficient village, with kerosene and gasoline lamps, coal stoves, water supply, and telephones.

"Anyway," someone remarked, "we won't need a refrigerating system."

Meanwhile the vast unknown areas around Little America awaited aerial exploration. We made the first flights in our Fairchild monoplane. We heated the engine with a torch under a fireproof covering, put warm oil into the tank, turned over the inertia starter, and snapped the ignition. The engine sparked and settled down to a smooth, even roar.

We flew east and discovered mountain peaks running north and south for 30 miles. I named them for John D. Rockefeller, Jr., one of the expedition's backers. Later we sighted mountains beyond this range. I named this land for the person who, as Peary said of his wife, "bears the brunt of all my undertakings" – I called it Marie Byrd Land.

Our first exploring season ended all too quickly. On February 22 we watched the *New York* disappear in the mist. The men joked and horseplayed, tipping one another into the drifts, then turned inland.

W E WERE ALONE in the Antarctic. Beyond the orange shacks, the tall masts, and the spectral shapes of anchored planes were the vast stretches of the barrier. Overwhelming solitude and a terrible stillness brooded over that immobile, frozen scene.

The sun bade us goodbye on April 18, and we became a family of moles scuttling through glistening snow tunnels with lanterns and flashlights. At one o'clock on any morning the man on watch, parka hood over his head, threw more coal in the stove while his shipmates huddled in a row of double wooden bunks, each

TARGET: THE SOUTH POLE! *To reach it and return to Little America, Byrd pinned his hopes on the* Floyd Bennett, *a stripped-down Ford trimotor with a top speed of 122 miles an hour. To pull the load, Byrd replaced one of the three 225-horsepower engines with a Wright Cyclone twice as powerful. The plane spent the Antarctic winter in a canvas-roofed snow pit where mechanics could work on the engines.*

When the sun reappeared in August, men dug the plane out and tuned her up. Into the drafty fuselage went survival gear—tents, sleeping bags, fur clothing, sacks of food, pressure stoves, skis, a light sledge. Photographer McKinley added his heavy mapping camera to be aimed through sleeves in the door windows. Could the plane lift its 15,000-pound burden over a 10,000-foot mountain pass? At 3:29 P.M., November 28, 1929, Byrd and three companions took off to find out.

head drawn inside a sleeping bag. Every half hour the watchman ducked out in the bitter cold and eyed the aurora as it painted freakish, gyrating pictures across a dead sky. He noted clouds, checked each thermometer and thermograph to make sure the cold had not stopped recording mechanisms. At six he made the fire in the kitchen stove.

The clock struck a high-pitched note, for the cold affected the bell, and the watchman signed off by calling Dr. Larry Gould, my second in command. Gould's job was to get everyone up for breakfast.

The men called him Simon Legree, but they appreciated that lying in bed was bad for morale. Our main winter job lay in keeping happy, and the way to keep happy is to keep busy.

After the sun rose in late August we sped preparations for the South Pole flight. Our Ford trimotor was hauled out of the snow. Its center engine roaring, its thick wing rising, the plane soon perched on top like some prehistoric bird of this lost continent. We had named the plane *Floyd Bennett* in memory of my beloved companion in adventure who died four

PARAMOUNT PUBLIX CORP. OPPOSITE: NEW YORK TIMES AND ST. LOUIS POST-DISPATCH

months before we set sail for Antarctica.

Mechanics checked engines, rigged controls, changed gas lines, installed a new gas gauge, altered cowlings, made innumerable adjustments, and jacked the plane up to put on new ski pedestals. It was desperately cold. At times the men could not work with gloves. They smeared their hands with grease; still the metal tools burned and blistered.

Sledge parties were working south, laying food depots to the foot of the Queen Maud Range bordering the polar plateau. Here Gould's geological party would establish their depot. It could serve us in an emergency.

The major purpose of our flight was to make an aerial survey of the lane of vision to the Pole. To make it possible to take Capt. Ashley McKinley and his 100 pounds of camera gear on the nonstop polar flight, we flew to Alex Heiberg Glacier to set up a refueling base for our return from the Pole. This strip of the lane we named Gilbert Grosvenor Trail for the President of the National Geographic Society, which had helped us with financial support and unwavering faith.

Near the glacier we dropped smoke bombs to determine wind direction, landed, deposited fuel and food, took astronomical sightings, then headed back. About 100 miles from Little America, over an area reported to be almost impossible for a landing, all three engines began to sputter, then stopped. We were out of gas.

We bumped hard, rocked along crazily, and came to rest. Chief pilot Bernt Balchen, who had been monitoring the flight, soon flew out with gas, and 36 hours later we managed to get off.

ON THE MORNING of November 28 the geological party flashed a weather report to meteorologist Bill Haines: Conditions over the plateau were favorable. Haines had a tremendous responsibility. "They could be more nearly perfect," he said, "but you had better go now. Another chance may not come."

Balchen, copilot Harold June, McKinley, and I climbed aboard. We took along a stone from Floyd Bennett's grave at Arlington to weight the American flag that we would drop at the Pole. Bennett and I had planned this flight together. Fate had sidetracked him. But he was not forgotten.

As the skis left the snow I saw my shipmates on the ground jumping, shouting, throwing their hats in the air, wild with joy that we were off for the Pole.

We circled, emerged from clouds into sunshine, and picked up the faint thread of the dog team trail. We passed over our snowmobile, abandoned wreck of the experiment of using automotive transportation in Antarctica. Snow-covered peaks 100 miles away glittered like fire in the sun's reflection.

What we faced far surpassed the demands of a simple flight of 800 miles to the Pole. For hundreds of miles we would fly over a barren, rolling surface, then climb a mountain rampart thousands of feet high and continue across a 10,000-foot plateau. We sped over the geological party 374 miles due south of our base. Now we began the climb. Before us, beyond the great mountains, lay uncertainty.

McKinley struggled with his camera, I navigated, June sent radio messages, fed gas from cans to tanks, and cranked his movie camera. We were heading for Heiberg Glacier, the plane near its absolute ceiling. Amundsen had reported the high point of the pass as 10,500 feet. Peaks towered on both sides. To our right stretched a wider glacier. Should we tackle Heiberg, altitude known but with air currents around those peaks that might dash us to the ice, or should we try the unknown glacier? We had to choose quickly—we were heading into the mountains at more than a mile a minute. We chose the unknown glacier.

Bernt Balchen fought for altitude while air currents tossed the plane about like a cork in a washtub. Suddenly the wheel turned loosely in his hands; the

DUMP IT! *Six weeks' rations go splattering out on the ice to lighten the stalling plane. Wheel flops uselessly in Bernt Balchen's hands as claws of an unknown glacier reach nearer; Byrd (at right) and copilot June shout orders to McKinley. Byrd wouldn't drop gas, since that meant "missing our goal."*

PAINTING BY BIRNEY LETTICK FOR NATIONAL GEOGRAPHIC

ailerons failed to respond. Above the engines' roar Bernt shouted, "It's drop 200 or go back!"

"A bag of food overboard!" I yelled. McKinley shoved a 150-pound bag of emergency rations out the two-foot trapdoor.

The controls responded. Slowly we climbed. But we were still too low. Again the wheel turned in Balchen's hands.

"Quick! Dump more!" he shouted.

I pointed to another bag. Mac nonchalantly shoved it through the trapdoor. Again the controls took effect.

Finally we reached the pass. We ambled over—a bit to spare. Bernt yelped in relief. We faced a clear route to the Pole, dead ahead over the horizon!

Our next thought was the engines. The plateau was so high that to fly above it the plane remained near its ceiling, re-

43

NEW YORK TIMES AND ST. LOUIS POST-DISPATCH. OPPOSITE: BYRD ANTARCTIC EXPEDITION

BRUSHING PAST *the Queen Mauds, Byrd aimed for the Pole. Over his goal he dropped this flag weighted with a stone from Floyd Bennett's grave. Injured testing the plane that Byrd later flew across the Atlantic, Bennett recovered and returned to the sky. He helped plan the South Pole expedition; then, on a rescue flight to Canada, he was fatally stricken with pneumonia.*

quiring full power for its lift. The loss of one engine meant landing in the snow.

Then the starboard engine sputtered. June rushed to the gas tank valves. Balchen manipulated the wheel. The gasoline mixture had been made too lean in our effort to conserve fuel. A quick adjustment and the engine sang again.

We had time to look around. The polar plateau at last—level, white, limitless!

We passed clusters of haycocks, small domes of snow that conceal deep pits. We saw glittering sastrugi, hard, wind-formed snow ridges with knife edges.

About 50 miles from the Pole, clouds approached—we would have to race them back to the pass. If we lost, our retreat would be cut off.

But the big moment had come!

I handed June a message to radio to Little America: *We have reached the vicinity of the South Pole. Flying high for survey. Soon turn north.*

The temperature was 15° below zero F. Clouds obscured the horizon in several places. No mountains were in sight. The Pole lay in the center of a vast plain. We opened the trapdoor and dropped our flag.

We circled at 2,500 feet, or about 11,500 feet above sea level, and at 1:25 A.M. turned back. A job lay ahead of us. We must hit the mountain pass and find our fuel depot. Patches of drifting snow below warned of ground winds. Like hawks we watched the sun compass and drift indicator. Time seemed to crawl. The mountains were now partly shrouded in clouds.

Balchen gave a happy shout. Soon we were sliding down a pass into Axel Heiberg Glacier. We refueled at the base we had previously set up. We reached Little America at last, having covered 160,000 square miles in 18 hours, 41 minutes.

We were deaf from the roar of the engines, tired from the strain of the flight. But we forgot all that in the tumultuous welcome of our companions.

AS THE ANTARCTIC SUMMER of 1930 came to a close we prepared to depart. Larry Gould's geological party returned. Gould's teeth formed a white line in a mask of whiskers and grime, his peaked cap stood up like a turban. No wonder the boys called him Abdul. Collecting rocks and making glaciological studies, they had covered 1,300 miles—one of the longest sledge journeys ever made for purely scientific purposes.

A few hours after the *New York* arrived on February 18, our radio station at Little America signed off for quits. It had handled 15,000 messages in 14 months.

Our expedition had carried the American flag 1,000 miles farther south than it had ever been before, and we were proud of that. But what meant more, we left not a single man in Antarctica. For this we give thanks to Providence.

45

WINTER MOON TOUCHES MASTS AND RAWIN DOME OF SOUTH POLE STATION;
AUTHOR SCANS NATIONAL GEOGRAPHIC MAP AND INVERTED GLOBE.
PAUL A. SIPLE. INSET: THOMAS J. ABERCROMBIE, NATIONAL GEOGRAPHIC STAFF

Long Night at the Bottom of the World

Hubbard Medalist Paul A. Siple relives the vigil of man's first winter at the South Pole

TUGGING at the wolf fur ruff of my parka, I step through the snow tunnel exit of our South Pole village. The cold is more searing than usual. The vapor in my breath blows back into my face and freezes instantly on my gray, ten-month-old beard.

Today, September 18, 1957, is no ordinary date. We have broken the world's low-temperature record. I want to see how it feels to walk around at 102.1° below zero F.

There is another reason to venture out. With eight other scientists and nine Navy technicians dug in at Amundsen-Scott Station as part of the International Geophysical Year program, I watched the sun set on March 22. Now it is nearly due to rise. Brilliant orange dawn colors sweep across the sky.

Lt. (jg) Jack Tuck, Jr., chief of the Navy unit, joins me. We plod over wind-hardened snowdrifts toward the geographical South Pole, about half a mile away in the direction of Australia. For conversation we grunt and point. The exertion of walking in bitter cold at an elevation of more than 9,000 feet makes talking a chore.

SNUG OASIS *in a desert of ice, Amundsen-Scott Station grew from prefabricated aluminum-plywood buildings linked by burlap and chicken wire tunnels. Bulldozed snow buried the camp to the eaves; wind swept the rooftops clear. Despite modern*

We cross the drop zone, where the huge Globemasters of Rear Adm. George J. Dufek's Operation Deep Freeze parachuted supplies last summer. As scientific leader of the station I flew in with the construction crew from McMurdo Sound, 850 miles from the Pole (map, page 52). I recall the windy day we chased a batch of steel girders 25 miles as they skidded across the snow behind a billowing chute. Then there was the crate that held 47 well-packed eggs. Not one cracked.

A red flag marks the Pole. Hundreds of star shots by theodolite pinpointed it for the first time. We tramp around the flag 100 feet out and realize that we have crossed the Date Line. This will get us out of time with the rest of the personnel. So rather than risk such a hypothetical mixup, we take another walk around the world in the opposite direction.

We turn back toward the camp that has harbored us through the coldest winter known to man. All we can see are a vapor-shrouded rawin dome and a rectangular tower amid an orchard of radio masts. We sense more than ever a feeling of isolation. There is little question of what lies beyond the gently rolling white plateau that leads to the horizon: more of the same for hundreds of miles.

I N HIS WILDEST DREAMS Robert Falcon Scott, last explorer to sleep at the South Pole, could never have imagined the comforts of our camp. He weathered his heartbreaking ordeal of 1912 in only a tent and sleeping bag. We have warm rooms, a light over each man's bunk, movies three times a week. I remember one afternoon in the mess hall. Our cook was turning a dozen sizzling steaks. A Navy technician was reading for the third time a letter from his girl in Florida. On a lounge chair sprawled Tuck, a hi-fi tape recorder lulling him to sleep. At the South Pole he was listening to Beethoven.

I think back to the Boy Scout named Siple who followed Richard Byrd south in 1928. I'm not as rugged as I was then and can certainly put up with all these conveniences. Yet hot showers and washing machines seem strange. In the good old days we spent weeks without a bath or a change of clothes. We called ourselves Knights of the Gray Underwear.

Now our snow mine provides us with more than 200 gallons of water a day. With an ax we chip at the ice, scoop it into parachute bags, load these on toboggans, and winch them to the surface. At 60° below, it's a painful job. For the first hour a man sweats. Then the chill knifes in. Back upstairs it takes hours to restore the lost body heat.

We talk occasionally with our families. Amateur operators can make radiophone patch connections right to our hometowns. The funniest call was made by our physicist. He got a wrong number. The man who answered accepted reversed charges but hung up when our man asked, "May I speak to my wife?" I wonder if he could make his friends believe that he had been awakened at 1:30 A.M. by a wrong number from the South Pole!

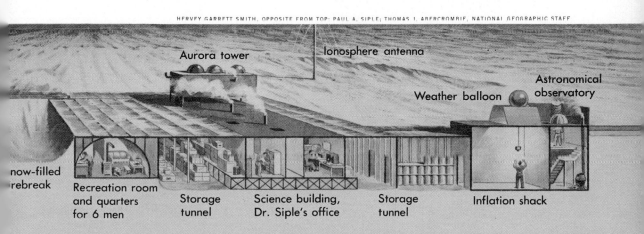

Aurora tower

Ionosphere antenna

Astronomical observatory

Weather balloon

now-filled firebreak

Recreation room and quarters for 6 men

Storage tunnel

Science building, Dr. Siple's office

Storage tunnel

Inflation shack

comforts, many of the 18 pioneers longed for new faces and privacy. On October 17, 1957, a Globemaster cascaded mail and supplies (top left). Joyfully, the men hauled in an air-dropped heater to warm up the planes that would fly them out.

PORTRAIT OF A GEOGRAPHIC STAFF MAN!
*Tom Abercrombie drew a seat on the
plane that flew in to end the vigil. He
was one of the first two correspondents
to stand at the Pole. Here's how he
looked after a hitch in the snow mine.*

Although we can talk to the outside
world we cannot order so much as a paper
clip; either we have it, or we make it, or
we do without it. Ingenuity is the key.
When the electrician runs out of equipment, he keeps the lights on in the snow
mine by using baling wire and junction
boxes made from tin cans.

No one has turned out to be more adept
at such improvisations than our medical
officer, who has invented some astonishing gadgets. For weeks he worked on an
"insomniometer" to record the movements men made while they slept. Built of
tin cans and powered by dripping water,
it marked with a stylus on smoked paper
the motions of strings running to a mat-
tress. He finally gave up in disgust when a
test graph showed a monotonous straight
line. His subject had slept all night without moving a muscle!

Of the essential jobs fulfilled by each
man, none is more critical than the cook's.
He must plan carefully. Food stored in
tunnels at 60° below takes days to thaw,
and each man puts away an average of
seven pounds a day. The cook makes gallons of iced tea, oddly our favorite bev-
erage. Once when he couldn't make his
cakes rise, he radioed for help. The Pills-
bury Company radioed back from Minne-
apolis: Add more flour. The cakes rose.

Our four weathermen have been working around the clock. Every three hours
one bundles up and stumbles over the
snow to check exposed instruments 100
yards away. He has to hold his breath
while he reads the thermometer lest ex-
haled vapor blur or warm it. Others fight
gusty winds of up to 50 miles an hour to release weather balloons which are tracked
by radio from the rawin dome.

The seismologist watches for earthquakes. His pit is located 1,000 feet from
the station to keep his delicate instruments from detecting camp vibrations.

A physicist keeps a 75-foot antenna
bouncing radio signals off the ionosphere
to study this rarefied layer of upper air, a
giant mirror for long-range communication. One sleepless specialist scans the
sky for the greenish-white aurora austral-
is, working constantly to keep the clear
plastic domes of his tower free of frost.

In the mine the glaciologist hacks out
blocks of ice to study the history of snows
piled layer upon layer over the ages.

SEPTEMBER 23: The arrival of the sun
brings us outside for a solemn ceremony. We stand at salute as the flag
is raised for the first time since the sun
set 186 days ago.

Almost a month later the first plane flies
in to drop supplies and mail. "You look
nice and big and beautiful!" shouts Tuck
over the radio.

With faraway looks in their eyes, the
men retreat into corners to read letters
from parents, wives, or sweethearts, ad-
vertisements flashing new auto designs,
headlines screaming of sputniks.

The first replacements arrive on October 26. It is difficult to fight down a feeling of annoyance when a "foreigner" fails
to show proper respect for some cherished
trophy of the winter's toil.

But our time is up. To the new men will
fall the honor of greeting Vivian Fuchs,
now starting an epochal journey.

SNOWBOUND SCIENTISTS *probe and plumb nature's icebox. Meteorologists (above) plot data from balloons launched twice daily. Glaciologist studies icecap history in slabs hacked from the snow mine. The camp doctor, almost jobless because germs were so rare, experimented in growing fungi from spores long locked in ice.*

The Crossing of Antarctica

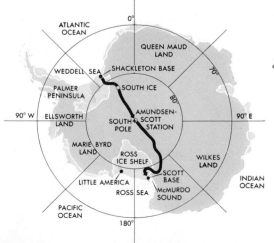

Join Sir Vivian Fuchs on his great polar trek from sea to sea—99 days over hidden crevasse and blizzard-lashed waste!

SUBZERO GALES RAKE A BEDDED-DOWN CAMP; DAVID PRATT. INSET: FUCHS AND HILLARY CONFER BEYOND THE POLE; JON STEPHENSON

Antarctica threw some of her worst pitfalls in our way at the very start of our 2,000-mile journey. Before our clanking caravan of snow vehicles had traveled 30 miles, we found ourselves in a maze of crevasses more diabolical than traps deliberately set. "It reminds me of driving a tank over a mine field," remarked one man, "except that in this case you are waiting for something to go *down!*"

We did not have long to wait. On the second day out David Stratton and I suddenly felt a horrible, sinking sensation, then a nerve-shattering lurch. A snow bridge had fallen away beneath the Sno-Cat we called Rock 'n Roll. Hardly daring to breathe, we peered out. We were suspended in mid-air over an impressive chasm, our front pontoons clinging to the far edge!

The situation was decidedly uncomfortable. David touched my sleeve. On his side he could just reach the rear pontoon. With infinite care I followed him out, crawling up the ladderlike pontoon as it hung in space. Snow and ice underfoot had never felt so good.

It was November, 1957. We had struck out from Shackleton Base on the 24th, ten men in six vehicles, hoping to accomplish what had never been done before—the overland conquest of Antarctica and exploration of an unknown area between

53

the Weddell Sea and the South Pole. To reduce our load Sir Edmund Hillary, conqueror of Mount Everest, was already pioneering a route to the polar plateau from the other side of the continent, caching fuel and food. Almost 900 bleak, wind-lashed miles still separated us from the Pole, however, and we weren't ticking off any of them with Rock 'n Roll literally on the brink of disaster.

We maneuvered the two Weasels — Rumble, and Wrack and Ruin — across a snow bridge and attached them to Rock 'n Roll's front end to keep her from nose-diving into the pit. Now our other two Sno-Cats, using the emergency low gears we called "Grandma," strained against the rear of the stricken Cat. Weasels whined, Grandmas growled. We held our breath. Rock 'n Roll lurched and sagged. One of her front pontoons had jammed against the edge of the chasm! But Hopalong, our little Muskeg tractor, clanked into action to free the pontoon. An instant later, against all odds, Rock 'n Roll was safe on solid ice.

We roped the vehicles together like mountain climbers and changed to night travel, reasoning that lower temperatures would add strength to the snow bridges. We probed ahead on foot with six-foot-long aluminum tubes, and rammed the butt ends of our ice chisels on the frozen surface. We could tell crevasse bridges because they reverberated like metal roofs. We called them boomers.

AT LAST, after 29 days, we arrived at South Ice. At this previously established scientific station 300 miles inland, we added two men and two dog teams. I radioed Hillary: *Consider this worst stage of journey and expect rapid travel from here on....*

But it was not rapid. Scouts marking the trail ahead with the dog teams reported fields of iron-hard sastrugi. It was impossible to go around them, for they extended out of sight in all directions. Mile after mile we bumped on. Day after day the trial of tempers and equipment continued.

"What a labour!" I wrote in my journal on January 2. "All vehicles in first and second gear all the way, over the most corrugated fields of continuous sastrugi. The strain is prodigious...."

Hillary radioed from the Pole, suggesting that we call off completion of our journey until next year. As I and all my party had complete confidence in our ability to carry it through, there was virtually no decision to make.

On January 5 we saw the last of the frightful sastrugi. Now the dog teams ran with us, and the next day we made 30 howling, yelping miles. Yet our troubles were not over. A mysterious illness, bringing fever and nausea, ran through the party. This puzzled us, because infections are rare in the Antarctic. All recovered. We never learned the cause.

On Sunday, January 19, almost two

CAT ON A COLD THIN ROOF!
A whisker either way would have plunged this Sno-Cat and Fuchs into a crevasse. Perilous snow bridges slowed the 2,158-mile trek. "Brilliant leadership" of the British Trans-Antarctic Expedition, 1955-8, and "extraordinary contributions" to geographic knowledge won Sir Vivian the Society's Hubbard Medal.

months out of Shackleton, we topped a snow ridge and looked down on a most welcome scene—the cluster of huts of Amundsen-Scott Station at the Pole. A reception committee headed by Hillary and Rear Adm. George Dufek met us.

"Hello, Bunny," Hillary called.

"Glad to see you, Ed," I replied.

We left the Pole on January 24, setting out northward to the other side of the world. We had to reach the Ross Sea, 1,250 miles away, before McMurdo Sound froze over. If we were late we would miss the New Zealand ship *Endeavour,* and be forced to winter over again. Four days later geophysicist Geoffrey Pratt was found unconscious in the cab of his Sno-Cat, stricken by carbon-monoxide poisoning. We radioed for help, and American Neptune planes from McMurdo Sound parachuted oxygen bottles to bring him round.

Foglike whiteouts, when the sky merges with the snow, made travel almost impossible. One day I was driving with eyes firmly fixed on the magnetic compass. Suddenly Stratton shouted. I looked up and saw three Sno-Cats lumbering toward me! I had turned around and was heading back along our track. We were so near the South Magnetic Pole our magnetic compasses were useless.

To keep in a straight line we marked

the trail. The men in the lead vehicle planted flags at 200-yard intervals; the man on the last sledge picked them up as he passed. To keep the flags aligned the leading driver had to steer with one hand while looking backward out the open door —all the time hanging grimly to the window frame. Forward vision and throttle control were provided by the passenger.

The strain on the arms and neck of the man behind the wheel was considerable. But most important, we were able to keep moving ahead.

By mid-February we were averaging 35 miles a day. Soon the distant mountains bordering McMurdo Sound swam into sight over the horizon to the east— the first rock we had seen in 1,450 miles.

As we started the long descent of Skelton Glacier the sky clouded over and blowing snow obliterated the guiding rocks. The temperature was 38° below zero F. and a following wind began filling the cabs of our vehicles with snow. It was gusting to more than 60 miles an hour as we pitched camp. All night we listened to the shrieking gale and watched the tent poles bend ominously.

At last, on March 1, we saw far off the dark specks of Skelton Depot on Ross Ice Shelf. In our excitement we made 75 miles —the longest run of the whole journey.

Next afternoon, as we neared our goal, Scott Base, with all flags flying, Weasels, Ferguson tractors, and Bren-gun carriers streamed out to meet us. With this escort, the Sno-Cats thundered and weaved between ridges. Scores of figures, cameras clicking, stood at every vantage point.

At precisely 1:57 P.M. we climbed down from our sturdy Cats for the last time. The long trek was over. We had traveled 2,158 statute miles across Antarctica in 99 days. Speeches were made; an improvised American band did their worst with our national airs. But the finest reward for all of us was a "well done" cable from Her Majesty the Queen.

QUILT-SUITED surveyors charted unmapped peaks west of McMurdo Sound. Hillary designed the gear on the basis of his Everest experience.

Shackleton had called the crossing of Antarctica "the last great Polar journey that can be made." Fuchs made it, gathering valuable scientific data en route. A sample: Soundings at the Pole showed ice 8,000 feet thick. But seismic shots 25 miles before and beyond it put the depth at less than 2,000 feet — indicating the Pole is at the center of a 50-mile-wide, ice-filled basin.

57

THREADING THE GOBI WASTES OF MONGOLIA, *camels bring supplies to Roy Chapman Andrews at the Flaming Cliffs of the Gurban Sayhan.*

Trailblazing Across Continent and Ocean

FOR THE ANCIENTS, horizons were not to seek beyond. Their saucered world dropped off abruptly into a void—or into seas roiled by ravening beasts. Go beyond? Ignorant and learned alike quaked at the thought. Then, in the 4th century B.C., the concept of the world as a globe grew with Aristotle's telling, and Greeks ventured over paths laid down by Phoenician traders. Rome rose, ruled, and died; and Medieval Europe, preoccupied with other worlds, forgot some of the lessons learned on earth. Once more the world was flattened, once more terrors lurked beyond its lip.

But now a new breed of men was born, daring men with restless souls— Marco Polo the Venetian; Eric the Viking; Da Gama, Columbus, Magellan, Cook. Over the horizons they pressed—afoot, on horse and camel, in longships and caravels—cracking the barriers of ignorance and fear. Spray from unknown seas salted their tunics, dust from distant lands chalked their boots. Filled with what Joseph Conrad described in the March, 1924, *National Geographic* as "that unappeasable curiosity," they went forth "each according to his lights and with varied motives, laudable or sinful, but each bearing in his breast a spark of the sacred fire."

THEODORE ROOSEVELT—
*Rough Rider, President,
big game hunter, explorer—
recounted his 1909 African safari
before a National Geographic
audience and belittled
his contributions to geography.
Several years later he risked
his life to put a jungle river
on the map of Brazil.*

LIBRARY OF CONGRESS

SYRIA'S SANDS *test the half-tracks as the Citroën-Haardt
Expedition starts its 7,300-mile grind across Asia.
Ahead lie Himalayan passes, bandits, and warlords.*

MAYNARD OWEN WILLIAMS

The earth had its true shape at last, and still the sacred fire burned on, undimmed by centuries. Modern trailblazers fathered the National Geographic Society, nourished it in infancy, gave muscle to its growth. Among the founders was George Kennan, who mushed a dog sledge 5,000 miles across Siberia. John Wesley Powell lost an arm at Shiloh, then turned to science. Braving hellish chasms in small boats, he made the pioneer survey of the Colorado River.

Another survivor of bloody Shiloh trailblazed in Africa. Henry Morton Stanley found the lost missionary-explorer David Livingstone in an adventure that thrilled the world. In the twilight of his life, Stanley recalled for *National Geographic* readers of 1902 his circumnavigation of Lake Victoria in days when "slingers of the islands stood ready to welcome the wayfarer...with showers of stones...sighing and thirsting for blood."

What trails does the questing spirit seek? In 1914 Theodore Roosevelt jumped at what he called his "last chance to be a boy" and explored Brazil's River of Doubt by dugout. In 1931 Georges-Marie Haardt wrestled his motor caravan through Himalayan passes that had led Marco Polo east. With him, to chronicle "the stately tread of caravans" and the "zig-zag of Cathay's Great Wall," rode

SECRET MISSION *accomplished,*
Capt. Edward L. Beach and U.S.S. Triton
emerge into the sunshine of world acclaim.
The nuclear submarine was first to
circumnavigate the globe without surfacing.

CRIES OF "WELL DONE!" *greet*
Hugo Eckener at Lakehurst,
New Jersey, after Graf Zeppelin's
globe-circling flight in 1929.
"The whole world held its breath"
during the 22-day adventure, said
Gilbert Grosvenor as he awarded a
Society medal to the dirigible pioneer.

Maynard Owen Williams, first Chief of National Geographic's Foreign Editorial Staff. Roy Chapman Andrews tackled Mongolia's forbidding Gobi by automobile and camel. His discoveries, said Gilbert Grosvenor, presenting the Society's Hubbard Medal in 1931, "have pushed back the horizons of life upon the earth and filled in gaps in the great ancestral tree of all that breathes."

Pushed back the horizons! When men sprouted wings a new galaxy of adventurers blazed trails across the sky. "The aeroplane is the nearest thing to animate life that man has created," Sir Ross Smith wrote in the March, 1921, *Geographic* after flying from London to Australia in an open-cockpit biplane at 80 miles an hour. "Wings!" exulted Comdr. Francesco de Pinedo in September, 1928, recording his 60,000-mile odyssey by seaplane to six continents. "Sindbad, tied to a roc's foot, flew over no stranger sights than I.... In 26 years Marco Polo made less mileage than I in a few weeks." Lindbergh flew across the Atlantic and into the hearts of nations, predicting with missionary zeal that the airplane would make "every spot on this planet accessible to man."

Accessible to women too. Five years later Amelia Earhart duplicated his feat, soloing the Atlantic in 16 hours. Accepting the Society's Special Gold Medal

TWO SHY MEN *share the National Geographic spotlight as President Calvin Coolidge presents the Hubbard Medal to Charles Lindbergh on November 14, 1927. The Lone Eagle was fresh from his Atlantic crossing and a 48-state tour in the* Spirit of St. Louis.

from President Herbert Hoover, she recalled that on a previous transatlantic flight as passenger she had been called a sack of potatoes. "That," she said, "probably as much as any other single factor, inspired me to try going alone."

In the brief and glorious day of the great dirigibles, America turned out to watch the *Shenandoah* follow the sun from coast to coast. The *Geographic* carried a first-hand report of that 1924 flight. Hugo Eckener girdled the globe in the *Graf Zeppelin* in 1929, and related the adventure to a National Geographic audience. He received the Society's Special Gold Medal.

The harnessed atom carried man undersea and the *Geographic* welcomed new trailblazers—*Nautilus*, the world's first atomic submarine, knifing under Arctic ice from the Pacific to the Atlantic; *Triton*, following Magellan's wake around the world submerged.

We have come far on the "great ocean of discovery," putting behind us horizons undreamed of by the ancients, each new generation building a rung on the ladder of knowledge. At Gibraltar, so the legend goes, Phoenician mariners found a rock inscribed *Ne Plus Ultra*, No More Beyond. We can give thanks that men in every age have scorned the warning and pushed impatiently by.

From Mediterranean to
Yellow Sea by Motor

*Half-tracks growl across Asia in the wake of ancient caravans.
Maynard Owen Williams records the dramatic journey.*

TROOPS SALUTE CITROËN-HAARDT EXPEDITION OUTSIDE WALLS OF FARAH, AFGHANISTAN, ONCE RAVAGED BY GENGHIS KHAN; MAYNARD OWEN WILLIAMS

MOONLIGHT gave way to clear dawn beside the Mediterranean. The camp camel bell sounded. For almost a year this relic of earlier caravans was to order our uprisings and downsittings. On this April 4, 1931, it heralded the beginning of a great adventure.

To follow pilgrim and trade routes older than either idols or money, to record the sights and sounds of the changing Orient, and to share our experiences with millions —this was our purpose. Across deserts and plateaus, over snow-clad mountain passes, through lands where ancient civilizations had flourished, and into teeming China—such was our route.

In the words of our leader, Georges-Marie Haardt, "No greater difficulties faced Hannibal in getting his elephants over the Alps."

In the 1920's Haardt crossed Africa's deserts and jungles in tractor cars built by André Citroën. Then Asia's vastness challenged the Frenchmen. For two years they planned. At last the Citroën-Haardt Trans-Asiatic Expedition was ready to roll,

63

PALMYRA, *Syria's city of Solomon, long welcomed the caravans of Asia. The author, "Mr. Geographic" to a generation of readers, camped beside its ruins. As Chief of the Foreign Editorial Staff, Maynard Owen Williams probed the earth's far corners.*

and I—the only American—joined it as representative of National Geographic.

Our original plan was to drive from Beirut to Peking in one set of half-track cars, avoiding Asia's mountain heart by cutting north beside the Hindu Kush ranges and then turning east. But the Soviets barred us from Russian Turkistan.

So we split into two fleets of cars. Seven, the China group, started rolling west from Tientsin on the Yellow Sea. Seven others, the Pamir group to which I was assigned, headed east for the mighty barrier of the Himalayas, Karakorams, and Pamirs, hoping to rendezvous with the China group in the heart of Asia.

Leaving Beirut, we swung out onto steep sand dunes where our tractors were in their element. Our engines were new and lugged us powerfully up the slopes of the Lebanon, mountains of Biblical story. Outlined against the sky a string of camels

slowly passed. And at the side of the road a handsome patriarch uttered that deathless oriental blessing, *Maa Salaameh!* Go in peace!

We camped among the hills and slept cold. Then down the valley of a swift stream to a hot parade ground and a highway once known to Saul—the Damascus Road from Jerusalem and Galilee.

We reached Damascus in time for me to roam the bazaars, gaze at mosaics in the Omayyad Mosque, and visit the tomb of Saladin, gallant adversary of the Crusaders. That morning troops of Spahis flashed their red-and-white burnooses before us, and wild-riding Circassians wove in and out among our gray cars, then reined in to escort us through "the oldest city in the world." Beyond the gardens of Damascus, we crawled toward Palmyra.

Syria's French administrators had cleared the hovels from the Great Temple of Palmyra and built a new town on the plain. I saw workmen dig a well shaft and strike damp clay—assurance that abundant water would bless this lonely desert post of the French Foreign Legion.

In the morning Legionnaires stiffened to "Present arms!" as the tricolor rose to the sound of a lone bugle. Our cars swung into line and our hands swept to a mute *Vive la France!*

Two days later we halted on the desert trail to Baghdad. Near our encampment were slovenly tents of canvas or goat hair. And we saw that the oil can, raw material for scores of oriental utensils, was used here to build fences. Each tent had its ugly wall of rusting tin. The soft-tinted ridges and mesas in the distance took on a splendid dignity in comparison with the man-made rubbish heap nearby.

The man who swore to be faithful "till the sands of the desert grow cold" was

65

THIS BEDOUIN SHEIK, *sketched by expedition's artist, came to Palmyra to arbitrate a blood feud caused by the abduction of a woman. This crime normally cost seven lives.*

At Behistun, near Kermanshah, Haardt's men saw "Rosetta Stone of Asia" (below) with sculpture of Persia's Darius triumphant over captive kings.

DR. GEORGE C. CAMERON

BLACK SEA

MEDITERRANEAN SEA

LEBANON
SYRIA
Beirut
Damascus
Palmyra

CASPIAN SEA

Euphrates
Tigris

Baghdad
IRAQ
Kermanshah
Teheran

IRAN (PERSIA)

Nishapur
Meshed

Herat
Farah
Bamian
Kabul
Farah
AFGHANISTAN
Dakka
KHYBER PASS
Helmand
Kandahar

Faizabad
Kashgar
ULUGH RABAT PASS
PAMIRS
HINDU KUSH
Hunza
Gilgit
BURZIL PASS
Pashwari
Srinagar
Kashmir
KARAKORAM
Misgar
HIMALAYAS

INDIA

MAYNARD OWEN WILLIAMS. BELOW: THOMAS J. ABERCROMBIE, NATIONAL GEOGRAPHIC STAFF

DESERT DUNES *delayed but failed to halt the motor caravan. Swift streams yielded to veteran boatmen; turbaned "Father of the River" (center) bossed the expedition over the Helmand. But at Meshed, in Iran, a wall of faith stopped Haardt's men. The shrine of Hazrat Imam Reza (right) was barred to Unbelievers.*

SKETCHES BY
ALEXANDRE IACOVLEFF

66

MIGHTY BUDDHA, *defaced by Moslem invaders, guards Bamian, in Afghanistan.*

MONGOL SOLDIERS, *whose forbears served Genghis Khan, met expedition at Gobi's edge.*

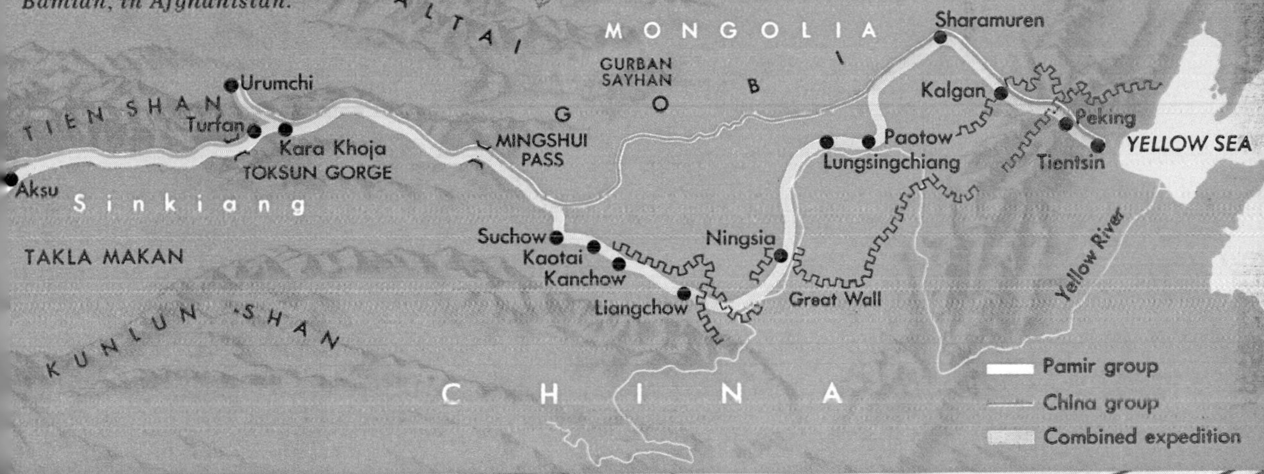

Map showing the expedition route with labeled locations:

ALTAI

MONGOLIA

GURBAN SAYHAN

G O B I

Sharamuren

Kalgan

Peking

TIEN SHAN

Urumchi

Turfan

Kara Khoja

TOKSUN GORGE

Aksu

Sinkiang

MINGSHUI PASS

Paotow

Lungsingchiang

Tientsin

YELLOW SEA

TAKLA MAKAN

Suchow

Kaotai

Kanchow

Liangchow

Ningsia

Great Wall

Yellow River

KUNLUN SHAN

C H I N A

Pamir group
China group
Combined expedition

FIRST CAR OVER THE ROOF OF THE WORLD! *Haardt's Golden Scarab grinds up Burzil Pass in the western Himalayas as Kashmiris tug at ropes to forestall a skid to disaster. Camels and ponies replaced cars on the stretch from Misgar to Aksu.*

0   500
STATUTE MILES
NATIONAL GEOGRAPHIC MAP BY
KARL GUDENBERG AND SNEJINKA STEFANOFF

either a poor geographer or a philanderer. Touch the roof of a low desert tent with your bare shoulder at dawn, and the condensed moisture feels like ice.

But the days are hot. And the dust clings in unbelievable ways. It tells from which direction a man has come, for one cheek is hidden under a deep layer of it. Shaving is purgatorial. The dust discourages the best-advertised soap from making a lather, and when you finally manage to work one up it dries while you reach for a razor.

Eastward we rolled through this bleak wasteland, along a road whose signboards seemed a little ironic. For in the land of camel and goat, of gowned horseman and nomad tent, our tarred trail was labeled "For Motors Only."

After the rigors of the desert, the air beside the Euphrates had a softness almost feminine. To the east of our green tents white marl cliffs bulged up against the blue. A few hundred feet away stretched verdant grain fields with fleecy flocks nibbling along the edges.

On April 16 we ferried the Euphrates to Mesopotamia—land between the rivers. My tentmate, expedition historian Georges Le Fèvre, never lost the light touch. Seeing the palm fronds, he noted that Allah's wisdom was great: "In such a dusty land He provides the dusters."

Between the Euphrates and the Tigris we met the semiweekly desert convoy— bus after bus crammed with Iraqi Boy Scouts, car after car jammed with travelers. In a back seat a desert woman hand-fed a black sheep while her own chubby infant nursed at her breast.

Beside the Tigris lay Baghdad—and disillusion. For 20th century improvements have erased much of the flavor that the *Arabian Nights* reader expects. My body enjoyed my private bath; but my thoughts

MINARET *of Maradiya Mosque rises like a jeweled finger above Baghdad. From the rail where a stork alights, muezzins call the faithful to prayer.*
Mighty Demavend, volcanic fires banked, towers over Iranian shepherds (right). The 18,934-foot cone guided the motor caravan to Teheran.

lingered with storybook characters beside some fictional marble pool.

After Baghdad we crossed more desert. We hurdled a rise and saw a wide bridge spanning an unexpected river where women in bright colors washed clothes in the muddy water. It was as if, at the rubbing of Aladdin's lamp, the desert had dissolved into a mirage. Close beside us lay Persia. We entered a wire-fenced enclosure where the ministering nipples of gas tank and grease gun nourished our cars, then reached the frontier and picked up an official escort.

Green valleys tucked between hills, wide-reaching plains with purple rims, emerald pockets among tawny slopes — springtime Persia proved to be a lovely land. At Kermanshah coveys of black-clad women with visored veils sat like a chorus of crows. Facing them spread a charming view across fertile plain to barren mountain where a crystal stream tumbled. From time immemorial that must have been a place for picnics. If so, the habit persists, for we passed gay parties of men in shirt sleeves and women with veils thrown back.

WE HASTENED toward Teheran, our path joining Marco Polo's. The morning after our arrival a camel was sacrificed in the central square. Stolid troops in long lines, natty officers on horseback, men and women spectators grouped separately, a Persian fife-and-drum corps shrilling barbaric music, guild leaders on plumed horses — and the gaily decorated camel advancing haughtily to his doom.

A swift flash of the knife and the moment of tension was over. The crowds, in holiday humor, flowed into the streets,

THOMAS J. ABERCROMBIE AND (LEFT) J. BAYLOR ROBERTS, BOTH NATIONAL GEOGRAPHIC STAFF

spread among the grubby shops, passed the green gardens and fine palaces of a city that is both fact and dream.

Our half-tracks thundered through Nishapur, city of turquoise mines and the burial place of Persia's ancient laureate, Omar Khayyam.

We approached the gold dome in Meshed and saw a procession of pilgrims on donkeyback riding slowly toward this sacred shrine of Hazrat Imam Reza, Eighth Apostle of Mohammed the Prophet, on whom be peace!

In the evening, when the shrine's radiant bubble floated in soft afterglow, I stopped outside the arch of the North Gate. An imaginary line here separates Believer from Unbeliever. A Persian called: I must go no farther. I drew him aside until we both could see the dome, the bright lance of the minaret. And there we stood, side by side, religious differences forgotten in the glory of that sight.

The sidewalk beneath us was made of tombstones which mark the final resting place of the rich. Perhaps "resting place" is not the word, for when space was needed the bones of a former tenant were removed and another's took their place. Finally all have been taken away.

A salt-crusted stream bed cutting a mirage-filled plain marks the boundary between Persia and Afghanistan. We passed through and found that Afghan hospitality has a long arm.

In this land, if you come upon what seems to be a palace, walk in, for it is the local guesthouse. Again and again we were entertained in gardens of delight where tables were bountifully spread. If we had a difficult river crossing to make under the hot sun, there would be a fine tent, brought from afar and pitched simply to offer us shade and refreshment. If our schedule was too hurried for us to keep an invitation in some distant place, behold a friendly shelter risen beside our

SLATS OF SUN *strike a strangely silent throng in the Herat bazaar. Williams persuaded these Afghan followers of the Prophet to pose for a three-second exposure. His creed: "A smile is good in all languages."*

MAYNARD OWEN WILLIAMS

path, with plenty of green tea and cardamom-flavored hot milk.

From 20 miles away we sighted four minarets towering above Afghanistan's town of Herat. Passing between them, we crossed into the unspoiled East. Men squatted in cubicles or stood so close that our creeping cars almost brushed their breasts. Wonder was on every face.

For two days I worked in the crowded bazaar. When I perched my big shiny camera on its chin-high tripod and dodged in and out of the sheetlike focusing cloth, curious Afghans came running.

There is nothing spiritless about the Afghan. He feels lost without a gun and a 40-pound corset of cartridges, but he caresses tame birds and fondles flowers. Where else on earth do wild-looking men play hide-and-seek with partridges? We saw an Afghan run races with his chattering playmate and, on being discovered, have his bare legs pecked as a sign that he was "it."

When we forded the Farah River, between Herat and Kandahar, we shocked the Afghans. For after our blistering ride we reveled in the cooling water. An Afghan modestly reefs his shirt as he enters water. We stripped to the buff.

ANOTHER CROSSING—over the swift, deep Helmand. Getting the seven-ton radio car across was a ticklish task, shared by our mechanics and the Afghan rivermen. *Baba Daria,* Father of the River, dubbed our chief mechanic "Baba Motor." There was enough picturesque cussing all around to make a play.

"May spit cover your faces!" screams Baba Daria.

"What does he say?" asks Baba Motor.

"That the truck is heavier than you said," replies the translator.

It took three days, but Old Man River and the Father of Autos did the job. We were lucky, as we realized later.

We pressed through Afghanistan to Kandahar, Bamian, Kabul, and Dakka. The morning we left Bamian a puncture enabled me to set out on foot. Up an avenue of willows, in early morning light, I met a tribe moving, their camels and donkeys stretching far along the road. A little girl strode beside two lambs which

71

KASHMIRIS ON DAL LAKE *net fish for nearby Srinagar. From here, two tractors teamed with*

nuzzled her knees. Young boys, coins dangling from their tight caps, sat atop towering gray camels. A bearded old man, too old to walk, rode slowly, sheltering a youngster with his shrunken chest. The caravan moved on.

In late June we threaded the Khyber Pass, northern gate to Kipling's India. And so we came to Srinagar, 3,445 miles and 81 days from Beirut. Gaudy posters decorated the bund, or esplanade, of this capital of Kashmir, a mountainous state whose borders held the Karakoram Range and the western flank of the mighty Himalayas. The streets were alive with boatmen, tailors, barbers, and tonga drivers, their light carts sharing the way with the Ma-

haraja's red and orange limousines. Dealers in papier-mâché, woodcarving, ring shawls, and silverware flourished testimonials. Shady canals led between floating gardens. And the full moon looked down on Dal Lake.

As I write, makers of leather-covered boxes and cashmere-lined boots wander in and out. My bearer comes to clear off the breakfast things and turn my stockings as if he were a lady's maid.

RAIN. The Vale of Kashmir was a lake. But Georges-Marie Haardt decided to push on. Beyond the mountain barrier of the Pamirs, 1,000 miles away by an air route no crow could follow, the

ponies and porters to launch the drive over 13,775-foot-high Burzil Pass.

heavier cars were plowing westward across the desert from Peking. We had to make the rendezvous.

With two cars, Golden Scarab and Silver Crescent, we left Srinagar July 12. From the windows black-haired Kashmiri girls smiled goodbye.

Our camp-breaking next morning was more chaotic than usual. For ugly little ponies had been herded together to help us across the Pamirs—a journey the experts said was doomed. Porters pounced on coils of cable, only to slink away when they felt the weight. Spare wheels with doughnut tires were slung on half-hidden ponies; axles and gearboxes swung awkwardly between four protesting coolies.

The cinema tripod was carried upright like a young tree; cameras, sleeping bags, toolboxes, tents, beds, and cases of food made up 150 pony loads.

A scouting and road-repair party was already ten days ahead in the mountains. Our second in command, Louis Audouin-Dubreuil, would leave eight days behind us, carrying a portable wireless to prolong our contact with the world. Each of our parties could in turn make use of the coolies and ponies at the worst spots during the crossing of the mountains.

Along our route waited grades too steep, trails too narrow, hairpin turns too sharp, underpinning and side walls too infirm. For a brave rider on a surefooted pony this could be the ride of rides. But no magic wand had transformed the mouse suggested to me as a riding animal into a horse. So I went ahead on foot.

All around were heavily wooded slopes bathed in morning mist. Then an ominous rumble, and the majestic silence was torn by the roar of engines. A gang of coolies strained the two cars around a narrow bend, and away they roared, impressive in their relentlessness.

For hours I stumbled upward with my large camera while a lad from the Hunza highlands of northern Kashmir puffed along behind with my films. The hairpins retarded the tractors, so I was able to keep ahead. When a car moves, the pedestrian is left behind. When it stops, he forges ahead. Thus our group moved.

At river crossings we unloaded or partially dismantled each car, then hauled it across with two ropes on the steering wheel to keep it to the straight and narrow. Thus the collapse of a bridge would risk no lives.

At the village of Pashwari the ether crackled bad news. A Moslem revolt had broken out in the Chinese province of Sinkiang. The China group had been halted, the men imprisoned!

For us, all was going well. We rumbled on toward dread Burzil Pass in the Himalayas. One bridge across an ice chasm seemed too weak. So the cars plunged up to their chins in the icy flood and climbed steeply to a resthouse more than two miles above sea level. They must lift themselves another half mile before crossing the 13,775-foot-high pass.

By nightfall we had plowed through two snowfields, and tired mechanics slept in their bags on the snow. Tomorrow we would try the long wallow to the top.

Dawn broke with fine clouds and blazing sun. Snow melted rapidly, and rivulets filled every gully. We added heavy iron teeth to the tractor treads, but the front wheels churned deep. Gangs of coolies hauled at long ropes to keep the machines from sideslipping. The struggle up the pass lasted ten strenuous hours.

My pony was brave but useless, sinking to his belly at almost every step. Once on foot, I was soon soaked with sweat, and my snow goggles clouded over so that I could not see. Our pack animals, badly blown, finally reached the top. Later came the cars, and the Kashmiris — not a demonstrative race unless they're trying to sell you something — cheered wildly. The Himalayan crossing lay behind!

NEXT DAY the Scarab nearly came to grief. When I caught up, it was perched 40 feet above a mountain torrent, shouldering a precipice and with most of its left tractor wheel poised in midair. The outside wall had collapsed under its weight. But brawny Hunza men, to whom heavy stones were lifelong playthings, built a new wall. Getting the car around that rocky corner involved enough pulleys, cables, and fixed points to give an engineer a headache.

After the cars cleared the danger zone, I rode through magic beauty beside the stream, down a valley clustered with spirea, lupine, and wild rosebushes. I passed a mirrorlike overflow gleaming at the foot of tall pines. After dark I could hardly distinguish the path, which often overhung the torrent, but the thunder of huge boulders grinding down the riverbed was ever in my ears. Now I noticed the nerve-tingling tendency of my pony to hug the outer edge.

Farther along, within view of 20,000-foot peaks, a mudflow had burst from the cliffs and obliterated the trail. The ponies had to be unloaded before they could pass. The cars were stopped.

A lesser leader than Haardt would have quit right there, for "Mile Seven" was a nightmare for weeks afterward.

The cars, stripped even of headlights and windshields, went through acrobatics that would break an ordinary auto's back. Finally there was nothing to do but carry them past the break in the trail.

I joined a gang and helped carry one engine a mile. The rough pine trunk to which it was wired scarred my shoulder,

HANGING BY A TREAD, *Golden Scarab teeters over a Himalayan gorge. This rocky trail beyond Burzil Pass had never known motors before. Brawny mountain men rebuilt it, and the expedition ground on.*

MAYNARD OWEN WILLIAMS

and though my shoes were better than the rawhide wrappings of the natives, and I was larger and better nourished, I soon had to depend more on grin than strength.

We reassembled the cars on a narrow path only slightly more promising than that just crossed. Progress was slow. Inches of rock were broken away to let the cars squeeze past; small metal gangplanks were laid down endlessly, one after the other, where the crumbly outer edge of the path overhung the distant river. The inner edge of one hairpin after another was battered down so the sturdy machines could turn in their tracks and mount a new incline. Cables strained the cars inward on rocks where a slip meant a crash. There was no breathing space.

When we reached a hamlet that night, the light of the moon peering through clouds touched the slopes with spirit glow. It was as if some of Titan's children, caught playing with phosphorous matches, had hurriedly wiped their hands across miles of mountainside.

O N OUR WAY again. Picture a shady forest with clear springs and the song of birds. Then you round a ridge and descend. There the scene is enough to break your heart.

For nearly four miles the trail zigzagged down to a valley. Before our arrival a square mile of mountainside had slipped, leaving enormous crevasses and ridges. Rocks big as a house barred the way. Ponies shuttled amid the disorder in a way that no motorcar could copy unless its chassis were made of soft rubber. In two days and nights a small group of peasants drove a rough but passable path for us through that infernal chaos. Then the cars tobogganed downward.

On August 4 the expedition pulled up for a well-earned rest at sandfly-bitten Gilgit in the Hunza district. Hundreds of Hunza men ran along in the dust behind

MILE SEVEN *on the trail to Gilgit. The author hefts an engine sling over the treacherous debris of an avalanche. Cars were reassembled beyond, in the shadow of 26,660-foot Nanga Parbat.*

HUNZA—*where oxen drag primitive plows through rocky soil, and lusty*

patriarchs dye beards red and boast of many sons. Here the expedition traded   *horsepower for horseback to cross the lofty Karakorams (above) and Pamirs.*

79

WAR-TORN SINKIANG *swarmed with bandits, rebels, and provincial troops. Victor Point, leader of the China group, was held by the swaggering, befurred governor (below) but got free and met Haardt in Toksun Gorge (lower right).*

the first wheeled vehicles they had ever seen. The colorful, crowded bazaar emptied. Everybody cheered. Our cars had blazed a trail where wheels never before had rolled.

The Silver Crescent, having served its purpose, was presented to the town. The Scarab crossed the Gilgit River and made a daylong run of a few dreadful miles toward the Hunza gorges.

End of the motor advance. Ahead lay a 700-mile horse- and camelback ride.

THE PRECARIOUS ROUTE through the rugged Karakoram Range of Kashmir was a medley of beauty and danger: walls of everlasting ice; a tightrope walker's path now hung in midair, now lost in the turbid torrent; peaceful villages with orange splashes of drying apricots on mud roofs; friendly folk offering fruits at every turn.

Until 1891 the men of Hunza levied tribute on all who passed. Their welcome is as enthusiastic as ever, but less expensive. A more delightful host than Mir Mohammed Nazim Khan would be hard to find. We climbed to his hilltop castle, dwarfed by an overhanging mountain. At dinner in his garden he confessed that his beard was dyed and that he was not the gallant he once had been.

At Misgar, between the Karakoram and Hindu Kush ranges, we were joined by our "rear guard." Near the Chinese border we picked up our advance units—a joyful reunion after so many days.

The precision of our caravan was something to wonder at as we crossed the Pamirs. Like trains stopping at parallel platforms, one string of camels after another filed up. The beasts knelt to the light flogging of ropes, left their burdens, and stalked away.

We pasted customs labels on our wooden baggage chests—a letter explained that if rain washed them off it was heaven's fault, not ours—and lightheartedly entered China, the land toward which we had pushed for five months.

Soon my companions became acquainted with the "bottoms up" feature of Chinese hospitality. Between innumerable courses your host fixes you with unpitying eye, raises his tiny metal cup of Chinese wine or brandy, and each of you must drain the cup at a gulp and show its bottom to a fellow victim. I chose tea, but

MAYNARD OWEN WILLIAMS. BELOW: CITROËN-HAARDT EXPEDITION

found it increasingly alcoholic. Then I discovered my neighbor using my teacup as a substitute for his stomach.

In snow mist we rode over Ulugh Rabat Pass, almost as high as the Burzil but a mere hump on our high plateau route. Once I watched our long line of camels top a rise. Their legs were invisible. Their necks jerked forward ahead of their burdens. They looked like hunchbacked tortoises snapping at the sky.

We camped beside a still stream. Camels knelt to deposit their loads. Green tents rose in neat alignment. Rugs and felt were spread on a raised platform. Turki tribesmen in fur-brimmed hats and soft boots brought bowls of tea, pyramids of peaches, and succulent melons. Our Kashmiri helpers squatted around a fire and sucked their water pipes.

On September 19 we entered Kashgar, a caravan center since Marco Polo's day. After a week of courtesies in this mud-walled city, we sat in a kiosk and drank the *chah-jan*, or farewell tea. Our Himalayan holiday was over.

Day after day we rode forward into mystery. And day after day we found welcome. When shall we forget that delightful garden in Faizabad, east of

MOTORIZED MARCO POLOS *cluster around a fire in the bleak heart of Asia. Haardt sits in center; Point warms his hands. Bearded Iacovleff inserted his self-portrait at left. Mechanic idles engine of lighted car to keep it thawed.*

ALEXANDRE IACOVLEFF

Kashgar, where a pet gazelle stared wide-eyed at us through the shrubbery, and a lovely maiden with a fresh flower tucked in her hair arrived with a tray piled high with fresh fruits?

We swung onto the "Great Route," that ancient caravan artery linking China to the Mediterranean, and followed it along the edge of the Takla Makan, the vast desert of Sinkiang Province. We refreshed at tiny hamlets or walled towns, and saw how these oasis communities teemed with crowds on market days, then fell silent as the last brightly garbed visitors were lost to view.

The desert itself is fascinating, once autumn has tempered the summer glare and heat. The silver and gold tassels of false sorghum, bunched with purple blossoms of the dwarf tamarisk, have a regal splendor. The flight of a solitary, black-winged stork against the hazy blue becomes a wordless poem. We almost tiptoed out of night-cool towns to keep lone rendezvous with the desert dawn.

THE CHINA GROUP, meanwhile, had invaded the sands of the Gobi in late May. After 19 days in the desert the caravan of cars reached Suchow and learned of the Moslem uprising in Sinkiang. The Great Route was closed to them by the authorities.

Lt. Comdr. Victor Point, leader of this arm of the Citroën-Haardt Expedition, swung north over an abandoned desert trail and on June 26 reached the threshold of Sinkiang. On the edge of a well a message was found from the last caravan to pass through: to avoid trouble, all travelers must flee to the mountains! But Point refused to be frightened. His cars were already within Sinkiang. The rendezvous with the Pamir group was drawing near. Forward march!

Two days later Point's caravan came upon the wreckage of war—horses killed, carts overturned, corpses lining the road and in the ditches; soldiers, women, and children huddling together in utter disorder. "We continued our way amid burning homes," Point later reported.

At Turfan in eastern Sinkiang he received a radio message from Haardt: He had reached Srinagar. Point was over-joyed. The rendezvous seemed certain.

But the governor of the province had other ideas. Please come without delay, with all men and cars, to Urumchi, the provincial capital. Point decided to risk only himself and one car.

He was royally welcomed by the governor. No hint of trouble. But as he tried to leave, two guards barred the way.

"Am I a prisoner?"

No explanation.

After three days Point was informed that he must await the arrival of his men and cars from Turfan. Since they would not leave without his order, he was asked to give it.

He refused.

"Think it over."

After a week of confinement Point decided to give in. The cars arrived.

Next came a telegram from Nanking ordering the provincial authorities to stop all activities of the expedition. The China group must return to Peking.

Soldiers surrounded Point's camp. The use of radio was forbidden. But he must warn Haardt at any price. Ingeniously his radio technician and mechanic rigged an antenna in a tree and muffled the sound of the generator by racing an engine. After a month of silence contact was renewed with the Pamir group. This was the message we received at Pashwari.

Five weeks later the governor permitted four cars to continue toward Kashgar to meet Haardt, on condition that Point go into the war zone and install a radio for staff headquarters. When he returned from the Chinese lines, Point learned that Haardt's caravan of 60 camels and 80 horses had joined his four cars at the town of Aksu, in western Sinkiang.

From the moment we met the vanguard of the China group in the dusty road at Aksu until the candles burned low that night, October 8, 1931, was a day of days. The shining tableware, the bright cloths, the Chinese lanterns in the soft darkness, the neat valises with clean clothing, the big cars so spick and span after their adventurous crossing from the Yellow Sea through the Gobi to forbidden Sinkiang—all these added luster. But the warmth of the occasion came from the hearts of men who had planned a rendez-

LIKE DESTROYERS *laying a smoke screen,*
cars of the combined expedition
trail dust as they wind across Sinkiang.
Ahead: gunfire and bitter cold.

MAYNARD OWEN WILLIAMS

vous half a world away and, after hardships and frustrations, had kept it.

The men and materials of the Pamir group were transferred from animals to cars, the cars turned around, and the whole party set out eastward to meet Point and the rest of his group. On October 27, fully united for the first time, the expedition sat down at Urumchi to sup and sing with barracklike virility. It was a red-letter day.

We lunched with the governor who had given Point so much trouble. From Point's men we knew what to expect—that we would be surrounded by soldiers with their hands on their guns, and that no one would dare reach for a handkerchief. As a matter of fact I reached for mine several times without thinking.

From Urumchi to Peking is 2,300 miles. Sand dune and river, desert and rocky defile lay across our path. And astride it the rebel Ma Chung Ying waited for us.

In the cold of the Sinkiang uplands we donned fur coats, boots, and sheepskin-lined trousers, and carried blankets for our engines. With early winter piling snow along our route, Audouin-Dubreuil and expedition artist Alexandre Iacovleff went ahead to study archeological sites. I joined them with the cinema and photographic crew. Iacovleff, with a gasoline heater keeping his palette from freezing, copied frescoes. The rest of us shivered in dark caves beside our cameras.

THE MAIN PARTY overtook us at Kara Khoja, and the drive to Peking was on. Our tents were seldom pitched. We ignored baggage and wash basins for days at a time. Night after night we felt our way over atrocious trails, halting for a so-called rest from two to five in the morning. Each driver slumped over his wheel. His seatmate, who could doze during the day, watched temperature gauges. When the radiator got cold or a bearing stiff the engine woke with a roar.

In each tiny village of sparsely settled

CHINA'S GREAT WALL, built 22 centuries ago to repel Mongol invaders, was a welcome sight to Haardt's weary drivers. They followed it down the homestretch.

Sinkiang our passing triggered an impromptu feast. But near the province's eastern border, war had altered the very dust. In a little hamlet called "Ever Flowing Water," I was recording my notes with a pen that I thawed by sucking, when someone interrupted. *"Eh bien*, it seems that there are two or three dirty rooms, one occupied by 15 frozen corpses."

Better sleep with 15 tonight than be one of 16 tomorrow, I thought. For many nights my breath had been freezing at the edge of my sleeping bag. So I made my bed in one of the rooms. It proved to be empty. The other two I left alone.

WE LEFT SINKIANG at Mingshui Pass with a cold early morning wind at 6,600 feet. After a 30-hour run without sleep, we overtook a flood of refugees fleeing Ma Chung Ying. He and his rebels were near and drawing nearer as we arrived at Suchow's gate.

A night attempt to use our radio brought a Chinese colonel down upon us. Our interpreters were instructed to lose $30 to him at mah-jongg, and the flurry passed.

Next morning another officer permitted us to leave. The city gates swung open for our cars. Twenty-four hours later Ma Chung Ying's troops entered Suchow. By then we were at Kaotai, 150 miles away. A bandit's head dangled from a cord beside the city gate. We hurried past.

On Christmas day we halted in Kanchow, a city where Marco Polo spent a year. Our missionary host sat beside Haardt at a table where "N-O-E-L," spelled out in candles, gladdened our eyes. Roast suckling pigs arrived on iron spits. At every place was an individual menu card with the owner pictured in one of Iacovleff's sketches.

With Ma Chung Ying just behind and the promise of needed spare parts in Liangchow only 200 miles away, we moved out on December 26. We passed through villages where armed men prowled silent streets. Then on through countryside shaken open in deep cracks by an earthquake years before.

The score of parallel ruts beside the Great Wall of China, here merely a succession of bulky towers, showed little evidence of recent use. Ages of traffic have worn them so deep that even a high-wheeled cart is trapped in the track it enters. There was dust at the bottom of all.

That night the caravan lights swept luminous shafts to right and left, now turning a dusty companion car to buffed silver, now making a shadowy mesa leap toward heaven's dark void, now adding a fairy brightness to coarse desert plants, now changing black walls to chalky whiteness. Each driver was responsible for the car behind. If he lost contact he stopped and extinguished his headlights, a sign to the car ahead that something was wrong.

Red sky ushered in the dawn. From the far edge of the plateau we saw a wide plain cut by silvery watercourses. The frozen flood delayed us. The ice would not bear our weight, yet when we stopped, our wheels froze solid.

Catholic fathers from near Liangchow brought peasants to smooth our way across irrigation ditches, and offered us shelter in the mission. We were tired. Fifty-two hours at a stretch is enough. Only 600 yards from the mission a driver dropped beside his car from sheer fatigue.

On January 5, 1932, we turned north toward Ningsia. The *Da Han*, or Great Cold, was due. Le Fèvre recorded his impressions of the route: "Two hundred and fifty miles! A six-hour drive on a decent road. Here, though advancing 20 hours out of 24, it is a six days' struggle across the eroded, worn-out no man's land."

Near the Yellow River we hit sand dunes — slow but dramatic going. We extricated ourselves only to face more and higher dunes. After two miles of them, we crossed 40 yards of ice, then waddled aboard an

archaic ferry and floated downstream for a mile before landing on the same bank beyond the wall of sand.

A guide conducted us to a house where we dined on Chinese noodles. While the mother mixed the paste, two youngsters played on the bed platform. At its end lay a wrinkled old granny, smoking opium.

After the noodles we rolled on. The route now was better. The wide plain beside the Yellow River had a rich look, even in winter. Skirted men on bicycles gave us a sense of arriving somewhere.

North of Ningsia at midnight, Silver Crescent II crashed through the ice of a canal. Suddenly my camera was afloat. Ice water poured into my boots. I scrambled over the roof to the bank. The car settled lower and lower. With help I bridged the watery gap and managed to

drag to safety the trunk of photographic records which had been expressly stored as high as possible. Flashlights threw the scene into wild relief. One man stood on the submerged radiator, wielding a crowbar against the ice. After a long struggle in bitter cold, three tractors dragged the Crescent, spewing water like some submarine monster, to the opposite bank. Thirteen hours delay—and I found my stored clothing frozen into blocks of ice.

SUNDAY, January 24. We set out with a following wind. The cars moved slowly ahead in a cloud of dust that filled our nostrils and mouths. With cold-cracked fingers we scooped out gobs of grit between our teeth and lips. Dust crept into cylinders as if no air filters were there. Pistons developed unusual wear, and oil fouled the spark plugs. When we made some trifling repair, water froze about the cylinders. A camel or horse would have seemed very efficient.

While pistons were being changed, parties on horseback came to visit or spy on us. At midnight we started toward a region against which we had been warned: "Don't talk when you should fight and don't fight when you should talk."

At Lungsingchiang, Chinese officers inspected our passports and invited us to enter. But walled towns aroused our suspicions. From several we had escaped only after long negotiations. We skirted the walls of this one and continued our drive to the east.

At still another town uniformed men pointed their guns at us and then jumped on our running boards, asking for information. We gave it without halting.

Farther along, just before nightfall, the Silver Crescent came to a narrow bridge which our other cars had already crossed. From my seat beside the driver I looked down the barrel of a gun held by a handsome young soldier. At three or four miles an hour it took a long time to

CITROËN HAARDT EXPEDITION

CRASHING THROUGH *the ice of a Chinese canal, Silver Crescent slowly sinks. Author peels off his sheepskin to rescue priceless film records. After a 13-hour trial by water, the Crescent pushed on.*

roll past that swinging rifle. Just beyond, we drove between chest-high mud walls lined with troops. Slowly we chugged by— then a salvo of shots rang out. Eleven bullets hit our car.

Deploying behind a diagonal bank, we brought our machine gun into action.

"Fire high or at a wall," ordered Audouin-Dubreuil.

Four rapid shots, then a wave of silence. Four more shots. Silence. We fired 12 cartridges. Then the Chinese hoisted a flag.

Men from both sides advanced for a conference. The Chinese called it a "slight misunderstanding." After having tea with them, we agreed to call it that.

Soon after midnight we passed into Inner Mongolia. Next day we met a 1919 Dodge truck, laden with 22 men coated with dust. They were on their way to Lungsingchiang. We learned later that three were killed, the rest stripped of everything before the truck arrived there.

Night was settling down when we approached Paotow, where there were electric lights and the nostalgic whistle of a train. We hadn't heard such a sound for seven months. Here I met my National Geographic colleague, W. Robert Moore, come to take charge of my photographic records. He left with film that had survived temperatures ranging from 120° above to 30° below, and had been through flood, gunfire, the ravages of time.

From Paotow we embarked on the last leg of our journey. Great herds of gazelles lightly leaped across our line of march. We lunched at a lama settlement so white that I dubbed it "Spotless Town." Then on across the Mongolian plateau.

One night fireworks blazed in the sky over a camp of Mongolian *gers*, or felt tents. Scores of old-world figures stepped into the glare of our headlights to investigate us. A local prince invited us to attend Chinese New Year ceremonies. We accepted. And in bitter cold we witnessed a meat offering to the rising sun and watched gaily dressed Mongols pass in and out of the compound where motorcars were lined up along with scores of ponies.

High noon, February 12, 1932. The Citroën-Haardt Trans-Asiatic Expedition swung into the grounds of the French Legation in Peking. The elite of many nations welcomed us grandly, and the Chinese, our real hosts, tendered us a friendly reception—a gratifying finale to months of barbaric living.

We were to have continued south across Indochina, through well-known lands. But a month after our arrival in Peking, Georges-Marie Haardt was dead—at 47 a victim of pneumonia. He had blazed a 7,370-mile trail across Asia, the first overland exploration from the Mediterranean to the Yellow Sea since Marco Polo's day. Thanks to his expedition, scientists may delve deeper into the largest continent.

To have lived with these brave Frenchmen and helped record their triumph— this was the greatest adventure of my life.

PEKING WELCOMES *the expedition, rumbling toward journey's end after ten months in the bleak heart of Asia. Elders paused in ritual exercise to bow; officials feted the weary explorers; the world acclaimed their feat.*

Trails to Discovery in the Gobi

Roy Chapman Andrews scoured a forbidding land to find buried monsters and dinosaur eggs 100 million years old

MUSCLES AND MOTORS FORCE A WAY THROUGH TRACKLESS SANDS WHILE AUTHOR'S DOG HITCHHIKES; AMERICAN MUSEUM OF NATURAL HISTORY

TEN THOUSAND BRIGANDS swarmed like locusts around Kalgan, gateway to Mongolia. Every camel, car, or cart that left the city was sure to be robbed within 50 miles. The merchants faced ruin, and the bandits were starving because they had no one to rob.

As usual in China, the matter was settled by the chamber of commerce, with a tax of $5 a camel payable to the bandits. Since their chief was an old friend, I argued that I ought to get cut rates. He finally agreed, and I paid only $2.50 for each of my camels. But for my cars he wanted the usual $100 apiece. I balked and hinted at a machine gun. We didn't have a machine gun, but the word went out and we were not attacked that year.

Thus began one of the five Central Asiatic Expeditions that we carried out for New York's American Museum of Natural History between 1922 and 1930. Our purpose: to probe isolated Mongolia's geologic history and to determine whether the Gobi had been the nursery of many of the dominant groups of animals.

War in China shut us out in 1926 and 1927, and arctic temperatures restricted our exploring seasons to the months from April to October.

Using automobiles, we found we could start as soon as the heavy snows disappeared, penetrate the farthest reaches of the country, and return before the cold set in again. Our camels, carrying gasoline, food, and other supplies, would set out first. The cars would follow, rendezvous, then fan out to explore.

I recall old Merin, the Mongol caravan leader, swinging aboard his camel at Kalgan (map, page 67) and waving farewell with a happy smile. He was headed into the desert where he had been born. Blizzards and brigands were part of his daily life. He would abandon the main caravan road and strike across the plains, traveling only at night. Playing hide-and-seek with the bandits, he arrived at the rendezvous safely and on time.

I estimate that with cars we made about 100 miles a day, while camels averaged only ten. Thus we could accomplish about ten years of work in one season. But both cars and camels performed extra services. The camels shed their wool at about the rate we collected fossils. There is little packing material in the desert, so when

93

LIKE AN ANCIENT CARAVAN, *camels plod the Gobi dunes. These "ships of the desert" carried*

we needed some for delicate specimens, we pulled it off the "living wool trees."

The cars helped our topographer, Maj. L. B. Roberts, develop a new system of desert mapping. Stumped by the scarcity of landmarks, Roberts used hubs, fenders, and windshields as stadia rods, while speedometers measured the distances between surveying points. Roberts carried his survey straight through the heart of Mongolia for more than 1,000 miles, greatly improving existing maps.

Speedometers also clocked the speed of desert animals. We proved beyond a doubt that the desert gazelle can reach 60 miles an hour in its initial dash. We followed one buck for ten miles. He left us easily in the first three miles, and we

just kept his bobbing white rump in sight. Then he settled down to a steady 30 miles an hour for seven miles. At that point we got a puncture but he did not.

At Tsagaan Nuur, a lovely desert lake near the foothills of the Altai Mountains, we raced the Mongolian wild ass, a mammal little known to science. During an amazing endurance run, we followed one as he hit a peak of 40 miles an hour and continued for 29 miles before he gave up and lay down.

Photographer J. B. Shackelford and I caught a baby wild ass. I have never seen such an untamable animal. Though treated with great kindness, he never lost his fear except with Buckshot, a Chinese assistant, who tended him. If anyone else

400-pound cargoes of fuel and supplies to Andrews' motorcade, and brought back fossils.

approached, fear dilated his eyes, and he kicked viciously.

A black vulture proved more sociable. Dr. R. W. Chaney, our botanist, took it from a nest at Baga Bogdo, a snow-covered peak near Tsagaan Nuur. It grew tame as a chicken and refused to eat carrion. If meat had the slightest odor of decay, the bird shunned it. When near water it bathed two or three times a day, and delighted to drowse in the sun, wings half spread, drying its feathers. The vulture's favorite sleeping place was the rear of my tent. My police dog, Wolf, also liked to sleep there and was usually worsted in the contest for supremacy.

The vulture consumed enormous amounts of water. Drinking from a pail was too slow. It preferred to open its great beak, toss back its head, and have someone pour water down its throat. One day the bird strode into my tent and rapped on a gasoline tin of water. I paid no attention. It came up, jerked my coat, and returned to the tin. I gave it water.

In the coarse grass around Tsagaan Nuur green insects swarmed in countless thousands, rising at dark with a hum like distant motors. Though their noise was appalling, the insects proved to be strict vegetarians and did not bite us. The lake area also abounded in many species of small desert mammals; collecting them was an important part of our work. Each afternoon our three Chinese taxidermists set out 50 or 60 traps baited with peanut

95

butter. In the morning they gathered kangaroo rats, hamsters, voles, sand rats, and other small species.

Pit vipers, the only poisonous snakes of the Gobi, annoyed us when we tented near a religious monument at Sharamuren. Two visiting lamas informed us that the place was sacred, and the spirits would be angry if we took life. I agreed to respect their wishes, but I had promised more than I could fulfill.

The temperature dropped and an army of pit vipers invaded our tents seeking warmth. Norman Lovell, our motor expert, caught two trying to crawl into bed with him. A geologist killed five in his tent. A Chinese chauffeur found a big one coiled in his shoe; another fell out of his cap. We named the place "Viper Camp" and broke our promise to the lamas 47 times, but our Mongol helpers held firm. They would shoo the snakes out of their tents and the Chinese would kill them.

These vipers are about the size of our copperheads. While their fangs probably do not have enough poison to kill a healthy man, a bite would make him very ill. Wolf

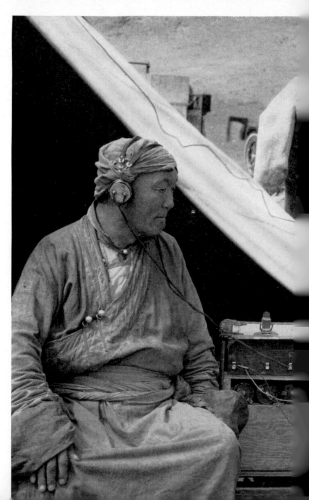

96

DOES IT BITE? *Where's the tail?*
Most Mongolian nomads had never seen
an auto until the expedition showed up
with its rugged Dodges.
Desert dwellers leaped on their horses
and fled for the hills, leaving women and
children behind. When families survived
the encounter, sheepish spouses
backtracked to take a second look.
Soon Gobi traders were paying more for
Andrews' used cars than he had paid
for them new. But the Mongol's first love
remains his horse. Toddlers (right)
will soon be in the saddle.

Radio was a miracle to Gobi nomads.
They liked Vladivostok programs,
but listened spellbound to time signals
beamed from the Philippine Islands.
The explorers checked chronometers
with these signals to ensure
accurate longitude observations.

was the only one of us to get bitten, and
he recovered.

The Gobi is harsh country and forces
its pastoral and nomadic people into a
strenuous existence. Mongols are fond of
children, but I have seen babies of only
two or three running about stark naked
while I was shivering in a fur coat. When
a child is about four he is taught to ride,
for a Mongol's real home is on the back
of a horse. To go a hundred yards he will
jump on his pony.

Life in the Mongolian desert is much
like that of our own West in the pioneer
days; assistance to a traveler is a matter
of course. When one comes to a Mongol
ger, he sits down beside the fire and helps
himself from the common pot without
the slightest question.

The old fighting spirit which drove the
Mongols to the conquest of Asia and half
of Europe is mostly gone. It stirred in
1921, when 300 Mongols massacred some
4,000 Chinese troops. The victorious general told me how "we rode at full speed
through the camp, killing everything we
saw." A wild horde, these Mongols were,

WEATHERED MONGOL FACES *express
the desert refrain, "Come be our guest,"
and prove that Gobi welcome hasn't
waned since Roy Chapman Andrews
explored here in the twenties.
Caught in a sudden May snowstorm,
the famed naturalist shared a crowded
ger with a family of four—plus calves,
goats, and a dozen lambs.*

*Some gers are now factory-built and
electrified, but the design is centuries old.
The trellised wall expands; ribs slip
into the roof ring; felt covers the frame;
a roof lid controls light and air. The ger
is up in 20 minutes without benefit of
nails or bolts. Supreme Court Justice
William O. Douglas noted in* National
Geographic *that these "beehives" linger
even in today's modern cities.*

DEAN CONGER, NATIONAL GEOGRAPHIC PHOTOGRAPHER. OPPOSITE: JORGEN BISCH

unhampered by a commissary, making almost superhuman marches. If there was no mare's milk or meat, they tightened belts and laughed at hunger. He was not a man who could not go 36 hours without water and fight at the end.

Before our first season in Mongolia ended we knew we had hit upon one of the world's richest fossil fields. The expedition was made famous by our discovery of dinosaur eggs embedded in 100-million-year-old strata at the Flaming Cliffs, sculptured red bluffs in the Gurban Sayhan Range.

In the hundreds of dinosaur deposits throughout the world, not a trace of eggshell had been known. We supposed that dinosaurs laid eggs, for most reptiles do, but no one knew for sure.

Then in 1922 we found a bit of eggshell and on later trips we found more. The most perfect nest was a chance discovery. Searching for eaglets against the face of a cliff, Lovell scratched his hand on something sharp — the knifelike edge of a broken dinosaur eggshell. Lying full length to avoid being blown over the brink by a high wind, Walter Granger, my second in command, removed a section of sandstone weighing several hundred pounds. It held 18 upright eggs.

The largest eggs are only nine inches long. They were laid by a small species of dinosaur, about nine feet long. That means an inch of egg to a foot of dinosaur — which isn't such a bad effort when you come to think of it. How do we know they are dinosaur eggs? Two of them contain parts of the embryo skeletons of unhatched dinosaurs.

Near the Flaming Cliffs, in an area of old sand dunes, Shackelford found handworked flints in some eroded ravines.

INCHING OUT OVER AN AERIE, *Andrews bags a pet for the expedition's "traveling zoo." Chopstick-fed eaglets (right) gobbled* two pounds of meat every four hours. Urtyn Obo's roller coaster canyons were so rich in fossils that bones could be spotted with field glasses. "After days of heat and pain," said Andrews, "at last the desert has paid its debt."

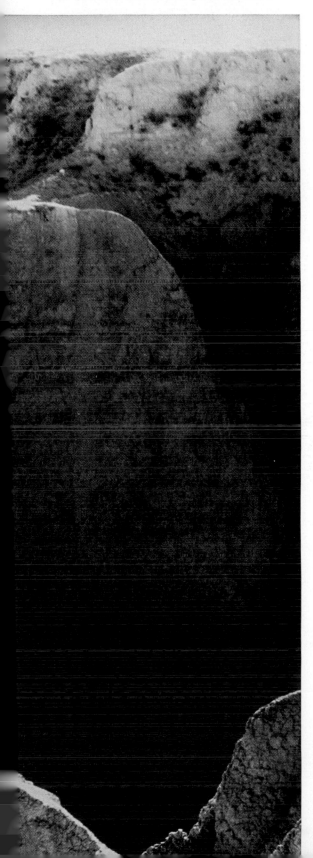

AMERICAN MUSEUM OF NATURAL HISTORY

Flakes of jaspar, slate, and chalcedony were scattered like newly fallen snow. Among them were pointed cones, neatly shaped. Tiny scrapers, delicately worked drills, arrowheads! We held a consultation: Could these artifacts have been washed down from the upper surface of the dunes? To date the deposit geologically we must find flints actually embedded.

We were in a fever of excitement. Archeologist Nels C. Nelson, most conservative of conservatives, skipped about like a boy. At last we found half a dozen flints deeply embedded in the sandstone floor. Now the advantages of correlated work were clearly displayed. Geologists, paleontologists, topographers, and botanists were right there to help the archeologist settle many puzzling questions.

Nelson concluded that we were dealing with a late Paleolithic or Mesolithic culture. Then Chaney played a joke. He planted a bit of rusted iron saw blade neatly in the flint-bearing layer. Its discovery threw the camp into consternation, upsetting all theories. We sat around racking our brains to account for its presence. Then Nelson found the other part of the blade near camp.

We determined to get even with Chaney. He spent leisure moments collecting birds' eggs, and blowing and labeling

101

them. We hard-boiled a pair of hen's eggs, then stained them beautifully in potassium permanganate. I found a bush splashed with droppings and set the eggs in a depression. When I announced the discovery of a demoiselle crane's nest, Chaney was all excitement. He photographed the "nest" from three angles and made close-ups with the portrait lens.

His attempts at blowing out the eggs were unsuccessful, so he decided to remove the embryo through a hole in one side. I shall never forget the expression on his face when he discovered that they were hard-boiled. With a roar he hurled one at Mac Young, our transport chief, and the other at me.

The true artifacts that we found represented a new culture not closely related to any known in other parts of the world. We named the people "Dune Dwellers."

PERHAPS the most important achievement of the expeditions was the finding of fossils which show that the Central Asiatic plateau was a great center of the origin and distribution of world life. Shackelford announced at lunch one day that he had found a bone as big as his body. We all laughed but went with him to a deep ravine. Ten feet down lay a great white ball. Until I examined it I would not believe it was part of a bone.

We moved 15 feet of hillside to expose two enormous ribs, a humerus, a five-foot radius, and a tooth as large as an apple—all from the giant *Baluchitherium*, the largest land mammal that ever lived. We were able to show that "Baluch" was an aberrant browsing rhinoceros that stalked the earth some 30 million years ago. It stood about 17 feet high at the shoulder and 24 feet long—a mountain of flesh, much larger than the biggest elephant.

Since we had found this huge vegetarian, it was proper that we should also discover the world's biggest flesh eater. Buckshot found the skull of a hyenalike carnivore which measured about 15 feet in length. It was named *Andrewsarchus*.

In a badland basin near Urtyn Obo we came upon an animal belonging to a group called titanotheres, massive beasts supposed to have existed only in America. We called this creature the "battering-ram beast" because the front of the skull turns upward like a two-foot post. Paleontologists suggest that this remarkable proboscis was a kind of periscope enabling the animal to browse on aquatic plants with its nostrils out of water.

Scientifically, the most important group of specimens the expeditions discovered were several tiny skulls. They belonged to the most ancient mammals known, which lived at the end of the Age of Reptiles when the dinosaur was dying out and nature was trying to establish the warm-blooded mammals that now dominate the earth. These little skulls, which represent her first attempts, were found near the Flaming Cliffs.

A letter from a paleontologist stated that a tiny skull discovered by Granger on the second expedition and labeled "unidentified reptile" was in reality one of these oldest mammals. In paleontology's 100-year history only one mammal skull from the Age of Reptiles had ever been found. "Do your utmost," said the letter, "to get some other skulls."

"I guess that's an order," said Granger. "I'd better get busy." He walked out to the base of the cliffs and was back in an hour with another skull!

Granger and his assistants kept at their search under a scorching sun for a week and came up with seven skulls. It was possibly the most valuable seven days' work in the history of paleontology.

We left the Flaming Cliffs for the last time with much regret. This single spot had given us more than we had dared to hope for from all the Gobi.

When we took the field in 1922, we were told that Mongolia was barren paleontologically and geologically as well as physically. Yet the first dinosaur eggs known to man, the skeletons of previously unknown dinosaurs, the oldest known mammals, and the relics of the primitive Dune Dwellers—all had come from these few square miles.

Is it surprising that a wave of sadness swept over me as I looked for the last time at the Flaming Cliffs, gorgeous in the morning sunlight? I knew that I would never see them again, for the active years of an explorer's life are short, and new fields were calling.

SIFTING THE SANDS *of Mongolia's "treasure house of life history," Andrews bared the bones of rhinolike Baluchitherium (top). Largest known land mammal, it stood 17 feet high and was built like a "grounded blimp." Dinosaur eggs (left) made world headlines. But the most significant fossil finds were rat-size skulls (above) of the oldest known mammals, which scurried between the feet of dinosaurs at the end of the Age of Reptiles.*

Down the River of Doubt

Where it went, no one knew.
Theodore Roosevelt traced it
through jungles of Brazil—
almost to death's door.
Ill, and in weakened voice,
he reports on his discovery.

IT IS A PLEASURE to tell this National Geographic audience about our trip in South America. I think it unnecessary to say that Columbus could not have discovered America had it not been for the knowledge gained by Portuguese sailors from the days of Prince Henry. Peary could not have reached the North Pole had not generations of explorers pushed northward the limits of knowledge. To take a far less important instance, I could have done nothing in Brazil had it not been for the work of others.

Spanish explorers descended the Amazon River nearly 400 years ago. They discovered the mouths of a number of rivers, but three centuries elapsed before anything else was discovered about those rivers. In the case of the river of which I am going to speak, what was reported about the mouth was entirely wrong.

I did not go to South America with any intention of exploring this stream. But when I got to Rio de Janeiro, Mr. Lauro Müller, the Foreign Minister of Brazil, told me that he had something which might appeal to me. The Telegraphic Commission, working in the western portion of Brazil, had found the sources of two rivers that ran north toward the Amazon. The larger was called the Dúvida, the River of Doubt, because no one knew where it came out. If I wanted to find out, the head of the Telegraphic Commission, Colonel Rondon, would accompany me.

"We cannot tell what may happen," Müller told me. "There may be unpleasant surprises. But we'd be delighted to have you do it."

"Well, by George," I said, "that is just what I would like to do!"

We started up the Paraguay River, then for 37 days took our mule train and pack oxen across the highlands of western Brazil—healthy country, in places more than 3,000 feet high.

It is almost impossible for me to show you our exact route because the standard maps are so preposterously wrong. We crossed many rivers. Two of them are close together and each has a waterfall about the size of the Yellowstone. Yet I can find no hint of those great waterfalls, nor even of the rivers, on this map. Farther along, where the map shows a mountain, we

PIRANHA'S SHARKLIKE TEETH *threaten any creature that enters the jungle waters Roosevelt explored. Attacking in schools, the voracious fish can skeletonize a swimmer in seconds. T. R. found the piranha worth catching: the little man-eater tastes good himself.*

came to a valley. This modern map, the best of its kind—obtained for me by Mr. Grosvenor—shows a river rising just here. It does nothing of the kind. Moreover, the map gives no suggestion of any big river between the Tapajós and the Madeira.

Yet we found such a river, the Dúvida, rising north of the 13th degree of latitude south. It flowed west, then south and north, a timber-choked mountain brook. We crossed the telegraph line at a point where the stream became navigable. There, on February 27, 1914, our canoe party broke off from the mule train and embarked. Our group consisted of Colonel Rondon and myself, ornithologist George K. Cherrie from the American Museum of Natural History, my son Kermit, two Brazilian army officers, and 16 *camaradas*, or paddlers—a strapping set of men, lithe as panthers, brawny as

bears. They looked like pirates. One or two of them *were* pirates.

For four days we ran slowly in calm water. Then we struck the rapids. We camped for 42 consecutive nights either at the head or foot of a stretch of white water, and in that time we made barely a mile and a half a day in a straight line.

At the end of that 42-day period we had gone only a sixth of the distance that we had expected to go and used up about three-quarters of our food.

We carried 50 days' half-rations which we eked out with nuts, fruits, parrots, and monkeys. I can assure my zoological friends that they can safely leave me in the monkey house without my making any assaults on the inmates. I have had all the monkey I wish.

We sometimes caught fish. These were piranhas, no bigger than trout but quite able to kill swimmers. Blood appears to madden them. An extraordinary incident occurred in the swamps of the Paraguay. The swamps were drying and the pools in them held quantities of these fish and a number of alligators. We shot an alligator. It was immediately attacked by piranhas and came right out of the water, preferring to face its human foes.

Colonel Rondon had his little toe taken completely off by a piranha. And when our dogs went into one lagoon after a tapir, two of the hounds lost the tips of their tails to these fish.

UNTIL a man has tried it, he can hardly realize the difficulties of going down a stream broken by unknown rapids. You come to the head of a rapid and you land and send people forward to explore. They may be gone six to eight hours, scouting the sides of the stream.

You must decide whether to run your boats down empty and portage the goods, let the canoes down by ropes, or, as we had to do sometimes, cut a road through the woods and, with block and tackle and bodily labor, drag the dugouts overland to the foot of the rapids. If you are over-cautious and travel too slowly, you will exhaust your food supply. If you are over-daring, you may lose your canoes.

We lost five canoes in the rapids. We built three others and lost one of those.

Under the strain, one of our boatmen went mad and murdered another, shooting him down on a jungle trail. Then he fled into the wilderness.

On March 15 we started in good season, drifted without incident through the forest, then rounded a bend and came upon a wide descent of white water with an island at its upper end. Kermit, as usual, was leading in his canoe, the smallest and least seaworthy. He had two paddlers, João and Simplicio, and his dog.

Kermit made his way across to the island to see whether we could descend better on the other side. Returning, the paddlers dug with all their strength into the swift current, but a whirlpool caught the canoe and swept it broadside into the rapids. Kermit yelled to his steersman to turn the canoe's head so as to run through. They raced down, wave after wave coming aboard, and reached the end of the stretch with the canoe nearly swamped. Another whirlpool swept them back to midstream where the dugout capsized.

João managed to swim ashore. Simplicio must have been pulled under at once and beaten to death on the boulders. He never rose. Kermit climbed on the bottom of the canoe and was swept into a second series of rapids. He was flung off and driven beneath the surface. When he rose at last, his strength almost spent, he managed to reach an overhanging branch and haul himself out. His dog had faithfully swum beside him the whole time.

The following morning we put a simple inscription on a post: "In These Rapids Died Poor Simplicio."

INDIANS lurked in the forest. Their hostility was due to timidity, but if a man shoots you because he is afraid of you it is almost as unpleasant as if he shoots you because he dislikes you.

Colonel Rondon was out hunting for monkeys with his dog. He heard what he thought was the howling of spider monkeys. The dog ran ahead, then yelped, and

DUGOUTS SCRAPE *along a corduroy trail carved out of the jungle as weary men portage past rapids. "Use light canoes,"* T. R. *warned all who would try the river.*

National Geographic Society

SIXTEENTH AND M STREETS, N. W.

WASHINGTON 6, D. C.

GILBERT GROSVENOR
CHAIRMAN OF THE BOARD OF TRUSTEES

3985 Douglas Road
Miami, Florida
December 29, 1962

Dr. Melville Bell Grosvenor
National Geographic Society
Washington 6, D. C.

Dear Melville:

You asked in your letter of December 21 for any recollections I may have
of President Theodore Roosevelt. As you know, he came to present the Hubbard
Medal to Robert E. Peary in 1906. That banquet was three years before Peary
discovered the North Pole. Theodore Roosevelt gave his first lecture to the
National Geographic Society on his return from Africa in 1910 and the second
after his Brazilian adventure in 1914. I entertained him on each occasion,
the last time at the New Willard Hotel in Washington.

After the dinner at the Willard, I accompanied Mr. Roosevelt to Convention
Hall. Several of the trustees of the Society were in the limousine with the
President. Admiral Peary rode outside, holding on to the window and con-
versing with the President and myself. The thermometer that night was in the
90's, yet Convention Hall was packed with more than 5,000 people. The entire
Supreme Court attended. We gave them seats in the front row.

Before Mr. Roosevelt left the United States for his South American trip
I had arranged with him to open the National Geographic lecture series in
November, 1914. But in May his party announced the exploration of a new
river. There was so much comment about this feat that I sent a wireless to
him aboard his steamer returning from Brazil, asking whether he would prefer
to give his lecture immediately. On a Friday afternoon I received a wireless
from him saying that he would arrive in Washington the following Tuesday
prepared to speak to the Society members Tuesday night. To print tickets,
send invitations, and arrange for the tickets to be distributed kept me and
everyone else on the staff working all Saturday, Sunday, and Monday. You can
imagine what a hectic time we had.

I presented Theodore Roosevelt with very few words that evening, as he was
anxious to start talking. He was worn from his travels and resultant illness,
and his voice was very weak. I sat in the front row and could barely hear him.
I don't think 30 people could make out his words. Yet he continued to speak
for nearly an hour and a half. Not a person of those 5,000 left the hall.

Your loving father

Gilbert Grosvenor

0   500

STATUTE MILES

NATIONAL GEOGRAPHIC MAP
BY SNEJINKA STEFANOFF

Amapá

Negro

Amazon

Belém

Manaus

Tapajós

Xingu

Aripuaná

B R A Z I L

Madeira

PERU

+Huascarán

Lima

Machu Picchu

River of Doubt
Later named the Theodore Roosevelt

Bocaiúva

*JUNGLE ORDEAL etches the faces
of co-leaders Roosevelt and Rondon.
Wracked by fever, T. R. once begged to be
left behind: "I am only a burden."
The strong arm and devotion
of his son Kermit saved his life.
Brazil named the river in Roosevelt's
honor, but the exploration took its toll,
as Gilbert Grosvenor notes (opposite). Said
the old Rough Rider: "I'm always willing to
pay the piper when I have a good dance."*

was silent. Rondon fired into the air. We hurried after him and found the dog's body with two arrows through it.

In the wilderness, people think of danger from Indians, alligators, and jaguars. They are not the things you mind. It is the mosquitoes, the poisonous ants, the maribondo wasps that are perfectly awful. It is the *borrachudos* and plum flies — like the black flies of the north woods, only worse. At one place where we stopped to build canoes the borrachudos were a torment. The bare feet of our boatmen swelled until not a man of them could work. They had to wrap their feet in gunny sacks. Life lacked a good deal of being undiluted pleasure in that camp.

We cut our belongings down to what we wore. The day after I threw away my spare clothing ants ate up my underwear. These were white ants. Driver ants try to eat the man instead of his clothes.

We threw out three-quarters of our tentage. But we saved our medicine, dosing ourselves with quinine the whole time to keep the fever from us. I think everybody got the fever more or less. Without quinine we would have been laid out.

The going was worst where the river cut through two mountain ridges with canyon walls too steep for a portage. If we could not get the canoes down, we would have to build new ones below the chasms — taking time we could ill afford. So we got them down, losing one in each chasm. We continued in the remaining canoes, so loaded their gunwales were within two inches of the water.

From there on our troubles were over. We reached a camp of rubber gatherers who had ventured upstream. There we got food, and in 14 more days we passed the junction of the Aripuanã River. A steamer took us to Manaus.

This River of Doubt has never before been traversed by any civilized man. It is absolutely unknown to map makers — English, German, French, American, or Brazilian. On the best maps issued today it is not even guessed at.

I do not know whether those in the rear of the hall can see it, but I have now put that river on the map. When I say "put it on the map," I mean just that. It is not on any map, and we have put it on the map.

109

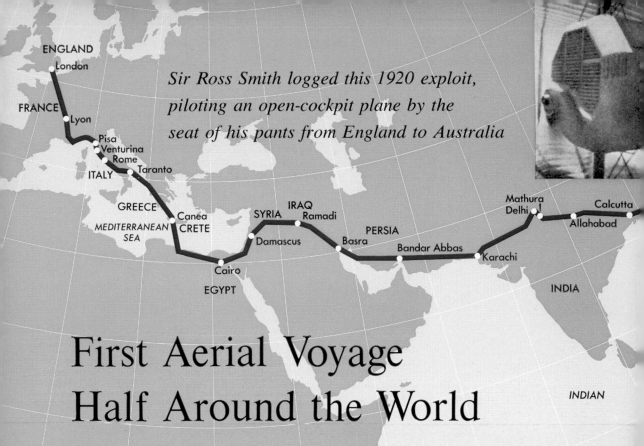

Sir Ross Smith logged this 1920 exploit, piloting an open-cockpit plane by the seat of his pants from England to Australia

First Aerial Voyage
Half Around the World

AFTER THE ARMISTICE of 1918 the Australian Government offered £10,000 for the first flight by an Australian crew from London to Australia in 30 days. I was keen to try, and Vickers Ltd. of England consented to supply a plane. I decided to take along my wartime squadron mechanics, Sgts. J. M. Bennett and W. H. Shiers. For assistant pilot and navigator I chose my brother Keith, who had been flying with the Royal Air Force.

Vickers gave us a Standard Vimy bomber with two 360-horsepower Rolls-Royce engines. With an extra tank for petrol, it could cruise at 80 miles per hour for 13 hours. We would fly by maps and direct observation of the ground. When clouds intervened we would rely on Keith's navigation. We had an Admiralty compass, a ground speed and drift indicator, and our own experience to fall back on.

We left the snow-covered aerodrome at London's Heath Row on the morning of November 12, 1920, in weather that the forecaster called totally unfit for flying. But at 2,000 feet we emerged into bright sunshine and set course for Folkestone. A rift enabled us to pick up the grand old coastline. Goodbye, England!

The machine was steady as a rock, bracing wires tuned to a nicety, dope on the wings glistening in the sunlight. The engines purred in harmony as we swept over the Channel. Beyond the coast of France stretched a sea of cloud. Thinking it might be only a local belt, we plunged into it and became deluged with sleet and snow. It clotted our goggles and windscreen and covered our faces with a mushy, semi-frozen mask.

We glided down, hoping to fly under the clouds, but snow blotted out all view. Back we climbed above the weather, where we set course for Lyon and entered another world: mighty towers of cloud, and chasms thousands of feet deep—a scene of utter extravagance.

For three hours we had no chance to check our position. The cold intensified. Hands and feet lost all feeling. Icy wind penetrated thick clothing. Breath condensed on face and mask and iced up goggles and helmet. When cloud barriers rose too high to climb over, I plunged into them.

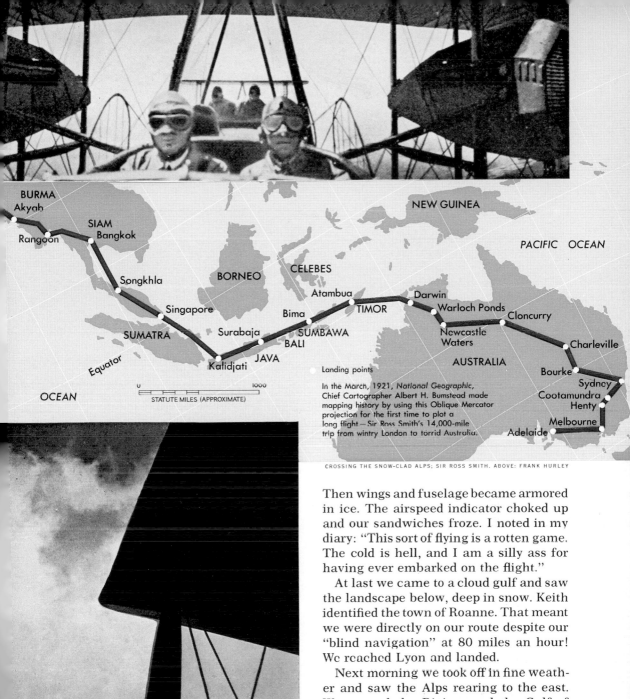

BURMA
Akyab

Rangoon

SIAM
Bangkok

Songkhla

Singapore

SUMATRA

BORNEO

CELEBES

NEW GUINEA

PACIFIC   OCEAN

Atambua

Bima

TIMOR

Darwin
Warloch Ponds

Cloncurry

Surabaja

SUMBAWA
BALI

Newcastle
Waters

Charleville

Equator

Kalidjati

JAVA

AUSTRALIA

Bourke

Sydney
Cootamundra
Henty

OCEAN

Landing points

STATUTE MILES (APPROXIMATE)

Melbourne

Adelaide

In the March, 1921, *National Geographic*,
Chief Cartographer Albert H. Bumstead made
mapping history by using this Oblique Mercator
projection for the first time to plot a
long flight — Sir Ross Smith's 14,000-mile
trip from wintry London to torrid Australia.

CROSSING THE SNOW-CLAD ALPS; SIR ROSS SMITH. ABOVE: FRANK HURLEY

Then wings and fuselage became armored in ice. The airspeed indicator choked up and our sandwiches froze. I noted in my diary: "This sort of flying is a rotten game. The cold is hell, and I am a silly ass for having ever embarked on the flight."

At last we came to a cloud gulf and saw the landscape below, deep in snow. Keith identified the town of Roanne. That meant we were directly on our route despite our "blind navigation" at 80 miles an hour! We reached Lyon and landed.

Next morning we took off in fine weather and saw the Alps rearing to the east. We crossed the Riviera and the Gulf of Genoa and set down on a very wet aerodrome at Pisa. Heavy rain kept us there for a day and so bogged the plane that when I opened the throttles to take off I felt the wheels begin to sink.

To hold the tail down, Sergeant Bennett crawled out and added his weight to it. This time we started to roll. Though Bennett was not secure, to stop once more would be to bog down for good. I was sure he would clamber back to his cockpit somehow. We gathered way and left the

111

ground. When I could look around I was delighted to see Bennett on board.

So to Rome we hurried, across the Apennines, down to the heel of Italy, and along the Greek coast. Weather closed in, and once I almost smashed into a rocky island that loomed out of a cloud. Then skies cleared, revealing a sea of wondrous blue. Soon a barren desert coastline appeared — Africa. We headed for Cairo and a rousing welcome from men with whom we had served during the war. It was quite like old times to climb into a car, spin along well-known streets to Shepheard's Hotel, and sink into the arms of a great and familiar lounge chair.

WE HAD PLANNED a rest in Cairo, but because of the delay at Pisa we were a day behind schedule. On the next stage of the flight the weather promised to be fine, and we would pass over the theater of the Palestine campaign where I had served with the Australian Light Horse before I started flying. We were keen to get on with the trip.

So to Damascus and Ramadi we sped, a following wind increasing our speed to 100 miles an hour. Basra, Bandar Abbas, Karachi. Each day the sun turned the propellers into shimmering halos. The engines sang merrily. Hour after hour I checked them — and scanned the ground for a safe spot to make a forced landing. My supreme difficulty was to keep my sleep-heavy eyes from closing.

Delhi. We had established a record by flying 5,870 miles from London in 13 days. But the congratulations fell on ears deafened by nine hours of roaring exhausts. Next morning we tumbled stiffly out of bed, climbed into our Vimy, and took off into the early Indian dawn. Of all the remembered scenes, wonderful and beautiful, that of the Taj Mahal at Agra remains the most vivid. There it lay below us, dazzling in the sunlight — a matchless white jewel in a setting of emeralds.

Allahabad. As we taxied out to take off, a bull broke onto the field and charged us. I frightened him by a roar of the engines. Then he took it for a challenge and stood in front of the Vimy, pawing the ground and bellowing defiantly. A Boy Scout rushed out, diverted the bull's attention, and we made a hurried ascent.

Calcutta. Our departure almost spelled disaster. There were a number of kite hawks flying around, and when we had cleared the ground by about ten feet, two turned straight into us. One struck a wing. The other flew into the port propeller with a shock and a scatter of feathers. It was a terrifying moment. Had the propeller broken, nothing could have saved us from a crash. And I have known a whirling propeller to fly apart when a cigarette was tossed into it!

Calcutta marked the end of the second stage of our journey. From now on we would have to land on racecourses or very small aerodromes hundreds of miles apart. Our chances of making a safe forced landing would be very slender.

At Rangoon, where no aeroplane had ever landed before, we came to earth on November 30 amid tempestuous cheering. Many people had brought food and bedding and camped on the racecourse to be sure of seeing us arrive.

Next morning we flew southeast over mountainous country. Our maps were poor, but they showed a 7,000-foot range to be crossed before reaching Bangkok. We neared a cloud bank that seemed to reach to heaven — one of the initial storms of the monsoon season. Somewhere in that dread barrier lay the high peaks we must cross, and I admit I was afraid.

Trying to get above the cloud barrier we went up to our ceiling — 11,000 feet. There was no alternative but to plunge ahead. Below lay the jagged peaks buried by cloud. Ahead, around, and behind, the mist enfolded us in an impenetrable screen. Struggling to keep control of the machine, I flew blindly for an hour. Then Keith and I felt we must surely have passed the mountains. I decided to take the risk and go lower and "feel."

Throttling back the engines, we glided down. I held the machine up to cut its speed to about 40 miles an hour. Lower and lower we went — ten, nine, eight thousand feet — and we anxiously peered over the sides for a glimpse of hidden peaks. At 7,000 feet we held on in anticipation of the crash. Minutes later we burst into view of a glorious world carpeted with trees 1,500 feet below.

All that night in Bangkok, Bennett and Shiers reground two cylinder valves by the light of a lamp aswarm with insects. By dawn our ship was ready to take off for Songkhla, halfway from Bangkok to Singapore. We were aloft some time before it began to rain. It came down like sheets of water. Goggles were useless. We removed them and, eyes narrowed to slits, took turns peering ahead. So it went for nearly three hours. I have never experienced worse flying conditions.

When we reached Songkhla we found half the drome under water. I came down low to examine a dry strip in the center, and to my dismay saw that it was covered with tree stumps. There was no other spot on which to land, so we touched and ran along, expecting to feel the undercarriage wrenched off. Miraculously, we came to rest safely, losing only our tail skid.

The whole population assembled. None had ever seen an aeroplane, and at first they would not venture near. But when they watched four ordinary humans climb out, they surged around. Some of them walked in front of the machine, flapping their arms to show how it flew. My brother, unobserved, climbed into the cockpit and moved the control column, causing the ailerons and elevators to flap back. There was a wild scamper.

With some scrap iron and a primitive lathe powered by coolies, we fixed the tail skid that night. The stumps were cleared and next morning we headed for Singapore. I had dreaded landing on the small racecourse. We glided in at low speed and, just before we touched, Bennett clambered out to the tail again, weighing it down so our craft pulled up quickly.

Eight days remained in which to make Darwin, Australia, within our 30-day limit. I decided to spend one at Singapore, working on the machine. We were asked to a dance that night, with assurances that it would end early, but weariness compelled us to refuse. When we went out to

TO QUENCH THE VIMY'S THIRST, *her crew worked long hours at the end of each day's flight, funneling 350 gallons of fuel through a chamois filter.*

SIR ROSS SMITH

SOARING *over paddies,*
Ross Smith saw Java as
"one vast bounteous garden."
On the ground he found it
a bog. Wide-eyed farmers
stripped off their bamboo
roof mats to make a runway.

SIR ROSS SMITH

take off the next morning, our would-be hosts showed up in evening dress—just back from the early dance!

We met rough flying on the way to Java. One immense bump made us hold tight. "The equator!" shouted my brother. We continued over fertile fields to Surabaja, and here we found the aerodrome a pool of mud. We landed and were easing off to the side when the machine seemed to drag. I opened the starboard engine to swing her, but the port wheels sank. In no time the Vimy subsided to her axles.

Only four days remained. And Keith

and I knew we could never get off this field without a firm roadway.

The villagers came to our rescue. Mats covered their huts, and we later learned that entire communities were stripped to provide us matting. We laid a bamboo pathway and tried to take off, but the mats were whisked up in our slipstream and blown into the tail. Then we interlaced and pegged the mats. This time we made a sensational takeoff, mats flying.

SKIRTING BALI, we landed at Bima, then made for Timor — last stop before Australia. None of us slept well that last night. On the morrow rested the destiny of all our hopes. We felt that if it dawned fine our homing was assured. But the morning brought haze, and we had to wait till it cleared.

At 8:35 A.M. the branch tops of a gum tree rasped along the bottom of the machine as we rose from the tiny aerodrome. Now for the final lap across the Indian Ocean. Our hearts beat quicker. Even our fine old engines seemed to throb faster.

It was 2:06 P.M. when, as our diary prosaically notes, we "observed Australia." At three we landed in Darwin, 27 days, 20 hours after taking off from London.

Zealous customs and health officials were anxious to examine us — and so were about 2,000 ordinary citizens. We shook hands with one another, hearts swelling. This was, and will remain, the supreme hour of our lives.

COCKPIT VIEW of Sydney, "sublimest spectacle of the entire flight," thrilled the Australian airmen. Rooftops swarmed with people as the Vimy landed. Cables came in shoals from all over the world, cheering the victors in the harrowing race against time. The author picked up his £10,000 prize, divided it four ways, and continued the triumphal tour of his nation.

In Darwin the fliers were carried like football heroes to a welcome—at the jail! In the smallest hamlets crowds turned out to gaze at the weather-beaten plane and its crew, even during morning tea under the wing. One youngster asked the meaning of the license letters, G-EAOU. Wryly, Ross Smith replied: "God 'elp all of us!"

FRANK HURLEY

Across America in a Leviathan of the Sky

A proud nation cheers the Shenandoah's *historic flight; Junius B. Wood reports it*

Dawn broke over the Naval Air Station at Lakehurst, New Jersey, as the U.S.S. *Shenandoah* was hauled from her hangar by 300 struggling men. They came running into the misty morn like ants pulling an immense gray worm out of its nest.

Nose to the wind, the 682-foot lighter-than-air ship was hooked to her mooring mast where an elevator carried her crew to the gangplank. It was October 7, 1924, and the first American-built, American-manned rigid dirigible was about to set out on her first transcontinental flight. Reporting for *National Geographic*, I went aboard as a civilian observer.

Down in the navigating gondola Lt. Comdr. Zachary Lansdowne, the skipper, waited for the sun to heat the helium cells inside the girder skeleton. As the gas expanded it gained lift. Then an officer pulled handles; water ballast splashed from the ship's belly. Slowly she lifted clear of her mooring mast.

"Standard speed!" Levers clicked, bells jangled. In five motor gondolas hands moved throttles. Lansdowne set course. This cruise would test new masts in Texas, California, and Washington.

The *Shenandoah* droned over Delaware and Maryland, soared above Washington, D. C., and paused beyond the Potomac to drop flowers on the Tomb of the Unknown Soldier at Arlington, Virginia. On she hummed southward through the night.

It was dark up in the keel, a triangular tunnel running the length of the ship. Beneath it stretched thin cotton covering; at its sides gas bags strained against the wire and twine network. Phosphorescent letters and numbers glowed from latticed frames. Flashlights blinked eerily as men

passed along its nine-inch-wide plywood catwalk, changing watch in the engine cars, measuring fuel in tanks, inspecting motors and gas bags.

The cotton cover 12 inches below the catwalk gave a false sense of security. The ground, usually 3,000 feet below on this flight, was only two steps away. A stitched rent in the cotton showed where one man made the first step; fingermarks showed where he clutched at the steel-hardened duralumin to save himself.

At the sides, distributed so the load was equalized, were gasoline tanks, oil cans, bunks for officers and men. One nerveless youth slept in a hammock—only fabric between him and space. Lateral runways led to open ladders from the motors. Men skipped up and down them, even stood on the gondolas to watch scenery while we cruised at 60 miles an hour.

The rising sun chased the *Shenandoah* across Georgia and Alabama. Over Birmingham open-cockpit Army biplanes buzzed out to meet the great ship while the city's whistles chorused a greeting.

Nightfall caught her at Dallas, Texas. At 8:30 Lansdowne maneuvered above the mast outside Fort Worth. By 9:45 the helium had cooled; its lift lessened. We dropped a cable, which was coupled with the mast cable and winched in. As frequently happens with new machinery, the winch balked. It was after 11 before we were wound down by hand and anchored. Through the night, officers and men loaded fuel, oil, and water. Fort Worth had planned a week of hospitality, but next morning we had to cast off. Ahead lay the crossing of the Rockies.

OVER THE PLAINS of Texas we caught up with a train which stopped so passengers could alight and gaze at us. In small towns children ran along the streets after us.

Gradually the vast spaces broke into hills and the *Shenandoah* began to climb. By dusk she was crossing the Pecos at 4,500 feet—pressure height, where gas cells bellied taut. Any higher and some of her life breath would escape through safety valves. Weight would have to be reduced to get up to the mountain passes.

Ballast poured down on the rising terrain. At 9:50 the ship was at 6,600 feet, still climbing. All water ballast had been dumped. We rushed toward the first pass.

Every man was on duty. Half the officers were in the navigating car. Others patrolled the keel, ready to cut away spare ballast. Time was figured in seconds, so close might be the difference between safety and destruction.

A full moon lit the clear sky. Shoulders of one tortuous, windswept gorge after another seemed to reach for the graceful intruder. A sudden swerve and she would be dashed to pieces. Over eastern Arizona she drifted for a breathless second within 100 feet of a mountain wall before the controls responded.

At one point a petty officer inspecting the gondolas found a closed door. Considerable kicking made him heard above the motor's roar. Why was everything closed?

SKIPPER LANSDOWNE *ran a taut ship,
impressed author Wood as a man
"who foresees difficulties . . . and
quietly avoids them." Smoking ban
grounded Wood's pipe on the
Shenandoah's coast-to-coast cruise.*

*In the cramped gondola below,
the rudder man stood forward,
the elevator man faced the port side,
and the navigator plotted course
at starboard. While the ship
cruised they guided its flight.
But to leave a mooring mast or gain
altitude quickly, water was dumped
and men scrambled up and down
the keel catwalk, balancing
the 682-foot tube like a seesaw.*

*Over the nation's capital, the
ship soared past the White House
(opposite) on the first leg of her trip.*

FROM JUNIUS B. WOOD. OPPOSITE: UNDERWOOD & UNDERWOOD

Pioneer Flight
Round the North Atlantic

First to solo the Atlantic, Charles Lindbergh flew it again with his wife, mapping today's airliner routes. Anne Morrow Lindbergh recorded the adventure for National Geographic.

CHARLES AND ANNE LINDBERGH PREPARE TO TAKE OFF FROM FLUSHING BAY, LONG ISLAND: UNITED PRESS INTERNATIONAL

IT WAS A HOT afternoon, the kind when one looks for ripening thunderstorms. At Glenn Curtiss Airport, Long Island, the red-winged Lockheed Sirius stood on a cradle at the ramp leading to the water. My husband signaled above the crowd that everything was ready. I scrambled to my cockpit, glanced at controls and radio equipment, fastened my safety belt.

The seaplane was pushed down the ramp while Movietone trucks took last-minute shots. "Hey! Give us a smile! Wontcha wave at us?" We watched the cradle approach the water. A push, and we were afloat in Flushing Bay.

The engine quickened, feeling its power. First, a surge of spray; then we were up on the pontoon steps. Rapid spanks as they hit the waves; then the run smoothed

out. We were off at 3:37 P.M., July 9, 1933.

We flew northeast along the coasts of Maine, Nova Scotia, and Newfoundland, first leg of a possible northern aerial route to Europe. We spent a week in Cartwright, Labrador, waiting for clear weather, then took off for Greenland. Three hours from our arrival time we saw "Greenland's Icy Mountains," like clouds on the horizon. They towered magnificently to meet us, a great wall against the sky.

Landing near Godthåb, we taxied into harbor toward brightly colored buildings —a red church with white trim, a green house with yellow shutters—a toy village set down by a child at play. The dock was jammed with people in gay reds and blues.

Two evenings later we watched them dance. They lined up for country dances

THE LINDBERGHS' FLIGHT:
AROUND THE NORTH ATLANTIC
IN 164 DAYS

○ Landing points
— Route of first commercial passenger flight, July 8, 1939

NATIONAL GEOGRAPHIC MAP BY ISAAC ORTIZ

brought over years ago by Scottish whalers and traders. But these had a different flavor, perhaps because of the women's red boots, the stamping of the men. As always there was one old man, bent in exertion, who clogged a little harder and kicked a little higher than anyone else, so that the crowd shouted with delight. He was one of those wonderful people, alike in every race, who know how to add a flourish to life.

We flew on to Holsteinsborg and stayed a week, making reconnoitering flights over Greenland and Baffin Island. From a window of the Danish governor's house we would watch fog curling over the mountains, boats trailing ripples in satin water, huskies snapping at flies in the dust, an Eskimo mother with a baby on her back, balancing from one foot to the other to put him to sleep.

The Eskimos came to see us off. Our plans were full of sudden changes, but the villagers always knew of our comings and goings. Long before anyone else could hear the hum of the engine, children would run out and set up the cry: "Ting-miss-ar-toq!" (The one who flies like a big bird.) Later an Eskimo boy sat on a wing of our plane and painted *Tingmissartoq* on the side.

From Greenland we hopped to Iceland with its white-topped volcanoes, to the misty Faeroes and the Shetlands, to Denmark, Sweden, Finland, Russia. A three-hour flight from Leningrad, and we were met by Soviet flyers as we landed between bridges on the Moscow River.

Moscow looked enormous, sprouting with new construction on all sides. Drab crowds formed long lines in front of stores. The people were intent on their work, but

GREENLAND'S CRUEL PEAKS *pierce the ice beneath the Lindberghs' wing. Exploring down the icecap from Clavering Island, their farthest north, they were startled to discover unmapped ranges.*

After soloing the Atlantic in 1927 Charles Lindbergh foresaw routine ocean flights. "Study of transatlantic air routes has become of immediat importance," he wrote in National Geographic.

On their 30,000-mile survey in 1933 the Lindberghs scouted routes in use today. But by 1939 the first North Atlantic airliners, with longer range, could shun the icy Greenland route, fly from Newfoundland to Ireland direct (map).

Idolized, Lindbergh still did his own refueling (right) like any good workaday pilot.

there was great interest in aviation. They lined a bridge to look down on our anchored plane.

We dipped our wings in salute to Moscow and went west—Oslo, Southampton, Galway, Inverness. We flew around Europe in vile weather. Our log shows that we took five hours to make the less than 40 miles between Amsterdam and Rotterdam. Why? Because we were trying to reach Geneva through what I considered thick fog but which my husband said "wasn't bad at all." Perhaps not. I only know that we spent a good deal of time circling small ponds under the mist. I thought we were about to make a forced landing, but Charles said he was looking at castles. I was glad to see Rotterdam.

IN SPAIN we looked for sunshine, but storms raged all down the coast. Leaving Santoña, we squeezed between low clouds and mountains. Then the fog lowered to the treetops and Charles put down on the Rio Minho on the Spanish-Portuguese border. We tied up to willow stumps, spread our bundles in the baggage compartment, and bedded down. The murmur of voices woke us. Men, women, children, and dogs were waiting for us to

CHARLES AND ANNE LINDBERGH (ALSO RIGHT). LEFT: WIDE WORLD

THRONGS GATHERED *wherever the Lindberghs landed. Russians jammed a Moscow bridge and nearby Dynamo Stadium (above) to watch the plane come in. Portuguese materialized magically after a forced landing on the Rio Minho. Greenland children gawked at the Lindberghs' window in Holsteinsborg. Turbaned Africans peered from their fishing boat off Villa Cisneros. Near Southampton, English greeters had to step lively to keep up.*

appear. I dressed, knocking my elbows on the sides of the narrow fuselage, feeling hundreds of eyes on me through the thin walls of the plane. Tripods spraddled, cameras ready to snap as we popped our heads above the cockpit. My husband jumped up and snapped our hosts first.

From Lisbon, by way of the Azores and the Canary Islands, we winged to Africa, then left for the Cape Verde Islands. It was a beautiful day and gave me one of the most thrilling half hours of the trip. Listening to the radio, I heard WSL at Sayville, Long Island, sending out a CQ (general call). I decided to call him. *WSL – WSL – WSL – de – KHCAL – ans (answer)* 24. I tapped it out easily, confident my 15-watt transmitter would never reach him. The CQ's at the other end stopped. Then, clearly: *KHCAL – KHCAL – KHCAL – de – WSL*. He was answering! *QRK (I receive you well)*, he went on. *QRU (Have you anything for me?)*.

QRU – casually, like that! Naturally he was not excited. He heard ships as far away as this every day. Still, I would let him know we were not just around the corner: *Lindbergh plane en route Cape Verde Islands – min pse (minute please)*.

I sent a message from Charles and got back, *Received OK*. More than 3,000 miles away! I decided to leave the set just as it was, not to move anything – just as, waking in the middle of a good dream, I try to stay motionless in the hope that it will return. But I had to call Cape Verde for weather and that was like turning over in my sleep. I never contacted WSL again.

In late afternoon we flew over Santiago in the Cape Verde Islands. The harbor of Praia, where we had planned to land, was small and open to the sea. A big swell rolled right to the beach. A few miles west we set down outside a sheltered inlet.

That night we fell asleep in our plane listening to the wind. I waited for its long roar to break – like a wave on the beach – but there was no relief. During our stay I had the feeling sometimes that the wind was an inward illness, a fever, a pressure on my temples.

"Is it never calm here?" we asked.

"Yes, it is sometimes calm. But never at this time of year. It will blow like this for six months."

We had planned to refuel here for the flight of 1,450 nautical miles across the Atlantic. Now we saw that we would never get off these rollers with enough gas to reach South America. So we returned to Africa for a start from Bathurst, Gambia.

BATHURST – gently waving palms, sun-helmeted British officers, cricket grounds, a harbor filled with little boats – here was a restful haven in which to study an Atlantic crossing. Speed for best fuel economy was 100 knots. At that rate it would take us about 16 hours to reach Natal in Brazil. We would have to leave when the wind was up, to help lift our load. We decided to try at daybreak.

On December 3 we taxied into the bay, pontoons almost submerged under the weight they carried, the plane lurching from side to side. We opened the throttle. Spray sluiced over the wings continually and we never got up on the step. We unloaded extra gas, tried again, but could not get off.

At midnight, with the moon lighting a path, we tried once more. I watched the red wingtip light glow, disappear, glow again as the spray flew over it. I held my breath to lighten the load. No use.

Charles spent the next day inside the plane cutting out an unused gas tank. By the following evening we had trimmed more weight: emergency chocolate, anchor, bucket, tools, flying suits, sleeping bag, extra clothes – about 150 pounds. That day had seemed unusually calm. At sunset there was not enough wind to lift a handkerchief. The moon rose about nine, reddish and lopsided. Certainly the last night we could use its fading light.

"We could still take off at daybreak, couldn't we?" I asked my husband.

"No. You see, the moon rises later every night. It wouldn't be high enough to land by when we reached the other side."

We pumped out the pontoons – so heavily loaded that their back ends had to be lifted from the water. I stuffed lunch into the map case at my left shoulder, put the radio bag beside me, and fastened my belt. Out in the bay there was more wind. Throttling down, we paused for breath.

"All set?"

"Yes, all right."

Then the roar, the spray over the wing. This time the spray stopped. We were spanking up on the step. We're going to get off, I thought, but how long it takes! We're off. No—spank, spank, spank....

Again I held my breath. We're off! The engine smoothed out into a long sigh, like a person breathing easily. We turned from the lights of the city.

For hours I bent over the radio dials, sending our position, straining to hear weather reports from Brazil through the crashes of static. Flying under clouds, we lost the moon, but I could still see a horizon. Then we lost that and flew blind. We climbed. I kept sending: *QRX (stand by)— going through clouds —min pse.*

Near the halfway mark, I flew while my husband took sights with the sextant. Between times I tried the radio, but could not make anything work. My back was stiff from bending and my ears hurt from the clamp of the phones. I sent with my eyes closed. Nothing seemed to be worth the effort.

Now Charles was coolly taking the sextant to pieces in the front cockpit! What was the matter? Had the sights turned out badly? More than ever we needed radio contact. I sent a CQ, signing *Lindbergh plane.*

Stations deaf to KHCAL sometimes answered *Lindbergh plane.* It was like changing the fly on a fishing line when your luck is bad.

We quickly got a bite. *Lindbergh—Lindbergh*, came the answer. *S.S. Caparcona bound Rio.* A ship off the coast of Brazil!

After that everything was easy. The ship said it would relay our position; the sextant was intact again; we saw several other ships. Then I made contact with Fortaleza, a Pan American station north

of Natal—we had reached the other side.

From Natal we flew up the Brazilian coast to Belém. I expected an easy flight home over the usual route—Paramaribo, Georgetown, Trinidad. How wonderful it would be to see a familiar place. But my husband felt ready for new adventures.

"How about stopping at Manaus on our way to Trinidad?" He looked sheepish.

"On our way! You mean that place a thousand miles up the Amazon? Would we come back here afterward?"

"Oh no," he said casually. "We'd just cut across to Trinidad."

"Charles!" My map showed a large

CHARLES AND ANNE LINDBERGH

COPILOT, *radioman, and navigator, Anne Lindbergh spells her husband at the controls. Her vivid narratives of their flying adventures launched her writing career.*

blank space in that thousand miles.

"It wouldn't be so bad." He did not wait for me to argue. "We could get down there anywhere—might smash the plane up, but we'd get out all right. Besides, I'd like to see that country."

"Why didn't you say so?"

So we found our way to Manaus with its stucco houses, rubber factory, and opera house, then over the flat llanos and thick jungle to the Orinoco Delta. At last we reached familiar places—Trinidad, Puerto

MANAUS GREETED *the Lindberghs after 1,000 miles of hazy Brazilian jungle. Rubber built this river port (with opera house!) near the junction of blue Rio Negro and brown Amazon. It still grows; houses built on rafts and served by floating hawkers (above) handle population overflow. Home at last (below), Lindbergh eases the Sirius up the ramp in Flushing Bay.*

Rico, Dominican Republic, Miami, Charleston, and rising out of haze, the towers of Manhattan. As we circled to land I tried to hold on to the trip, turning over in my mind the pictures, fingering them with pleasure like lucky pieces: the white peaks of Greenland, the view from the window at Holsteinsborg, the lights of Bathurst in the dark.... In the log I wrote, "Landed Flushing Bay 1937 Greenwich Mean Time, December 19, 1933."   133

LIKE AN AIRPLANE PILOT, HELMSMAN AT CONTROL PANEL GUIDES TRITON: J. BAYLOR ROBERTS, NATIONAL GEOGRAPHIC STAFF

36,000 Miles Under the Sea

Following Magellan's wake,
Capt. Edward L. Beach
takes the atomic submarine
Triton *around the world*

THE SUN lay low in the southwest and dusk was gathering. A shrill wind swept cutting cold over our exposed cockpit. I raised my glasses and scanned the sea. Our wake—a long, straight, broad furrow of white water—reached beyond the horizon. The coast of Long Island had receded from view.

I swung onto the ladder to go below. "Take her down," I ordered. The diving horn sounded, stopped, sounded again. Now in the control room, I watched legs clattering down the ladder beneath the conning tower hatch; then I heard the report to the officer of the deck: "Hatch secured, sir!" Effortlessly, the 447½-foot nuclear submarine U.S.S. *Triton* slipped under the waves.

As I took *Triton* south the ship was steady as a church, as solid and as quiet. But not the crew. Already the men had hints that we were in for more than the traditional shakedown cruise. They had noted our passengers: scientists, engineers, a psychologist, even a photographer from the National Geographic Society. They had pondered our advice to file income tax returns—though the deadline was still two months off.

On February 18, 1960, two days out from Groton, Connecticut, I revealed our mis-

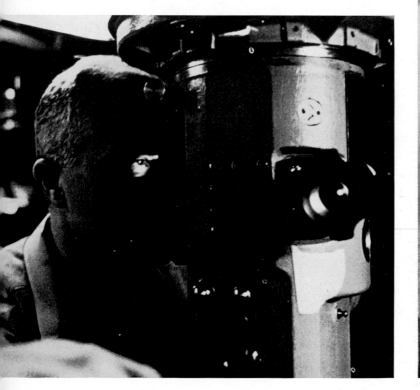

"**HAVE WE BEEN DETECTED?**" *Captain Beach (below) asked a thousand times in 84 days, this time while a gaff-rigged merchantman sailed through Makassar Strait off Borneo. Triton, as usual, ran deep. The 184 men aboard her saw the world of sun and wind and rain only through a looking glass. "Periscope liberty" became very dear liberty indeed.*

sion over the announcing system: To circumnavigate the globe along the route Ferdinand Magellan took 441 years before; to do so submerged, unsupported, undetected; to bring back new knowledge about the oceans, our ship, and ourselves.

I had the feeling a penny dropped would have sounded like a hammer on an anvil. Around the world without surfacing!

On February 24 we made our first landfall on St. Peter and St. Paul Rocks, jagged tips of the Mid-Atlantic Ridge, 600 miles off the coast of Brazil and "home plate" for this voyage. Enthusiasm soared. The first leg of the circumnavigation was now under way—and we were in for our first emergency.

On March 1 Chief Radarman John R. Poole developed a kidney-stone attack.

Many kidney stones take care of themselves without surgical treatment, but not all. To give Poole proper medical care would require X-ray and other equipment that we did not have.

As if a sick man were not enough, our echo sounder chose this time to lose sensitivity. In open sea, surface ships seldom run their sounders, since they are rarely concerned with how deep the water is. But a deep-diving submarine can easily strike bottom on a seamount over which surface ships have passed in ignorance for centuries. At 20 knots the impact could crumple the bow like an accordion.

Moreover, failure of an echo sounder is so rare that spares are not ordinarily carried. Should we lose ours for good, the cruise would be endangered. Luckily,

J. BAYLOR ROBERTS, NATIONAL GEOGRAPHIC STAFF

the electronics crew put the recalcitrant sounder in operation again within a day. One weight lifted from my mind. But the other, the responsibility for Poole, settled more heavily upon it.

FOR THREE DAYS I wrestled with the problem. Although under sedation during his attacks, Poole was often in extreme pain. To turn back would mean time lost and possible exposure of our secret mission. But to go on.... The Falkland Islands were visible in our radarscope when Poole had his fourth attack, by far the most severe. I made my decision.

At two in the morning on March 5 we met the cruiser *Macon* off Argentina. We eased our conning tower out of the water, and Poole, bundled for protection against the water sweeping over the submerged main deck, stepped groggily from the arms of his shipmates into those of the *Macon*'s boat crew. We learned later that he recovered without an operation.

We accomplished this mission of mercy without surfacing the entire ship, but it had cost us nearly 2,000 miles. Now, powered by all the energy of her twin nuclear plants, *Triton* raced back down the coast of South America.

On March 7 *Triton* entered Estrecho de Le Maire, between Staten Island and Tierra del Fuego. Just before noon we sighted Cape Horn. I directed all hands to file into the conning tower and look at this landmark, so important in our country's history. At 1408 we passed from the Atlantic to the Pacific Ocean.

137

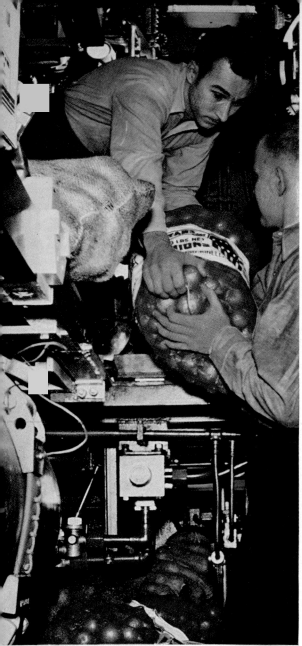

And now, as 8,000 tons of nuclear warship moves unnoticed from one end of the Pacific to the other, what keeps us occupied? We work a 12-hour day—eight hours of watch, then training, because carrying your weight on this ship means a lot more than knowing your job alone. You'll find a cook making his way the length of the ship, periodically looking up from a blueprint. He's "walking pipe"—perhaps tracing the 400-pound air system. If a compartment should be flooded, we would use air to force out the water. The man on the spot might be a cook.

In off time many men pursue hobbies. Commissaryman Ramon Baney, one of our five cooks, tools a leather holster for his Western-style six gun. Electronics Technician Martin Docker paints a New England seascape.

Others attend classes in English, French, Spanish, mathematics, or civics at *Triton's* "College of Undersea Knowledge." And every day our psychologist collects confidential questionnaires from 50 volunteers whose self-ratings range from "Happy" to "Bored stiff."

ON MARCH 27 we passed due north of the spot where our namesake, U.S.S. *Triton I*, was lost in action in 1943. Japanese destroyers had attacked her with depth charges. Then engineering officer on the submarine U.S.S. *Trigger I*, a few miles away, I heard those explosions. Now we held a memorial service on *Triton II*.

A ship on the surface would fire a salute with guns. This we could not do. But the salute we could fire was one that the people of the old *Triton* would best have appreciated. With the crew at attention, the empty forward torpedo tubes were discharged three times. We

heard the echo of the water ram—the slug of water which ejects a torpedo from its tube without telltale air bubbles—then the clear notes of taps.

Next day off the coast of Guam we heard a note of homesickness: "There's my father's house! I know it from the pictures. . . ." Crewman Edward C. Carbullido, at the periscope, was describing Agat, village of his birth and a place he had not seen for 14 years. Someone suggested shooting him out through a torpedo tube. "Negative," I said, "He might scratch the paint." But when Carbullido finally left the periscope and *Triton* turned west, there was a lump in everyone's throat. Fourteen years, and now so near—and so far!

That night, while airing out with our ventilating tube, we spotted what we believed to be an aircraft's flashing red and green lights, apparently closing in. We dived. The following evening those same lights followed us again. Had we been detected? We became more cautious with our periscope, taking only short observations and spacing them, in case the plane had sensitive radar. But the bearing of the plane appeared constant.

"Let's check the star charts," someone muttered, and it hit me. I ran the periscope all the way up. In a moment Chief Quartermaster Bill Marshall reported from the chartroom: "Arcturus bears 070 at this time, at the altitude we have sighted the aircraft." Our red and green lights were results of refraction through spray and dampness of the lens.

The next part of our trip was a pilgrimage. Cutting across the Philippine Sea, we turned north in darkness through heavily traveled Bohol Strait. Twice, when we heard heavier-than-normal screw noises, we came up to

MEN WORK A 12-HOUR DAY, *though their sun neither rises nor sets. Jammed for space, sailors stow part of 40-ton food supply under torpedo tubes (upper left).*
Medic runs radiation checks on crew's film badges (lower left). Captain (center) and his officers plot and replot their undersea course. Torpedoman releases marked bottles (right); if found and turned in, they will aid study of ocean currents. Engineer (center right) logs the latest data on sea floors. Off stormy Cape Horn, radarman (top right) checks the mountainous coastline.

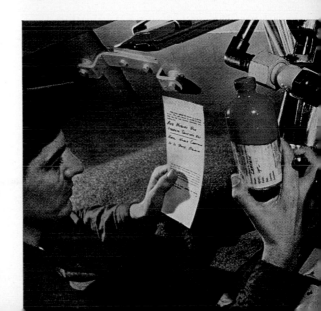

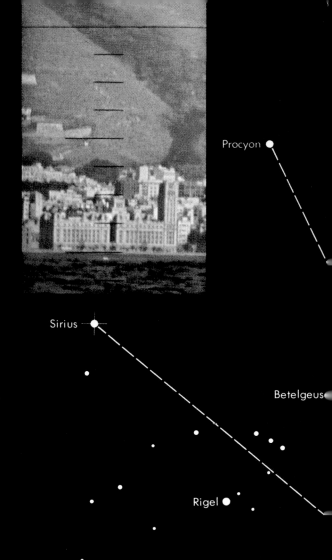

SANTA CRUZ, *gem of the Canaries, was "the most spectacular scenery" of the voyage for Captain Beach and his crew.*

Procyon

Sirius

Betelgeus

Rigel

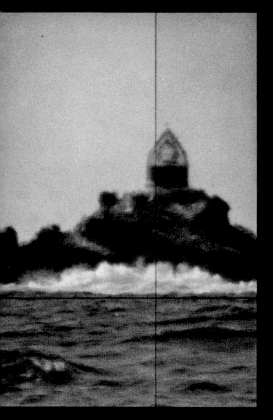

ABANDONED LIGHTHOUSE *on St. Peter and St. Paul Rocks, off Brazil, marked start and finish of the circumnavigation.*

GLIDING SILENTLY *below Bohol Strait in the Philippines, Triton runs by dead reckoning. Sonar pings bottom depth. Periscope up, navigators confirmed ship's position with star sights; by day, photographer Roberts took inset pictures.*

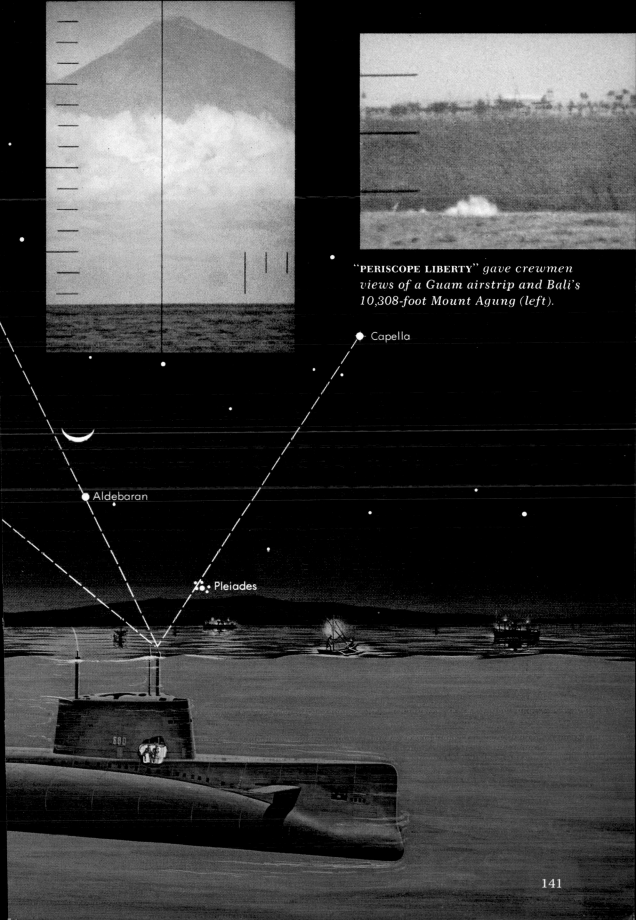

"**PERISCOPE LIBERTY**" *gave crewmen views of a Guam airstrip and Bali's 10,308-foot Mount Agung (left).*

Capella

Aldebaran

Pleiades

periscope depth and saw the brightly lighted decks of coastal steamers.

We worked our way up the Hilutangan Channel to Mactan, where Magellan was killed in a skirmish with natives. Here we saw a decrepit ferry powered by an old one-lung steam engine. It carried several people, but the only one looking in our direction was a woman with a child on her lap. She faced us directly, so close that I thought she might spot our periscope. But she seemed lost in thought.

At the end of the channel we turned into Magellan Bay. Here was the place we had come so far to find. On its shores we sighted a monument to the Portuguese navigator and explorer who dreamed so greatly and here lost all. His men continued on to complete the historic voyage.

A ND IT WAS in these placid waters that we met the sole unauthorized person to see *Triton* on the cruise. From the log: "Upon raising the periscope, I am looking right into the eyes of a young man in a small canoe, close alongside. Perhaps he has detected the dark bulk of our hull in the relatively clear waters of the bay,

or he may have sighted our periscope earlier. He and I study each other gravely. His boat is a small outrigger, perhaps 12 feet long, innocent of any paint and without mast or sail. His clothing is tattered, and he wears some kind of a battered hat.... He looks ahead and looks behind, looks down in the water and, with a paddle, maintains position."

"Down periscope!" I yell, and seconds later, "Up scope." There is our friend, leaning on his gunwales and impassively staring right at the periscope as it rises barely two inches out of the water. It is a ludicrous confrontation—an Asian in a canoe propelled by the brawny arm of its builder, and a U. S. Navy officer in a $100,000,000 submarine, the newest, biggest, most powerful in the world.

I snap the all ahead order. Minutes later, slowing for a last look, I spot our friend hundreds of yards away, paddling hard in the opposite direction.

Returning through Hilutangan Channel, we ran 150 feet deep at 10 knots, relying entirely on sonar—a feat no ship would have attempted a few years ago.

After traversing the Celebes Sea and

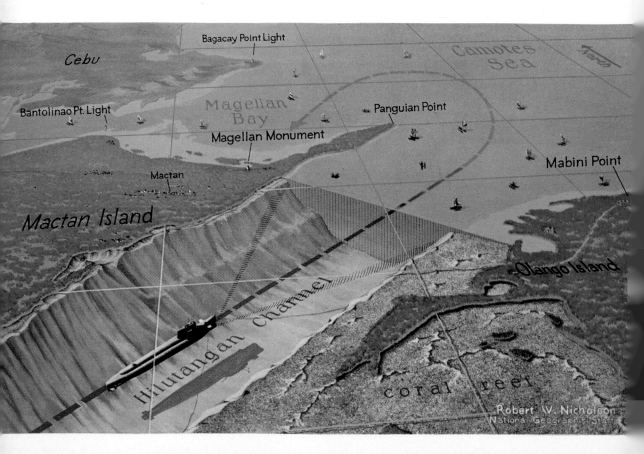

Makassar Strait we came to Lombok Strait, and I recalled what our wartime operation orders had said about this spot: "A most hazardous passage because of unusual currents and strange variations in water density." Shortly past noon we sighted a ridge of water ahead, several feet high. A few minutes later *Triton* slipped below periscope depth, blotting out my view.

"I'll have her back up in a moment, Captain," the diving officer announced confidently. But no. First gradually and then rapidly, the depth gauges spun. The ship involuntarily dived to 125 feet in 40 seconds. It was as though we had hit a hole in the water—similar to air pockets encountered by planes. At last a surge of increased speed pulled us out. Analysis of the data later revealed that at this point the deep and cold waters of the Indian Ocean meet the shallower, warmer waters of Lombok Strait, resulting in tumultuous vertical currents.

We had never been in real difficulty. But we could imagine the serious position of a diesel-electric sub of World War II days hazarding this passage with low batteries.

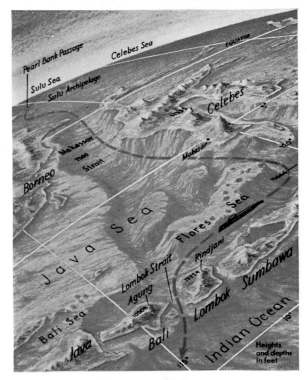

IN DEEPWATER CHANNELS *Triton wove through the Indies. Currents at Lombok Strait dropped her 125 feet in seconds.*

PHOTOGRAPHED THROUGH TRITON'S PERISCOPE BY J. BAYLOR ROBERTS, NATIONAL GEOGRAPHIC STAFF

"I **TRIED TO GET AWAY**," *recalled the Filipino fisherman who spotted* Triton's *periscope. The huge sub fled too. She had circled half the world undetected, threaded Hilutangan Channel (left) with sonar feelers, only to meet Rufino Baring eye to eye. Found later by the Society, he thankfully learned that he had seen no sea monster.*

On April 5 *Triton* entered the Indian Ocean. It was during this leg of the voyage that we ran our sealed-ship test and a no-smoking period. For two weeks we did not ventilate the ship, but refreshed our atmosphere with chemical candles. Later, smoking was prohibited. It was a trying time for many.

I am not a smoker, except for an occasional cigar, and felt little beyond a certain heightened sense of well-being—due, probably, to lessened tobacco fumes in our atmosphere. Most everyone else hated the no-smoking period.

Nonsmokers felt elated, at first. "Got a light?" they kidded their suffering shipmates. But soon, as men chewed unlit cigarettes and cigars cut in small pieces, the nonsmokers also were on edge. Everyone was much happier when, after three days, we decided to end the ban.

We sighted the Cape of Good Hope on April 17, Easter Sunday. It seemed a particularly good omen to make this landfall on that holy day and so begin the last leg of our circumnavigation. But a week later, shortly after eight in the evening, there was a loud report and a heavy spraying

noise in the after hydraulic system. Clouds of oil vapor rose from beneath the deck plates. A valve had burst.

"The stern planes aren't working!" reported the man at the diving controls.

"Shift to emergency!" ordered Lt. "Whitey" Rubb.

In the aft compartment, now filling with oil vapor, Torpedoman Allen Steele could see nothing. But he plunged into the high-pressure spray and found the quick-closing valves to the supply and return pipes. He struggled desperately to close them. Finally, with the help of Engineman Arlan Martin, he succeeded.

Not until afterward did we reflect on what might have happened. The heavy concentration of oil vapor might have caused a fire, possibly a severe explosion. Had Steele not acted so quickly and correctly, *Triton*'s main hydraulic system would have been lost in seconds—with the momentary loss of all diving-plane controls, and steering as well. I recommended Steele for a letter and ribbon of commendation for meritorious service.

The next day, Monday, April 25, at a bearing due west, we sighted St. Peter

and St. Paul Rocks. The log read: "First submerged circumnavigation of the world is now complete." We circled the bleak islets, as we had done two months before. The sun was shining brightly.

O N MAY 10 we surfaced off Rehoboth Beach, Delaware. Planes came to photograph us; a helicopter hovered with sacks of mail. Following radioed instructions, I was ready in my unaccustomed dress khaki uniform, and in little more than an hour the helicopter had put me down in Washington, D. C., on the back lawn of the White House.

Waiting to see the President, I thought of what *Triton* had accomplished. We had proved that a submarine can go around the world undetected, can go wherever there is deep enough water; that on long-range submarine exploits to come, fuel would be no problem; that when machinery was ready to produce oxygen from sea water, a submarine could stay down as long as rations and the nerves of the crew held out. I also thought of another voyage — and another captain.

Only eight days before, off the coast of Spain, *Triton* had transferred a plaque to the destroyer *John W. Weeks*. The plaque was presented to the country from which Magellan had begun his epic voyage. Its inscription, in Latin and English, reads: *Ave Nobilis Dux, Iterum Factum Est* — "Hail Noble Captain, It Is Done Again."

NO. 586 COMES HOME! *At New London, Connecticut, May 11, 1960, is a wet, cold day. No matter. The warmth of friends and families awaits* Triton's *men. Below: Captain Beach pins the ship's Presidential Unit Citation on Comdr. Joseph Baylor Roberts, USNR, a National Geographic staff man.*

B. ANTHONY STEWART, NATIONAL GEOGRAPHIC PHOTOGRAPHER. ABOVE: NORWICH BULLETIN

DAVID S. BOYER, NATIONAL GEOGRAPHIC STAFF

Unveiling the Hidden Past

"AS WE CLEARED THE SHAFT to the level of the floor, it appeared almost as if we were treading on a carpet of gold.... The 68 women, lying in ordered rows, were decked out after the fashion of the principal occupant of the domed chamber. Hair ribbons of silver or gold were almost invariable and many of the gold ribbons bore marks of exquisitely fine network.... The six men, perhaps the funeral bodyguard, were ranged in a row."

Here M. E. L. Mallowan captures one of archeology's great moments—the discovery of the "death pits" of Ur, in Iraq, grim scene of royal burial and human sacrifice 5,000 years ago. The quest for man's past is studded with such moments; this and many others have been shared with *Geographic* readers.

In Egypt's Valley of the Kings, Howard Carter pierces the burial chamber of Tutankhamun, and National Geographic's Maynard Owen Williams glimpses the magnificent coffin: "Secret eyes looked out reproachfully... and a serpent coiled near the top. The structure appears to be wood, covered with gold leaf or thicker gold.... It seemed to be about nine feet high."

On the Syrian coast, C. F. A. Schaeffer unearths clay tablets in the palace of ancient Ugarit: "We found that the majority had been inscribed in a language

OLDEST DATED WORK *of man in the Americas (291 B.C.) was unearthed by a National Geographic expedition in Mexico. Rubber effigy (below) came from Chichén Itzá's sacred well.*

HIRAM BINGHAM *clawed his way up an Andean ridge and discovered a lost Inca city—Machu Picchu. The Society backed his excavations.*

the existence of which no one had ever surmised! And—an extraordinary thing —it is in an *alphabetical* script of 27 cuneiform signs, a real alphabetical document of the second millennium before Christ!"

In Jordan, near the Gulf of Aqaba, Nelson Glueck excavates King Solomon's city of Ezion-geber and finds an earth-encrusted ring. "On it, engraved in retrograde, like an image in a mirror, is the inscription: 'Belonging to Jotham.'" *Jotham!* An Old Testament king comes to life.

We often call the Americas "the New World." Yet it is an ancient world indeed. In Mexican jungles, Matthew Stirling finds colossal stone heads and jade masterpieces from the La Venta civilization, which dates back 3,000 years. At Dzibilchaltun in Yucatán, E. Wyllys Andrews uncovers what may be ancient America's largest and longest-inhabited city, occupied perhaps 4,000 years ago. In an Alabama cave, Carl F. Miller digs past layers of bones and Stone Age tools. "At 23 feet we found a small pocket of carbon.... Using trowels and brushes, I gathered as much as possible and sealed it in a quart jar." Radiocarbon tests revealed that the charcoal—remains of a caveman's fire—burned 9,000 years ago! The National Geographic Society purchased Russell Cave and presented

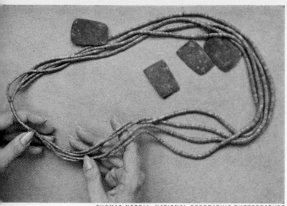

WITH THIS SANDSTONE HONE *an ancient American
sharpened bone awls in Russell Cave. Turquoise
necklace (top) adorned an Indian of Pueblo Bonito.
Society grants help Douglas Osborne (right)
unveil the life of Wetherill Mesa cliff dwellers.*

it to the people of the United States for preservation as a national monument.

Society-supported expeditions explored the cloud-scraped Inca citadel of Machu Picchu in Peru, the Maya sacred well at Chichén Itzá in Mexico, the prehistoric "apartment houses" of Pueblo Bonito and Wetherill Mesa in our own Southwest, and the sunken pirates' lair of Port Royal in Jamaica.

But man is earth's newcomer. Roland T. Bird discovered 135-million-year-old tracks near the Brazos River in Texas. "I don't know how long I remained in the footprint, staring at the unmistakable features of a sauropod's 38-inch hind foot," he reported in *National Geographic*. "Not until I realized that a walking brontosaur could have stepped all of 12 feet did I strike the next cavity." In the Badlands of South Dakota, one Society expedition came upon fossils of giant pigs, rhinoceroses, and saber-toothed cats that roved 35 million years ago. In Wyoming, another team dug from an ancient bog the remains of a woolly mammoth that Ice Age men killed and ate.

Each discovery has its price in toil and sweat. "From daytime highs of 130° F. the temperature plunged to freezing at night," wrote Theresa Goell, excavating on Nemrud Dagh in Turkey. "Fetching a bucket of water from the closest

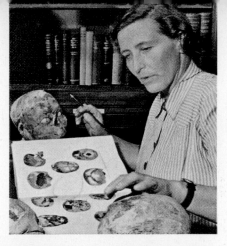

KATHLEEN KENYON *of London University unearthed these 7,000-year-old skulls at Jericho. The Society has supported her search for Jerusalem's oldest walls.*

DISCOVERERS *of* Zinjanthropus, *oldest tool-maker, Dr. and Mrs. L.S.B. Leakey receive the Hubbard Medal from Chief Justice Earl Warren, a Society Trustee, and Melville Bell Grosvenor, at left.*

ROBERT S. OAKES AND (TOP) DAVID S. BOYER, BOTH NATIONAL GEOGRAPHIC STAFF

spring required a three-hour round trip; there was not a single tree for shade, lumber, or fuel; on the unsheltered heights we were at the mercy of wind, rain, hail, and dust storms; roving bears added a final touch."

For years Louis and Mary Leakey labored beneath East Africa's blazing sun, often searching on hands and knees, before they beheld their most spectacular find: "The teeth projected from a rock face.... shining bits of fossilized matter .... the remains of the earliest man ever found!" Here was *Zinjanthropus* — the tool-maker who pushes the story of man back 1,750,000 years.

A century has passed since Heinrich Schliemann, a copy of Homer's *Iliad* in hand, set out to find the gold of Troy. Forty years have passed since C. Leonard Woolley and T. E. Lawrence excavated Carchemish, on the upper Euphrates, and "volleys of revolver shots would greet a discovery . . . and the sculpture would ever afterwards be known by the name of its finders—'Mustapha's bulls,' 'the lions of Hassan Ibrihim.'" Today's archeologists use aerial photographs to spot ruins, electric currents to probe for tombs, an "atomic clock" to date remains. Experts in a dozen sciences may join in a single dig. The treasure they seek is man's hidden heritage, far more precious than gold.

PAINTING BY BIRNEY LETTICK FOR NATIONAL GEOGRAPHIC

Machu Picchu: Lost City of the Andes

Hiram Bingham discovered this lofty Inca citadel, hidden for centuries under jungle growth

A FEW DAYS out of Cusco, we entered the magnificent canyon of the Urubamba River. Beside the roaring rapids wound our trail, shaded by vegetation—tree ferns, orchids, all the witchery of the jungle. Cliffs rose 2,000 feet, and above soared snow-capped Andean peaks.

Inca terraces climbed the slopes, but these were no novelty to us. Instead we were searching for the last capital of the great Inca Empire that had extended more than the length of Peru before the Spaniards came in the 16th century. With two Yale colleagues, a Peruvian soldier, and a mule train, I had investigated every rumor of a ruin. And now, camping beside the river at the base of a mountain called Machu Picchu, we were told of another ruin on the ridge above us.

Our informant was Melchor Arteaga, an Indian obviously overfond of firewater. I agreed to pay him the munificent wage of 50 cents if he would lead me up.

We started July 24, 1911, in a drizzle. My college companions decided (wisely, I thought) to spend the day in camp. Sergeant Carrasco and I joined Arteaga, crossed the river, and attacked the cliff.

On all fours we pulled ourselves up through slippery grass, digging with fingers to keep from falling. Far below, the Urubamba snarled angrily. The heat was oppressive. Arteaga moaned that there were lots of snakes—vicious fer-de-lances reputed to spring after their prey.

Calling on every reserve, I clambered through thinning jungle to where the ground leveled. Drenched with sweat, I straightened and saw a grass hut. Indians approached with gourds of spring water.

I drank in the view of steep summits between gulps of water and lungfuls of air. Our Indian hosts said there were old houses "a little farther on." With a small boy to guide and Carrasco to interpret, I set out along the ridge.

We rounded a knoll and suddenly faced tier upon tier of Inca terraces rising like giant stairs. Each one, hundreds of feet long, was banked with massive stone walls up to ten feet high.

What settlement of Incas had needed a hundred such terraces in this lofty wilderness? Enough food could be grown here to feed a city!

In my excitement I forgot my fatigue and hurried the length of a wide terrace toward the tangle of jungle beyond it. I plunged into damp undergrowth, then stopped, heart thumping. A mossy wall loomed before me, half hidden in trees. Huge stone blocks seemed glued together, but without mortar—the finest Inca construction. I traced the wall and found it to be part of a house. Beyond it stood another, and beyond that more again.

Under a ledge appeared a cave, its walls lined with niches of cut stone—a royal mausoleum. Above rose a semicircular building with sloping outer wall like that of Cusco's Temple of the Sun. Its straight courses of masonry diminished in size toward the top. The outer side of each stone was rounded to form the graceful curve of the building. No pin could penetrate between these blocks. It was the work of master craftsmen.

Stone steps led to a plaza where white granite temples stood against the sky. Here high priests in resplendent trappings had carried out rituals to the sun god. A gabled compound of beautifully built dwellings nearby must have sheltered the Inca himself. I could picture it floored with vicuña rugs and soft textiles woven by his Chosen Women—those "Virgins of the Sun" who figured so prominently in Inca religious ceremonies.

Down the slope, buildings crowded together in a bewildering array of terraced levels linked by at least 100 stairways. This beautifully preserved sanctuary had obviously never felt the tramp of a conquistador's boot. I realized that Machu Picchu might prove to be the largest and most important ruin discovered in South America since the Spaniards arrived.

Bursting with my news, I returned to New Haven to organize a complete archeological exploration of the forgotten city. I was greatly pleased when the National Geographic Society joined Yale University in sponsoring a second Peruvian expedition.

Our first tasks were to bridge the Urubamba and build a trail up the saddle of Machu Picchu mountain. Topographer Kenneth C. Heald solved these problems despite snakes and reluctant Indians, but a fire, started by the workers to clear the slope, almost proved his undoing.

"I was about a quarter of a mile above the workmen," he said, "when Tomás, a soldier who was with me, said, 'Look, they have fired the cane!' Sure enough, the flames were roaring toward us, reaching 20 feet into the air. There was nothing for us to do but run, and we did that, tearing through the jungle to get around the side of the fire. Suddenly, on one of my jumps I didn't stop, but kept right on through the air. The brush had masked a nice little

Continued on page 161

A portfolio of historic photographs by Hiram Bingham

The author compiled this unique album of the city and its setting. Atop Machu Picchu mountain, he looked straight down 4,000 feet at the foaming Urubamba (opposite).

HIDDEN *amid jumbled Andean peaks, the city clings to the saddle between dark-crested Machu Picchu mountain and conical Huayna Picchu (at far left). Bingham first glimpsed it through smothering growth (above); months of clearing revealed its full glory (below).* 155

WALLS OF THE CITY, *once more exposed above the Uruhamba's misty gorge, whispered their story to Bingham's men: Inca masons had labored lovingly to fit those even lines of stone (above), to align that straight, unblinking row of trapezoidal windows and niches, to carve the jutting rock beams where once a thatched roof was lashed. They even built a curving bay, in line with Huayna Picchu. Only a temple could have inspired such work.*

Temple of the Sun, Bingham called it, and found its footing locked against the jar of mountain earthquakes by a mighty boulder (below), hand-hewn to grip the square-cut blocks. Beneath it nestled a cave with bench and altar.

Steep gables, fashioned of rough stone mortared with clay, told another tale.

These roofs stood high enough to air
the smoke of cooking fires. Dwellings,
these must have been. Their well-cut
lower walls suggest they were homes
of Inca nobles, even royalty.

Who was Hiram Bingham? A lanky
young assistant professor of Latin
American history at Yale (page 147).
He led a University expedition in 1911
to seek Inca ruins, traced faint clues—

half-forgotten legends and musty Spanish
chronicles—to the wilderness of the
Urubamba, and stumbled on a city.
The National Geographic Society joined
Yale in sponsoring its excavation, 1912-15.

Bingham served as a pilot in World War I,
later as Governor of Connecticut and
U. S. Senator. At 72 he returned to Peru
to open the Hiram Bingham Highway up
the ridge he scaled that day of discovery. 157

"HITCHING-POST OF THE SUN"
stands on the topmost terrace of
the hilltop citadel. Upon finding it,
Bingham posed Sergeant Carrasco
and his small Indian guide and
took this photograph. Here, at
winter's solstice, Inca priests
"tied" the sun so it would return.

Keyed granite blocks (left) fit
so perfectly that few cracks are
wide enough for a pin to enter.

The main stairway climbs the
full height of the city. Where the
stairs divide, stone basins and
channels mark Machu Picchu's
famed fountains. Rain sends
rivulets cascading from basin to
basin—water to drink, to wash in,
to irrigate the farm terraces.

One house (upper right) boasted
a "modern kitchen" with built-in
mortars. The rocking pestle was
used to grind corn and potatoes.

Carved stone locking device
(lower) allowed a nervous
homeowner to lash his crossbar
to a solid granite pin, which a
capstone completely concealed.

158

eight-foot jump-off, and I got beautifully bumped. In a moment there was a thump and Tomás landed beside me. It amused me so much that I forgot all about my own jolted bones. There was nothing broken, however, and we made our way around the fire and fell upon the peons, who were gathered in a bunch, speculating as to where we might be."

I asked Heald if he could get to the top of Huayna Picchu, the sharp peak that adjoins the ridge on which the lost city stands. Arteaga had insisted that splendid ruins stood on the summit. When Heald tried to employ him as a guide for the climb, he refused—possibly realizing that his lies would catch up with him.

With Tomás and four Indian workers Heald crossed the river and started up the lower slopes—so steep that he had to cut steps. Progress was very slow and the Indians finally gave out. So Heald determined to conquer the mountain alone.

He pushed on up, following a bear trail and cutting his way through mesquite. "I had almost gained the top of the ridge, which runs along like the back plates of some spined dinosaur," he reported. "I was just climbing out on the top of the lowest back plate when the soil under my feet let go and I dropped. For 20 feet there was a slope of 70 degrees, then a jump of 200 feet, after which it would be bump and repeat down to the river.

"As I shot down the sloping surface I grasped a mesquite bush growing in a crack. I was going so fast that the jerk tore the ligaments in my shoulder. The strength left the arm, but I got hold of a branch with my other hand.

"After hanging for a moment or two, so as to be sure that I did nothing wrong, I started to work back up. It was distressingly slow work, but after about half an hour I had gotten back to comparatively safe footing. As my right arm was almost useless, I at once made my way down."

Five days later Heald tried again, and again he failed to reach the top. On the following morning he returned to the attack and eventually made the summit. He found it a jumbled mass of granite boulders with no houses, but a few stairs. It may have been an Inca signal station.

WORK, MEANWHILE, was humming in the ghost city. We felled trees that had found footing on ancient walls, hacked away bushes, burned debris, and scrubbed moss from stones. Gradually our axes and machetes chewed away the jungle to reveal all the breathtaking details of Machu Picchu.

A flight of some 150 steps formed the city's "Main Street." Down it ran the one aqueduct, a series of slender grooves in the granite, spilling water into basins hacked out of solid stone.

Another stairway led to the hilltop that commands the city. Here we discovered an *intihuatana*, a short, square-topped stone column where the Inca priests worshiped their solar deity. On festival days the nobles, priests, and Chosen Women ascended these stairs in colorful, solemn procession. Beside their sacred stone they blew kisses to the sun.

We found that the dwellings vary in construction. Some have carefully matched masonry of the finest Inca architectural period. Others were obviously built quickly with small stones set in clay. On many steep-pitched gables we found carved stone rings to which the thatched roofing had been lashed.

Apparently, Machu Picchu was divided into clan groups or wards. Each had its own gateway with rings and cylinders on the inside to serve as locks. Doors probably were rough-hewn logs of hard wood, fastened by two bars that crossed each other at right angles, and were lashed to these rings or pins.

One clan group boasted a private garden on inner terraces. Another's dwellings were built with unusually steep gables and monolithic lintels over the doors. Nearly all contained their own shrines— carved granite blocks in inner courts.

The stonemasons may have used bronze chisels but had no iron tools. Yet they fashioned keyed blocks as in the beautiful wall of the semicircular sun temple. Where it joins the wall of the next house,

MAIN CITY GATE, *at the top of town, opens on a stepped Inca road that climbs to a high pass. Here tradesmen drove llamas, and runners set out for Cusco.*

the stones hook into one another so that earthquakes could not spread them apart.

One of the windows in this same temple has several small holes near the bottom that connect with circular cavities within the wall. I think it possible that priests kept a few snakes in these interior nests and used their chance exits from one hole or another as a means of telling omens and prophecies.

What of the people of Machu Picchu? To find archeological clues to their life we sought burial caves where, according to Inca custom, pottery, implements, and ornaments had been laid to rest with the dead. We offered one *sol* to any workman finding such a cave.

The result was that before season's end we had opened about 100 caves, unearthing the bones of 173 humans. With the skeletons we found jars, dishes, jewelry of bronze and silver, and some stone disks, apparently used as counters. A concave bronze mirror lay beside the remains of a *mamacuna*, or high priestess. With it she could ignite tinder by focusing the sun's rays while worshipers watched in awe.

About 150 of the skeletons we had dis-

IN GIANT STEPS *the great terraces march past the city they were built to feed. Packed with dark loam that men hauled up from the river, these hanging gardens grew corn, potatoes, perhaps lima beans for the townspeople of Machu Picchu. Visitors cross about where Bingham did when first he saw the buildings.*

Even today the Andean farmer (left) tills the soil of ancestral Inca terraces.

EDWARDS PARK AND (OPPOSITE) KIP ROSS, BOTH NATIONAL GEOGRAPHIC STAFF

covered were found to be female. Apparently the last residents of Machu Picchu were Chosen Women. This strengthened my belief that here was indeed the refuge of the last Inca and his retinue. In the royal buildings had lived the emperor. His towering fortress had defied invasion and stood forgotten. This was the same "last capital" that I had originally sought.

Thousands of tourists now visit Machu Picchu, arriving at the base of the mountain on a narrow-gauge *ferrocarril* from Cusco, then sweeping up the switchback road by bus to the stronghold that hid from the world for so long. The traveler can climb the stairways and stroll the plazas where the Inca once paced. And all around, the great silent peaks look down on the secret they guarded so well for three and a half centuries.

163

On the Trail of La Venta Man

Hacking through southern Mexico's rain forests,
Matthew W. Stirling led eight National Geographic expeditions
to unveil the story of one of America's first civilized peoples

O UR LAUNCH slipped through a jungle channel so narrow that we could touch either bank from the gunwales. Hyacinths choked the water, and the vegetation grew denser as we wound deeper into high country. Close to Tuxtla Mountain we disembarked, shifted to muleback, and filed through the tropical forest to Tres Zapotes, a thriving farm village in one of the most isolated backwashes of Mexico's Veracruz State.

Two intriguing discoveries had led our National Geographic Society-Smithsonian Institution expedition here this January of 1939. One was the Tuxtla Statuette. At the turn of the century, a Mexican trudging in a tobacco field one day saw gleaming in the soil a pale green stone. He picked it up – a jadeite figure eight inches high – and smiled. The carving depicted a bald Indian priest whose wide-open eyes radiated good humor.

This figurine was destined to become one of the most celebrated archeological finds in the New World. Decorating its belly was a Maya-style calendar date of bars and dots corresponding to 98 B.C., far earlier than any known Maya date. The relic was baffling. It was found 150 miles west of the nearest known Maya site. Had the Maya come this way? Or had another pre-Columbian people invented the calendar, considered the greatest intellectual achievement of the Maya culture?

Then there was the great stone head. In 1858 a jungle worker's spade struck what appeared to be an enormous inverted kettle. Visions of buried treasure set him to excavating. But he dropped his spade in disappointment when only a carved stone face was revealed. Over the years erosion reburied most of the head.

I was determined to excavate it, for its origin intrigued me. I knew of no Middle American culture with such massive statuary. Who had carved it, and when?

These questions turned tantalizingly in my mind as we made camp a mile from where the head lay buried.

In two days our workers uncovered the head – an awesome sight – 6 feet high, 18 feet around. It weighed more than 10 tons. Despite its size, the workmanship was delicate and sure, the proportions perfect. True artists had carved the square, sullen,

"INVERTED KETTLE" *at Tres Zapotes
proved to be the top of a ten-ton head
carved in La Venta, or Olmec, style.
Dr. Stirling excavated it in 1939
on his first expedition to the home
of these great early American artists.
A replica of a similar "colossal head"
stands in the Society's Explorers Hall.*

pug-nosed face. Topped by an incongruous helmet, it looked like an ill-humored football player.

"How do you suppose it got here?" someone asked. The nearest source for this basalt was ten miles away. We could not imagine how ancient engineers, without wheels or draft animals, could have hauled the stone across the gorge between Tres Zapotes and Tuxtla Mountain.

This was not the only huge stone transported to Tres Zapotes and carved and erected there. Our spades uncovered other sculptured stones from more than 50 mounds that rose along a two-mile stretch. East of one big stela, I set a crew digging out a five-foot-long stone chest. When we

finally unearthed it, I marveled at its elaborate scrolls and figures of gods engaged in cosmic combat. Here was one of the finest examples of stone carving ever found in Mexico. What was it for?

Nearby we found the answer—a barrel-shaped stone with a shallow basin indenting its top. Suddenly I could envision high priests tearing the throbbing heart out of a victim spread-eagled over this rock. His blood would spill into the basin and then be poured into the carved chest—a precious offering indeed to grim gods. The Indians were practicing such rites when the Spanish conquerors splashed ashore here in Veracruz. The custom could well have dated from dim antiquity.

Such discoveries convinced us that our spades were cutting into the site of a great aboriginal city whose existence was unknown to the modern world. We were revealing an entire culture hitherto barely suspected. But how old?

One hot day I tramped to a distant section of the dig to examine a flat stone that a workman said bore traces of a design. I found the men on their knees clearing mud from it. Suddenly one looked up and called, "Chief! Here are numbers!"

And numbers they were! Peering close I saw a beautifully carved row of bars and dots in low relief—exactly the form of a Maya calendar date (page 147).

I copied the characters and hurried back to camp where Mrs. Stirling and I deciphered them as 6 Eznab 1 Uo. According to the Spinden correlation this was November 4, 291 B.C.—earliest recorded date ever found in the New World!

The stone was a fragment broken from a large stela. If our section had lost three inches more from top or bottom, we could never have read it. But enough was there to determine a year that predated the famed Tuxtla Statuette by nearly two centuries. Our find ranks as the Rosetta Stone of Middle American archeology.

DURING TWO SEASONS we lived in thatched huts beside the colossal head and calendar stone of Tres Zapotes. We shared our home with armies of ants which, when they found the house in their way, generally decided to go on through rather than change course. Fat

DIRT FLIES *when Dr. Stirling's diggers pick at giant teeth of basalt. Ancient engineers dragged these two-ton volcanic pillars to La Venta, rounded them, and set them to guard a green mosaic depicting the feared jaguar god. At Tres Zapotes (opposite), workers pry a yawning Earth Monster from the mud. Turn page sideways to see the carving, perhaps of a wedding, between his lips.*

worms dropped like manna from the roof – usually down our necks. Now and then a hairy tarantula would make a social call, and one evening when Marion was washing her face she felt something rough – a big black scorpion had taken refuge in her washcloth!

The worst pests were the ticks – "little brothers under the skin." They clustered in half-inch balls on twigs. Once these *pinolillos* got inside a trouser leg, they burrowed beneath the skin, gorged with blood, and set up an itch out of all proportion to the size of the burrow. We had to go over our bodies from stem to stern each evening under the light of a gasoline lantern, and pick the ticks off, one by one.

At times unseasonable northers lashed the site, halting work and filling excavations with muddy water.

Yet it always felt good to be back in camp. I recall those calm nights when moonlight filtered between the palm-ribbed walls of our house and cut slices through our mosquito nets as though they were loaves of bread. We would hear an amorous goatsucker warbling his mournful query, "Who *are* you?" and receiving the distant reply, "Who are *you?*"

I remember listening to the sound of a rhythmic stamping like the thumping of drums. Rising and falling with the breeze came lively strains of stringed music, the wail of falsetto voices. *Huapango!* The traditional folk dance of Veracruz was in full swing a mile away.

We knew it would last till dawn. The men lucky enough to own shoes would be stamping hardest. Perhaps the orchestra would stop by to serenade us; perhaps the dancers, stimulated by more than music, would pass by, shouting and firing guns in the air. Yet when the weekend was over, despite 48 hours of continuous huapango, our workmen would appear on time in the morning none the worse for wear.

Spades bit ever deeper into the mounds of Tres Zapotes. Beneath a layer of volcanic ash, 20 feet down, we turned up pottery fragments and figurines that established Tres Zapotes as one of the longest inhabited sites in Veracruz. Ceramic styles covered a span of 2,000 years, from ten centuries before the birth of Christ until ten centuries after.

A small mound yielded the second season's most exciting discovery: a group of pottery vessels covering figurines, among them what appeared to be wheeled toys. Never before had there been any proof that the principle of the wheel was known in the New World.

We started a new phase of exploration: side trips in southern Veracruz and neighboring territory. We recalled that a Tulane University expedition headed by Frans Blom and Oliver La Farge had pressed into Tabasco State to the village of La Venta. There they photographed the top of a stone head. It seemed possible that the one they found might be the twin to our colossal head at Tres Zapotes.

Thus we set forth for La Venta, a pinpoint of a place that was destined to give its name to a rich prehistoric culture.

We boated up the Tonalá River and into a coffee-colored tributary just inside the western border of Tabasco. The unruffled water mirrored immense webs of mangrove trees. Unseen monkeys chattered and quarreled in the topmost branches.

Oil prospectors had pitched camp at a derelict village along our way. With Mexican hospitality, the men made space in their storage tent for our cots, and their Chinese cook served us a superb dinner.

Next morning we trudged through foot-sucking thickets toward a dry, sandy rise in the heart of an expansive mangrove swamp. A half hour of easy walking on this island brought us to La Venta, a large clearing with houses.

A BREATHTAKING CACHE,
*the largest discovery
of jade in the New World,
comes gradually to light
as Marion Stirling
gently brushes away
the soil of centuries.
This priceless heap of 782
trinkets and tools lay buried
under a pile of sherds at
Cerro de las Mesas.
The pieces vary in age,
material, and workmanship.*

 *Ancient Indians prized
jade more highly than gold.
When Cortés demanded
treasure, Montezuma added
"a few jades" to the golden
hoard as a special sign of
homage to Spain's emperor.*

HUNCHBACKED HUEHUETEOTL,
*ancient god of fire (left),
wears an incense burner hat.
He lay broken near the jades.*

Fifty years before, an Aztec Indian named Sebastian Torres had come to this lonely spot with his wife and two sons. Clearing the virgin forest teeming with game, they found fertile soil and prospered. One night when the moon was full, armed bandits broke in, badly wounded Sebastian, killed his sons, and stole his wealth. Years later, after another bandit raid, he gave up the attempt to get rich. Now he said he would grow only what he and his clan needed to eat.

Many were the evenings when the 85-year-old patriarch regaled us with stories of his heroic efforts to keep his village going. Once, as a special treat, I brought Don Sebastian a half-dozen cigars. He declined them, but suggested that his wife was fond of cigars. For the rest of that evening she sat propped against the wall of the house, the picture of contentment, puffing away at one cigar after another and allowing the ashes to fall between her enormous, unclothed breasts.

"She's not much to look at, but she's a fine worker, loyal, and the best wife I ever had," the venerable don told us.

We asked him and his sons-in-law about archeological remains. Yes, there were

LA VENTA TOYS, *mounted on tubes and found with eight disks at Tres Zapotes, indicate the first known use of wheels in the New World — 12 centuries ago!*

carved stones, perhaps a great many covered by jungle growth. But take care. Here at La Venta the ghosts of Montezuma and his court come out on moonlit nights to dance among the ruins and hold ceremonies in the abandoned plazas.

We braved the ghosts and mounted the jungle-tangled top of a 105-foot mound where we could look down upon an enclosure walled by stone columns. The close-set pillars indicated that this once served as a sanctum. We realized that the mound on which we stood was the crest of a pyramid — a major ceremonial shrine.

Our excavations uncovered beautifully carved altars. One had a base in the form of a stylized head with a hole running from ear to mouth. We could imagine some ancient priest speaking into the ear, and stentorian tones emerging as if by magic from the mouth!

A workman recalled two other stones in the forest. He hacked through undergrowth and suddenly we stumbled upon a large pate almost smothered in vines. I looked at it closely and grinned. Here was Blom's colossal head. Excavated, it proved to be two feet taller than its cousin at Tres Zapotes. But the two looked alike — even to the dyspeptic expression.

Then a small boy approached. "Señor, I have seen some stones near the *milpa* [maize field] where my papa is working."

In the forest half a mile away he pointed out three round heads bulging from the earth, about 30 yards apart. We dug them out. Two had finely carved teeth. The third displayed a happy, befuddled smile.

We returned to La Venta several more seasons. Here was a fountainhead of Middle American culture. La Venta men were skilled engineers as well as artists. They raised no temples or palaces, but somehow managed to get their great monoliths to the island from quarries 50 miles away. The profusion of jade and serpentine axheads showed that the ax was a sacred symbol, and meant as much to La Ventans as the cross to Christians.

Two months of digging through rubble to a depth of 23 feet rewarded us with the sight of a green stone "tiger" mask. Tamped blue clay marked eyes, mouth, and nose. In early Middle America *el tigre,* the jaguar, was sacred. Natives today fear him as their forefathers did centuries ago. And with reason. We were awakened one night by terrible squealings. Next morning we saw the carcasses of three hogs that a jaguar had killed not 200 yards from the house.

AN EXPEDITION to Cerro de las Mesas in southern Veracruz bared a large quantity of well-preserved human remains, so valuable to archeology. We cut through an upper mound that enclosed another like an onion skin, and found five pottery vessels, each holding the sawed-off face of a skull. The inner mound was apparently built for just one person's remains. The body was tightly flexed, head cut off and placed face down in an orange shell filled with red paint. The head had been flattened, a mark of aristocracy, and the teeth were inlaid with pyrite.

Nearby, we turned up 52 pottery vessels, each cradling the skull of a young adult with two or three vertebrae attached. Obviously the heads had been severed, perhaps in a mass sacrifice performed on some grim occasion.

But the real treasure at Cerro de las Mesas was jade. One day toward the end of the season, Miguel, our Mexican supervisor, ordered his diggers to remove a wedge of earth that had been left as a wheelbarrow ramp in Trench 34. They struck fragments of pottery.

Miguel took over, easing the earth away with his trowel. He uncovered a stone monkey and turtle, both painted red, and a thin disk of polished jade. Then another piece of jade, and another.

At this point he sent for me.

Carefully we worked around the deposit until we had exposed a huge pile of jade — ear ornaments, beads, tubes, pointed implements, bits of human images, plaques. It took us three and a half hours to remove it, a fortune in stones ranging from porcelain white to deep blue, with all shades of green in between — 782 pieces!

This was the largest find yet made of the most precious substance known to Mexico's ancient civilizations. It may have been an offering. Perhaps it was buried upon the approach of Aztec invaders.

Though we scarcely expected to match that windfall, we did find emerald-green masterpieces of jade in rich tombs on subsequent trips to La Venta. In all, we counted 340 handsomely carved specimens, 300 of them imperial green jade, the first of their kind ever uncovered in the New World. Some of these La Venta pieces are of the finest Oriental quality.

One piece, found north of La Venta's high central mound beside the bones of three persons, was a carving of a seated female figure, highly polished, with a circular mirror of crystal hematite attached to her chest. This carving is possibly the most exquisite example of its kind in all American archeology.

On a trip to the San Lorenzo region we found further examples of La Venta culture. An old Mexican led us to a ravine and pointed to a huge boulder lying on the slope. The colossus of all colossal heads! He was face up, top of the head down, 30 tons of basalt finely carved and too big to destroy. The invaders could only shove him into the ravine.

El Rey we called him, and knew we were gazing on a La Venta masterpiece.

La Venta Man was one of the first Middle Americans to achieve civilizational stature. Carbon-14 dating shows that his culture, sometimes known as Olmec, began before 1000 B.C. and reached its peak between 800 and 500 B.C. He was America's first great artist and lapidary, and may have originated the calendar system that later gave the Maya their chief claim to intellectual fame.

And the great earth mounds of the La Ventans were precursors to the soaring pyramids that the Maya built in Yucatán.

HEADS FLATTENED *and stretched,
15 priests of jade and serpentine
enact a mysterious rite at La Venta,
religious capital of the pre-Maya
culture that Dr. Stirling uncovered.
Another figure, set against ax blades,
may be a leader — or sacrificial victim.
Buried 15 centuries, this scene
was unearthed by Drs. Philip Drucker
and Robert F. Heizer, leaders of
the 1955 expedition to this area,
the ninth cosponsored by the Society.*

In tropical America the Stirlings meet many faces

RIDING THE SURF to a desolate Panama beach, the Stirlings plunged into the jungle
by dugout to study links between the ancient cultures of Mexico and the
pre-Inca civilizations of South America. Up the swift, shallow Rio Coclé del Norte
they pressed, boatmen straining at the poles. East of the Panama Canal they
went among the Chocó Indians, who carve canoes by hand but run them with
outboards. Once plundered by conquistadores, the Chocó gave up wearing gold.
Now they decorate themselves with silver coins, paint, and flowers.
In Ecuador, Colorado Indians mash achiote seeds to make crimson hair dye.

Dr. Stirling, Director of the Smithsonian's Bureau of American Ethnology, 1928-57,
led four National Geographic expeditions to Panama, and a fifth to Ecuador.

175

Treasure Hunt in Maya Land

For decades the National Geographic Society has unearthed and chronicled the heritage of early America's most accomplished people

"SILENT are the temples, courts, and colonnades; gone are the rulers, priests, and sacrificial victims; gone the artisans and builders; gone those humbler folk whose unremitting toil made all this pomp and pageantry possible—back to Mother Earth, enshrouded by the living green of tree and bush and flower.

"But of a moonlight night, standing on the lofty terrace before the palace of the Itzán kings, the silent city at one's feet, the temples and pyramids rising white and spectral above the dark forest, breezes whispering through the trees bring stirring tales of other days, other men, other deeds, and he who would may listen then and hear."

In Yucatán, that sere, brush-clotted, limestone thumb of Mexico, Sylvanus Griswold Morley listened and heard—and

177

THE MAYA
Their Land and Their Trade Routes

- Tinted area shows regions the Maya ruled.
- Pyramids denote their principal centers.
- Broken arrows follow main trade routes.
- Fishing scenes copy murals on temple walls in the sacred city of Chichén Itzá.

0   100   200
STATUTE MILES
NATIONAL GEOGRAPHIC MAP BY R. W. NICHOLSON

burrowed through a thousand years of history. Excavating for the Carnegie Institution of Washington, he peeled back the overgrowth from the great edifices of Chichén Itzá. And as he fitted stone upon stone to re-create this holy city of the Maya, Morley captured for *National Geographic* the spirit of America's most brilliant aboriginal culture.

These Greeks of the New World gradually concentrated in Yucatán from a broader area in Central America and Mexico. "The former centers were abandoned," says Morley. "The forest returned, and again the jaguar, tapir, peccary, and deer stalked the courts where kings had ruled and priests performed their rites of hu-

man sacrifice. Meanwhile the cities of Yucatán became the new fountainheads."

Morley described "the so-called Castillo, which is not a castle at all, but the principal temple of Kukulcan, the Feathered Serpent god," rising more than 100 feet above Chichén Itzá's broad plaza. He told of astronomers mounting the spiral passage of the nearby Caracol observatory to determine the seasons for sowing and reaping, while wise men chiseled dot, bar, and glyph of a calendar system accurate to the day within a span of 370,000 years.

He was impressed by the Temple of the Warriors, atop its pyramidal base. "The front chamber is a long colonnaded hall; behind it is the sanctuary. Carved and

BATES LITTLEHALES, NATIONAL GEOGRAPHIC PHOTOGRAPHER

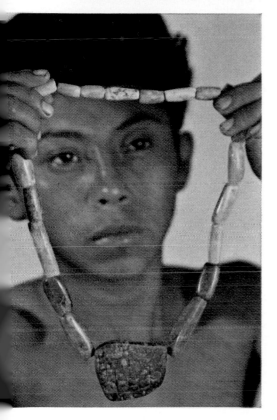

painted columns preserve their original brilliancy—red, blue-green, yellow, brown, black, and white. Enormous plumed serpents weave around the sides.

"Imagine the barbaric splendor of this building, broad summit thronged with priests gorgeously robed in jaguar skins, feather cloaks, and embroidered cottons, half seen in clouds of swirling incense!"

IN YUCATÁN no water flows above the ground. It is drawn from natural wells, *cenotes*. At Chichén Itzá there are two. One was for life—it supplied the city. The other was for death. This sacred cenote faces the Castillo and is linked to it by the *Via Sacra*, a stone causeway. In days of

TREASURES from all the Maya world were brought to Chichén Itzá's sacred cenote. Spanish chroniclers reported: "Into this well they have had . . . the custom of throwing men alive as a sacrifice to the gods. . . . They also threw into it a great many other things, like precious stones."

Diving and pumping, archeologists retrieved human bones and thousands of artifacts from the cenote's muddy bottom. Gold beads, and jade gem and necklace shine anew. Copal resin again burns brightly in an incense bowl. And a clay head of an eagle warrior still wears its ancient paint.

179

drought and famine, pilgrims from distant lands converged for the grim rite. Priests in solemn procession led the anointed and blue-painted victim along the Via Sacra amid music and dancing.

In some ceremonies the living victim's heart was cut out. In others—"a push, perchance a startled cry, a splash below, and silence." Then the pilgrims hurled in their personal treasures, gold and jade, pottery and carved wood.

"Could this old limestone water pit be given a tongue and made to tell what it had seen, what world romance could equal it?" wrote Edward H. Thompson, a former United States Consul in Yucatán, in the June, 1914, *National Geographic*. Years earlier, Thompson had hauled a dredge to the cenote and scooped from it startling treasures: gold masks and breastplates, bracelets and jade stones.

No one doubted that the well still hid many relics of scenes it had witnessed. In 1960 the National Geographic Society, the National Institute of Anthropology and History of Mexico, and the Exploration and Water Sports Club of Mexico came to investigate. An air lift vacuumed the bottom. Divers probed the murky waters, among them Bates Littlehales of National Geographic.

"The whole setting was eerie," he reported. "The water seemed to have turned to ink. With my underwater flashlight, I couldn't see beyond my arm. By touch I established the shapes of fallen boulders and twisted, waterlogged trees."

Yet the sinkhole yielded more than 4,000 artifacts: incense burners, jade amulets, gold and copper bells, a four-inch rubber effigy still holding its dancing pose after five centuries under water (page 147).

"ON A SUN-BEATEN thorny plain in northwest Yucatán, an expanse of overgrown, long-forgotten ruins is emerging as possibly the largest and longest inhabited city of ancient America."

Thus archeologist E. Wyllys Andrews introduced the lost site of Dzibilchaltun in the January, 1959, *National Geographic*. He continues in his own words:

In this vanished metropolis, our National Geographic Society-Tulane University team has opened new perspectives into the Maya story. We are uncovering the first continuous era-by-era record of Maya life over its entire span, from its rise thousands of years ago down to the Spanish conquest in the 16th century.

If you could stand with me upon the terrace of the Temple of the Seven Dolls and look about you, what would you see? Only the dusty scrub of Yucatán, perhaps the bone-white scar of a triumphal avenue, a few mounds of rubble. You would not see any great Maya center.

It is there nonetheless. It extends in orderly array—20 square miles by our current estimate, more than one-quarter the size of the District of Columbia. After long study I still have trouble bringing it into focus; yet I can sense the nobility of its proportions, the grandeur of its conception. Dzibilchaltun in its heyday—perhaps years before the rise of Chichén Itzá —had a ten-square-mile "downtown" zone thick with pyramidal temples, palaces, and thatched houses on stone foundations. Such early centers of Maya power were not previously known to exist in northern Yucatán. By the end of our first season's work we realized we had an archeological bear by the tail.

Behind a wing of an awesome complex of buildings which we christened the Palace, we cut a trench into what seemed a refuse heap. We sought something exceedingly rare in hardpan Yucatán—a deep deposit of undisturbed artifacts capable of giving us a kind of ledger of the centuries. That is just what we found. We recovered 250,000 fragments of pottery —a haul that will require years to assess fully. Here too we found the skeletons of two Maya girls. One had her incisor teeth filed down to points. We can only hope she found this fillip to her beauty sufficient to justify the pain.

In our second season I gave way to the fascination of a crumbling pyramid at the eastern end of the great white causeway and began excavating what appeared to be some buried chambers. Before long it became clear that I had stumbled onto an entire temple, intentionally and carefully buried. One day Eugenio May, chief of the labor force, rushed up and exclaimed, "Don Beel! We have uncovered the top of what must be a window!"

LUIS MARDEN AND (BELOW LEFT) BATES LITTLEHALES, BOTH NATIONAL GEOGRAPHIC STAFF. BELOW: WILLIAM W. CAMPBELL III

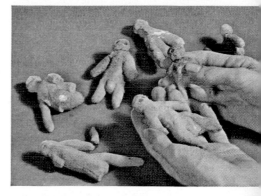

DZIBILCHALTUN, *a ghost amid fields of sisal, thrived for some 3,000 years as a Maya center. This excavated temple held seven strange dolls (above). Expedition leader E. Wyllys Andrews (left) brushes dirt from a burial urn.*

181

TEMPLE OF THE SEVEN DOLLS, *carefully restored, dominates three lesser structures at Dzibilchaltun. Today's Mayas uncovered it from 10,000 tons of rubble (right), the ruins of a huge pyramid their forefathers had built over this ancestral shrine.*

I snorted. "Eugenio, after 25 years! You know as well as I that the *antiguos* never built windows. Keep digging. You'll find this to be a small side door."

Two and a half feet farther down we came upon sills. Eugenio was right. We had uncovered windows as we use the term today, unlike the small openings in most Maya buildings. Carbon-14 dating indicated the temple had been built about 1,450 years ago. Our studies show that it was in intermittent use for the amazing span of more than 1,000 years. At some point the Maya, perhaps ashamed of its old-fashioned lines, decided to bury the temple. At great effort they stuffed it carefully with stone and used it as a foundation for a much larger edifice which, in turn, was destroyed.

Then, during the last gasp of Maya civilization, the Indians turned archeologists. Tunneling down through the structure, they cleaned out the rubble obscuring the inner sanctuary and rededicated it as a subterranean shrine. In its center they built a plaster tube leading to the rubble below. There they placed seven small clay dolls. None of us had ever seen anything like them. Two are hunchbacks, one is a dwarf, another has a swollen stomach.

On an altar two steps away from the top of the tube was a striking medallion covered with stucco and repainted with three different hieroglyphic texts. After much soul-searching, we painstakingly scraped away the upper layers, photographing and sketching the later texts to preserve them. We were lucky; an almost perfect inscrip-

BATES LITTLEHALES, NATIONAL GEOGRAPHIC PHOTOGRAPHER

tion emerged, its glyphs precise and clear. These are the only hieroglyphic inscriptions ever found from the last 650 to 900 years of Maya history.

Our findings show that this amazing center was founded around 1000 B.C., if not earlier. Its culture flowered. But instead of being abandoned, it thrived uninterruptedly into Spanish colonial times.

The gaunt, gray ruins of Dzibilchaltun have given us a unique record stretching 3,000 years.

Not all the treasures of Dzibilchaltun lie on the ground or even in it. One of the site's most striking features is the great cenote. Of its web-footed exploration, ace diver photographer Luis Marden writes with vivid authority.

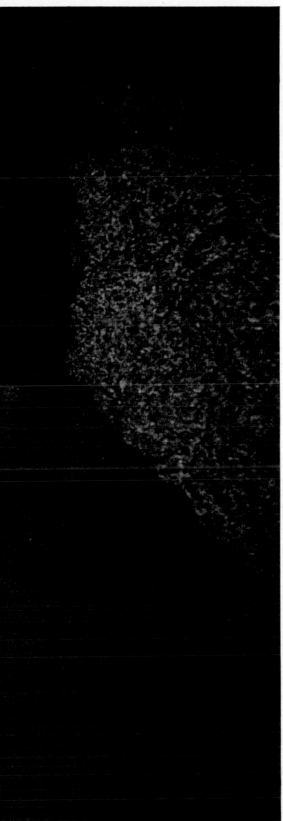

Into the Well of Time

At Dzibilchaltun, Luis Marden of National Geographic plunged a thousand years into the past

I CLENCHED THE AQUA-LUNG mouthpiece between my teeth, took a breath of bottled air, and slid downward into the cenote of Dzibilchaltun. I had often dived to the sea bottom. Now, for the first time, I was diving through it.

This deep natural well—one of hundreds that pock the flat face of northern Yucatán—emerged from an ocean bed perhaps a million years ago. I had come to hunt for artifacts dropped or thrown into the well by the ancient Maya.

Silvery characin fishes darted round my head. Beneath me the green carpet of water weeds stopped at the limit of sunlight. Under the rock overhang at the cenote's deep end I paused to turn on the flashlight that hung from my wrist. As my eyes adjusted to the gloom, I could see the vast curve of the roof and back wall receding in a dim semicircle, like an amphitheater seen by moonlight.

I expelled air and sank down a rubble-strewn slope that dropped at an angle of 50 degrees. The jumble of limestone fragments in the black ooze seemed to slide upward, reversing in slow motion their age-old fall. Here and there lay carved stones, evidence of human handiwork.

At 60 feet I looked up and saw, swimming in black silhouette against the blue rectangle of the entrance, Bates Littlehales, my diving companion and National

185

80 Ft.

144 Ft.

DZIBILCHALTUN'S CENOTE
*angles deep into the
limestone of Yucatán.
Divers with shimmering
lamps followed their
lifeline into Stygian
darkness to raise
6,000 Maya artifacts
and bones (opposite)
from the rubble
and silt of the ages.*

Geographic colleague. He came down, wagged his lamp reassuringly, and we continued to sink. At 80 feet the slope came to a landing of velvety mud, then plunged abruptly into blackness between two pylons of rock. Just here stood a big lintel of stone which I fingered for possible hieroglyphs. Its sides were smooth.

We edged between the pylons, our lamps throwing cones of light on the back wall which curved abruptly down to the cenote's toe. Past the columns we came to another landing where the bottom dipped again, flattened, and slid into a low-arched black tunnel. There the depth gauges read 120 feet. I looked up. Under the curve of rock the surface opening glowed faintly green, its dim arch of light slashed by the masses of rock, like monstrous jambs at the gate of some cold and silent hell.

We finned into the tunnel, swimming close to the floor of ooze to pass under the low arch. Suddenly muck swirled before my mask. I turned to look for Bates and saw the green disk of his lamp wink out. I turned my own light full in my eyes —and could see nothing. I could not tell up from down, or which way led back to the tunnel opening, to the surface, to air. For ten seconds I felt black panic.

Then reason returned. Inhaling deeply, I rose to the tunnel roof and clung there like a fly. As the roil subsided it left a foot of relatively clear water under the roof, and I saw Bates's light wavering toward me. We touched hands and started up.

In the dazzling sunlight I asked Bates why the mud had boiled up so suddenly.

"It was this," he said, holding up one arm. "I saw it lying half buried in the mud, and when I tugged at it, the ooze spurted up in a cloud." He was wearing an oversize armlet of terra cotta, the broken neck of a jar—our first artifact.

AT 60 FEET we struck our first rich lode. Necks of earthenware pots lay thick among a rubble of shaped stones, which, we thought, had slid from a pyramid on the rim. But Manuel, our camp caretaker, told us of his people's belief: that a king, whose castle stood where the cenote is now, once refused his mother a drink. His fine house sank into the water.

In one dive we could easily fill our wire

baskets. Lying head upward on the slope, moving as little as possible to conserve air and avoid clouding the water, we could stay down 40 to 50 minutes on a tank of air. Working with our Mexican fellow divers, we sent pail after pail of potsherds to the surface. The clay was soft when it came out of the water, but after drying in the fierce sun, the pieces hardened.

One day I heard Bates hooting through his mouthpiece. He held a slender object toward me. I took it, thinking it was an abnormally long thorn. With my lamp I saw it was a bone awl engraved with a row of hieroglyphs. We shook hands and started up. Like nearly all nonnumerical Maya hieroglyphs, some of these carvings proved undecipherable. The awl may have been a skewer, thrust into the glossy hair of a Maya girl who lost it drawing water.

In two weeks of digging we exhausted our rich vein and moved down to 80 feet. Here we worked standing on our heads, groping in ooze up to our armpits. Under a tree trunk we found a dozen buried pots, some of them still whole.

While probing deep in the muck at 90 feet, I grasped something that felt like a branching twig. When I shook it free from its coating of mud, I recognized a piece of sea fan, a gorgonian such as I had swum among many times on coral reefs. How did it come to be in the cenote?

Later I found more fan fragments, and these finds convince me that there must have been a special rite connected with the cenote, perhaps a cult of the sea.

Bates and I decided one day to see how far we could penetrate the cavern at the bottom of the cenote. We dived to where our lifeline plunged into blackness between the rock pinnacles. I had rigged two lines tied to bronze snap swivels. We snapped them to the lifeline and swam down into the murk.

In the light from my lamp a black catfish, eyes gleaming dull ruby, trailed its whiskers in the mud. Here, more than 50 feet into the tunnel, the floor ran level.

A cloud of ooze swirled around us. I looked at my depth gauge: 144 feet. We

FORGOTTEN FLUTE, *silent for
centuries, intrigues Dr. Andrews.
Made of clay, the flute broke
when Marden extracted it from
its grave of mud and stone.
Ethel Marden, the author's wife,
found the first figurine,
a hollow clay jaguar (left).
Discovery of such nonutilitarian
objects suggests that the well
may have received gifts and
sacrifices to the gods as did the
sacred cenote at Chichén Itzá.*

   *Diver Fernando Euan (below)
works carefully to prevent
shifting rubble from smashing
artifacts. His wire pail holds a
human femur. The squared stones
probably tumbled from a temple
that once stood beside the pool.*

remained only 15 minutes, then swam back to the amphitheater and rose at the prescribed rate of 25 feet per minute.

Within five minutes of emerging I felt a slight pain in my right upper arm. I put on a fresh air tank and went down to 60 feet. I stayed 10 minutes, then came up by decompression stages. Still the pain. I went down to 80 feet for 20 minutes. When I rose, again by stages, I was chilled through. The pain returned. There was no doubt now; for the first time in 17 years of diving I had the bends.

Bates and I raced to Mérida, 20 minutes away. There an engineer friend, Melvin Art, rigged a recompression chamber from a square-sided oil tank. Though he felt no symptoms, Bates decided to take the treatment with me.

Recompression tables called for a pressure of three atmospheres, equivalent to 100 feet of water. We lowered ourselves into the tank and lay in pitch darkness. The valves opened and air roared in. Then the roar died to a hiss. My ears told me we were not at 100 feet, but we lay quietly, knowing Mel was doing his best.

After 20 minutes we signaled for more air. None came. We hammered the signal for "take us up." The manhole cover clanged aside, and we climbed out.

"The tank wouldn't take any more," Mel said. "We hadn't reached two atmospheres when the sides began to bulge."

My arm still ached dully.

"I've got a cylindrical tank that should stand a lot more pressure," Mel said. The tank was too small for two men. Bates still showed no signs of the bends, so I entered alone. So much time had elapsed we decided to try five atmospheres, equivalent to a depth of 165 feet.

I spent 6 hours and 12 minutes in that steel coffin, one of the least pleasant experiences of my life. And when I finally emerged, blinking in the light, Bates said, "We couldn't get you down to 165. The tank wouldn't stand more than 100."

That night I slept under sedation. When I awoke I found Bates stretched stiffly on his bed. He felt pain in his spine and could not sit up. Now I was truly alarmed. If this was also the bends, he was in danger of complete paralysis.

An emergency call brought, that afternoon, a four-engine U. S. Navy plane with pressurized cabin. Three hours later we were in Panama City, Florida, where we spent 44 hours and 26 minutes in a recompression tank at the Mine Defense Laboratory. We emerged fully cured, thanks to the Navy and two of its doctors, Lts. Charles F. Aquadro and David M. Jewett. They took care of two unshaven and ailing civilians with unfailing good humor and we felt deeply grateful. I returned to Yucatán a few days later.

MY WIFE came to search with us, and on her last day of diving she found the first figurine from the cenote, a little clay jaguar. My own best find was a bone finger ring, incised with glyphs and a zigzag design, as fresh and sharply outlined as if carved yesterday. And several times we found, interspersed with the bones of cows and rodents, human bones.

Possibly the bones were of victims of drowning or even the *corpora delictorum* of pre-Columbian murders. But the increasing number of nonutilitarian relics —a molded head, noseplugs, a clay flute— in addition to bones, made Dr. Andrews think this well may have been the center of a sacrificial cult, like that which centered round the sacred cenote at latter-day Chichén Itzá.

On the final day, after the first heavy rain of the season had suddenly come and gone, and the sun was washing everything in a pale champagne light, I thought of the treasures so long hidden in the well beneath my feet.

Through the centuries the slow rain of pots and gourds, spears and lances, jade pendants and carved bone ornaments, even the bones of men and women, sifted softly down to their beds of ooze. Here they were held, safe from the erosion of sun and wind, inviolate in the green twilight until man found a way to take his air with him into the aqueous world.

MARDEN REPORTS FROM THE PIT *while his Geographic colleague Bates Littlehales massages away the cramps of a chilling hour's work. The bends sent both men racing to recompression chambers.*

MELVILLE BELL GROSVENOR

The Riddle of Pueblo Bonito

In a seven-year exploration for the Society, archeologist
Neil M. Judd restored New Mexico's "Beautiful Village" from
a heap of stone and traced the life of its ancient citizens

FOUR-STORY OUTER WALL OF D-SHAPED PUEBLO BONITO RISES BESIDE CLIFF FACE OF REMOTE CHACO CANYON; RALPH GRAY, NATIONAL GEOGRAPHIC STAFF

THERE IT LAY, surrounded by a sea of sand and mystery: the foremost prehistoric ruin in the United States, the largest, most complex, most impressive. A broken pile of once-terraced homes that rose four stories and covered ten times more ground than the White House. A massive apartment house sheltering up to 1,200 people, unmatched in size the world over until New York City's Spanish Flats were erected in 1882.

Pueblo Bonito. Beautiful Village!

It stands in the maw of Chaco Canyon in northwestern New Mexico. When the National Geographic Society undertook to explore it in 1921, I was struck by the challenge of the gigantic rock pile.

Who built this marvelous city? When? Why did they leave it?

In our first season we dug through more than 40 of the 800 rooms in this huge, D-shaped human hive. We carefully gathered usable stones from the fallen walls. We passed these building blocks from hand to hand and piled them at a central point amid the ruins until we needed them for repairing the walls.

In older portions of the city we found crude stonework. In some areas, blocks of rubbed sandstone had been laid in adobe mud and chinked with small chips. The later walls consist of evenly cut stones placed close together. Jack Lavery, our chief mason, became so skilled at imitat-

193

CEREMONIAL LODGES—*for men only—
rise once more. Horses haul out tons
of debris (below), then masons set the
stones as Indian artisans did 1,000
years ago. Men built these circular
kivas; women did the stonework on
dwellings. This "might explain the fact
that kiva masonry is invariably
inferior," the author suggests.*

HUB DEEP *in Chaco Canyon quicksand,
this truck stuck fast for six hours
despite combined efforts of ten men
and a team of horses. Seven National
Geographic expeditions fought
cloudburst and sandstorm to uncover
the Bonitian way of life.*

*Expedition leader Neil M. Judd
(left), then Curator of Archeology
at the U. S. National Museum, stands
with the leader of a pueblo whose people
still live much as the Bonitians did.*

194

ing the craft of the ancients that our Zuni workmen called him *Enote Nahme*, Prehistoric Grandfather.

We tapped a hidden desert reservoir for drinking water. As its surface rose and fell the number of men at the dig increased or diminished. When hot July winds blew across the mesas to pile the rain clouds back upon the horizon, we measured our cisterns twice a day, and work lagged. When the gods smiled the job progressed smoothly, with 35 Indians, 10 whites, and 8 horses at work in the ruins.

At such times our camp became the seventh largest settlement in San Juan County. All provisions for it had to be hauled from the railroad. Thus our corner grocery at Gallup was separated from our kitchen at Chaco Canyon by 106 miles of happened-by-chance road. In dry weather a one-way trip took seven hours. During the rains our drivers carried bedrolls and a week's rations.

If it wasn't rain, it was dust that we faced in our exposed camp. On the very heels of a saturating shower we would see a cloud of flourlike sand rolling over a distant cliff and up the canyon. Nothing

escaped this dust. It found its way into locked trunks, beneath watch crystals, and worst of all, into food served by our incomparable cook. Once when sand showered down like pumice we had to drag our stove to a vacant dugout, fresh with the unmistakable odor of goats.

Our dealings with the Indians called for diplomacy. If our Navajo neighbors arrived with empty lard buckets and complained of dry water holes, we shared our meager supply. When they returned with horses and herds of goats, we had to clamp on the lid and tell them to dig their own wells deeper. If one or more of our workmen threatened to flare up in mutiny over some imaginary injustice, we dissipated war clouds with a five-cent bag of candy or a sack of tobacco. I am a firm believer in the efficacy of the lowly gumdrop and the pipe of peace.

Then there was the mother-in-law problem. The Navajo is forbidden by tradition to look upon or speak to his wife's mother. If, during the working day, the mother-in-law of one of our Navajo passed by, he would drop his shovel and pull his shirt over his head until she left.

O. C. HAVENS

Our original Americans seem to possess some mysterious means of telepathy. Let some important event take place, and every Indian for miles around will know of it before you have a chance to send word. So it was when, in a deep room, I troweled away a covering of earth to reveal the most magnificent discovery of all the expeditions to Pueblo Bonito—a priceless turquoise necklace (page 148). Within minutes, every Navajo and Zuni on the job was draped over the insecure walls to watch what was going on.

We brushed away the dust of ages, and at last the necklace emerged—2,500 tiny blue stones shining in all their ancient splendor. How unbelievably hard the prehistoric lapidary must have labored, rubbing each bead back and forth against sandstone, drilling each minute stone

exactly in the center with a sharpened flint. Nothing was more highly prized by the Pueblo Indians of a thousand years ago, as by their descendants today, than turquoise. Symbol of the blue desert sky, of vaulted heavens, of mystic oceans!

FROM ORNAMENTS such as that marvelous necklace, from pottery and tools, from living quarters and ceremonial rooms, or kivas, we sought to reconstruct the wordless history of the vanished Bonitians. We found that despite the lack of written records their story sometimes seemed to flow from the specimen at hand.

We sensed pride in the maker of the necklace, joy of possession in its owner. We saw that this had been a wealthy community of home-loving, sedentary, backyard farmers. It had lured parrot venders

Tree rings unlock secrets of the Southwest

"PUEBLO BONITO guards her age well!" wrote Neil M. Judd in the July, 1923, *National Geographic*. "The exact date when it was first established and the year when it was abandoned remain unsolved problems." Yet even as he wrote, the riddle was under attack.

In 1923, 1928, and 1929 the National Geographic Society assigned astronomer Andrew Ellicott Douglass to head expeditions in the Southwest. The purpose: to fix the dates of Pueblo Bonito's building and abandonment by studying tree rings.

The life history of almost every tree is revealed by its growth rings. Thin rings mean dry years; thick ones spell years of abundant rainfall. Since wet and dry periods tend to alternate at fairly regular intervals, all the trees in any one district acquire a more or less orderly sequence of thick and thin annual rings. Some of these sequences appear often enough to be recognizable and thus serve as keys. The expert finds them in living and dead trees and in roof beams of prehistoric ruins.

Judd thought that enough old timbers

from Veracruz and seashell dealers from the Pacific. It had also tempted human wolves—roving hunters of the desert.

These nomads had slain lone Bonitian workers in the city gardens and dragged boys and young women away as slaves. In four burial rooms we found an astonishing example of their pillage. Most of the 71 bodies laid to rest here had been wantonly disturbed—skulls tossed aside, arms and legs torn from crushed torsos, bones scattered in hopeless confusion during a hasty search for turquoise.

Nomadic raiders eventually forced the Bonitians to seal off parts of their pueblo and were probably one cause of its abandonment. Disease, dwindling water supplies, and soil turned sterile by alkali surely added to the pressure. If there was an immediate cause for the Bonitians to leave their city, it is lost in the sands of the last thousand years.

How easy it would have been to tell the story of this great pre-Columbian experiment in communal living if we could have pictured the scenes that were witnessed from the canyon wall that towers over the ruins. But we saw only an accumulation of fallen walls and windblown sands.

Summer after summer, from 1921 to 1927, we dug deeper into the maze of empty rooms. We carted away 100,000 tons of earth and stone. And as we repaired the broken walls, we pieced together a little of the life of the ancient residents.

Now Pueblo Bonito again stands clearly outlined on the floor of Chaco Canyon National Monument. It will remain a splendid memorial to the primitive genius of its long-forgotten inhabitants.

could be found in Hopi villages and Spanish missions to establish a continuous calendar of rings reaching back from living forest to the oldest beams of Pueblo Bonito. Douglass proposed to find out.

From giant tree stumps, from old timbers in occupied pueblos, from rubbish-filled ruins Douglass slowly pushed back his tree ring timetable. At Oraibi, a sun-baked Hopi pueblo in Arizona, he took a core from an upright post and read the rings—back to 1260.

Meanwhile, from even older ruins, including those in Chaco Canyon, Douglass pieced together a continuous 585-year sequence of tree rings. But nowhere could he be certain that the rings of this early sequence matched those that stretched from modern times to 1260. Reluctantly, Douglass labeled his early series a "floating chronology" and set about finding a link between it and the later timetable.

He offered a reward for any living pine tree more than 600 years old. No luck. He poked through Hopi pueblos, smoothing his way with diplomacy. A gift of six turtles opened the door to an unused kiva, but he was forbidden to bore into the timbers. "I spent most of the time from five in the afternoon until midnight lying flat on the floor, a lens to my eye, counting and measuring the rings in the planks," he wrote. But it was to no avail.

Early in 1929 a charred beam from a buried Hopi ruin in the thriving Mormon town of Showlow, Arizona, was bound with twine to keep it from crumbling, and labeled HH39. Douglass recognized its outer rings as 14th century growth. Counting in toward the core, he passed 1260. The wood had begun life in 1237.

Now a quick comparison with the floating chronology. The rings overlapped! The 551st year of the floating chronology matched perfectly with year 1251 in beam HH39. Indeed the last years of the floating chronology clearly overlapped the year 1260. "We had closed the gap without knowing it," wrote Douglass.

"By the time I went to sleep that night, I knew that the earliest beam found in Pueblo Bonito was felled in 919, and that the 'Beautiful Village' reached its golden age by 1066, the year William the Conqueror faced Harold the Saxon at Hastings. Pueblo Bonito was still occupied in 1127, and was empty by 1299."

Tree ring chronology has dated hundreds of other Indian ruins in the Southwest. It clearly shows the years of the Great Drought, 1276 to 1299, a chief cause of the abandonment of these dwellings.

MEMBERS OF THE SOCIETY'S COMMITTEE FOR RESEARCH AND EXPLORATION INSPECT 700-YEAR-OLD
DWELLINGS IN WETHERILL MESA'S MUG HOUSE; ALBERT MOLDVAY, NATIONAL GEOGRAPHIC PHOTOGRAPHER

Sifting the Mystery
of the Vanished Cliff Dwellers

*In a remote corner of Colorado's Mesa Verde National Park
Douglas Osborne's archeological team works with spade
and computer to restore the forgotten cities of Wetherill Mesa*

To US THE ROOM WAS NO. 28 of Long House, a silent, crumbling cliff village on the jutting finger of high ground called Wetherill Mesa. There, some 700 years ago, a baby died.

His mother tenderly wrapped him in the feather blanket that had taken so many hours of work. Gently she buried him in the dirt of a back room, placing a turkey beside him, and returned, mourning, to the incessant toil of the living.

Soon, forces still to be determined drove the woman's people from their dwellings in the cliffs. Centuries passed.

Where the baby lay it was dry; perhaps a little drifting snow reached in, a sprinkle of hard-driven rain, but that would be all. The small body dried out. In time a wall crumbled, the roof fell.

For hundreds of years the silence of the buildings was broken only by the ravens' call, the coyotes' song. Then came a new race of men to dig among the ruins.

The National Park Service, with the support of the National Geographic Society, was conducting this exhaustive archeological search through the Wetherill Mesa section of vast Mesa Verde National Park in Colorado. We had come to learn more of the ancient Pueblo Indians, called by the Navajo *Anasazi*, "the Old Ones." We began in 1958, with a survey.

To understand how we worked, visit with our survey crew. You stand in a gnarled juniper-piñon forest that covers the mesa top. Beneath your feet is red, dusty soil, sparsely grassed. The sun beats down through thin foliage; sometimes a cool breeze touches your cheek.

Sounds move toward you: voices, the crackling of dead branches underfoot. Through the woods comes a line of men, 50 to 75 feet apart, their eyes swinging back and forth, each man covering his allotted section. From the end of the line comes a call: "Here are sherds. Several."

"What are they?"

"Black on white and corrugated. It looks like float" (washed out potsherds on the surface of the ground).

"Good going. We'll follow it up."

A moment later: "More sherds. They're getting thicker as I go uphill."

"Fine. Hold to the ravine. Bet there's a site on the ridge."

"Lots of 'em now."

"Here's the site! Here it is!"

That low formless mound beneath the trees, thick with gray-green sagebrush, was the trash dump—see the broken pottery? There's a *metate*—the corn-grinding stone; a chipped tool, arrow points.

That low curving mound with a few building stones sticking up helter-skelter through the forest duff was a line of dwelling rooms. That faint round depression was a kiva. A thousand years ago people worked and played and prayed here. Here some still sleep.

After discovering an archeological site the survey crew maps it, photographs it, and writes up a detailed description of its

OSWALD WERNER. OPPOSITE; WILLIAM BELKNAP, JR.

dwellings of articles left above ground. But they did not find all the caches. Some remained untouched half a century later.

Our painstaking survey located many of them. It was archeologist Al Hayes, working alone, who found the first. After recording the site of a small cliff ruin in Upper Rock Canyon, he started down, hesitated, then went back and peered into a crevice. To this day he can't say why he went back. But in that hidden crack he found a bundle of digging sticks—sharpened staffs used to break and hoe the soil—and a large black-on-white painted bowl. The bowl had lain there 700 years.

One of the most exciting climbs turned out to be the most valuable. One day Hayes and a fellow archeologist, Curt Schaafsma, circled an isolated, 100-foot-high butte, studying it as a boxer measures an opponent. They found a crack in one of its sheer sides and started up. Curt climbed Al's back to reach a foothold. Then he lowered a rope to Al, who pulled up to where he could return the favor.

Two-thirds of the way up, Curt shouted, "Loose rock. I'm afraid it's coming off!" It did. Al couldn't duck without losing balance. The crown of his Stetson absorbed most of the impact of the football-size stone. "That" he said later, "and the fact that I had my head pulled down until the hat brim rested on my clavicles!"

But the trip was worth the strain. They found a 13-room cliffside apartment.

The Anasazi were in this land a few centuries after Christ, living by hunting and gathering wild food. By A.D. 500 or 600 their pit houses were growing larger, and they had established corn, beans, and squash as the great triad of agriculture. By 900 they built homes of stone; by

surface features. Then the diggers begin.

In Long House, with the fallen roof and wall cleared away, a bit of fabric comes to light. Dropping his shovel, an experienced man gently reveals more with a trowel, then straightens to announce the rarest of finds, a scientific treasure trove: "This is a mummy! Call Art!"

Archeologist Art Rohn hurries over. His trained hands remove the small bundle and the mummified turkey, probably food for the journey into the hereafter.

The blanket tells how the people worked their textiles. The body shows the burial position, flexed as in the womb, the same position as that used by other Indians of the Southwest. Each clue helps solve the mystery of this vanished people, a mystery lingering since that snowy December day in 1888 when two cowboys reined up at a canyon's edge and looked across to discover a forgotten city of stone.

Archeologists and explorers of that day combed the area and stripped the cliff

the 1100's they were fine masons, shaping blocks to corners and curved walls. They created handsome pottery, domesticated the turkey, built waterworks, and even practiced soil conservation.

But time was running out. In the late 1200's drought may have made existence grim. The dwindling population crowded into caves and built cliff dwellings. A strange life these people must have led, jammed cheek by jowl, sheltered in the great sandstone alcoves. Yet few of the wealthy today can see from their picture windows scenery so wildly beautiful. The Anasazi knew their land in an intimate way that few of us can comprehend.

By the year 1300 or thereabouts the great pueblos were deserted. Juniper smoke hung no more in the valleys in the cool mornings; men went no more to the fields; the turkeys ran wild. No longer did the chants of the people, the shaking rattles, and stamping feet implore the gods for rain. After 1,000 years it was over. The Anasazi vanished from Mesa Verde.

To SOLVE this final mystery we have set up one of the most complete scientific programs ever undertaken with an archeological exploration. Scientists from no fewer than 19 specialties work with us. We use every type of equipment from mousetraps to computers.

Automatic weather stations record today's climate. Near them, mounted on trees, complex little dendrographs measure the trees' imperceptible growth. We correlate present climate and tree growth; timbers from the ruins show past growth. Thus we may determine past climate. If there was a change in the weather strong enough to make life unacceptable to the cliff dwellers, we shall find it.

A plant ecologist studies the present growth on the mesa. Under a microscope, ancient pollen grains, which are tough and last indefinitely, tell us what plants grew here in the past.

A soil conservation expert bores with a powerful hydraulic cylinder to study changes in the soil over the centuries. Perhaps he will discover evidence of erosion which made agriculture hopeless for the Indians of the 1200's.

An animal ecologist studies the living

SNOW MANTLES *the mesas where now-silent cities once rang with Indian chant and laughter. National Park Service-National*

mammals of the mesas. Ancient mammal bones, discarded after many a hearty meal, even insect remains, give us a good cross section of the life of former times.

Finally, we have the bones of some of the Anasazi themselves. We found more than 40 skeletons in a trash heap near Long House. Examine one with me.

It is on its side, knees drawn up, arms folded. You wonder if this was a man or a woman. I show you characteristics of skull and pelvis that tell us this was a man who died in his mid-forties.

Geographic Society restoration of the fortresslike homes and ceremonial kivas on Wetherill Mesa will relieve the pressure on nearby Cliff Palace (above), which each year feels the tread of nearly 200,000 Mesa Verde visitors.

You think this person was a large man? I match the right thigh bone against my own upper leg—it is at least an inch and a half shorter. The other bones are comparable, all smaller than mine. I am 6 feet tall; this man could not have been taller than 5 feet, 5 or 6 inches.

See how worn the teeth are, how smooth the surfaces? These people ground corn on sandstone slabs; grit was always present.

So goes the absorbing task of re-forming the past. Each object becomes a clue. Clue joins clue, the story comes into focus.

But we have been doing far more than digging and studying on Wetherill Mesa. We have been preserving. With aid from the National Geographic Society, we have strengthened ancient structures, shored up enfeebled walls, provided firm foundations and protection from the elements.

Someday Wetherill Mesa will have roads and trails. A museum will be built to house the artifacts we have found. Then you will be able to come and see with your own eyes this part of America's past in its splendid frame of cliff and canyon.

Exploring the Drowned City of Port Royal

Marion Clayton Link joins her husband's quest for a pirate lair smitten by an earthquake and buried under the sea in 1692

SHAKEN AND SHATTERED, PORT ROYAL SINKS INTO THE SEA; ROBERT W. NICHOLSON, NATIONAL GEOGRAPHIC STAFF

"LORD, SIR, what is this?" cried the Reverend Emanuel Heath. A rumbling like distant thunder rolled from Jamaica's mountains over Port Royal.

"An earthquake; be not afraid, it will soon be over," replied Acting Governor John White. On that late morning of June 7, 1692, he was about to take a glass of wormwood wine with Mr. Heath, rector of St. Paul's Church.

Then, in quick succession, three shocks rent the island. The waterfront lurched into the sea. "The earth heaved and swelled like the rolling billows," wrote a survivor, "and in many places the earth crack'd, open'd, and shut ... in some of these people were swallowed up, in others they were caught up by the middle and pressed to death.... The sky was turned dull and reddish, like a glowing oven."

Stout Fort James and Fort Carlisle vanished as if they had never been. A great wave formed and swelled and rolled in from the sea, capsizing several ships. But the frigate *Swan* worked in over the tops of houses and helped save hundreds of lives. The terrifying convulsions lasted only two minutes. Yet two-thirds of the

LUIS MARDEN, NATIONAL GEOGRAPHIC STAFF. FAR RIGHT: CHART DETAIL ADAPTED FROM THE ATLAS OF HERMAN MOLL, C. 1720

West Indian town disappeared and more than 2,000 people perished.

Sealed by the sea in an instant of earthquake, Port Royal is a unique archeological site. Unlike cities on land, which change with the years, this one remained exactly as it had been in 1692.

A startling contrast to the sleepy fishing village of today, 17th-century Port Royal was a carnival of riotous living—"the world's wickedest town." Gambling men and bawdy women thronged the dozens of taverns. Privateer Henry Morgan sallied out of the harbor to sack Spanish settlements. Port Royal's relics would truly indicate the old buccaneer city's life.

In June, 1959, my husband, Edwin A. Link, and I set out, under the sponsorship of the National Geographic Society, the Smithsonian Institution, and the Institute of Jamaica, to find these relics.

The sunken city sprawled beneath our new *Sea Diver*, the world's first ship built expressly for submarine archeology. Ed, the inventor of the Link Trainer which helped thousands of pilots learn to fly, designed the 91-foot steel vessel. High pressure water jets under the bow enable *Sea Diver* to turn in her length. A diving compartment aft, loaded with fins, masks, and Aqua-Lungs, can be entered directly from the sea. A jetting hose helps clear away bottom deposits. A compressed air lift, ten inches in diameter, dredges the sea floor like a vacuum cleaner.

A British Museum chart and Jamaican surveys helped us trace the old town's buildings. Portable sounding equipment checked standing underwater remains. The long waterfront warehouses, which probably had stored valuables, seemed like a logical starting place.

We slung the air lift from a barge alongside the ship. Divers descended to salvage

206

"PORT ROYALL SUNK." *The stark epitaph on a 1720 chart marks the grave of the prosperous buccaneer haven disinterred by the Sea Diver on her maiden voyage. The Links dovetailed data from modern echo sounders and old maps to pinpoint buried landmarks. Then, while the air lift spat bricks and brine, divers groped for mementos such as this fragile terra-cotta dish being passed up to Mrs. Link by her son Clayton.*

relics before the lift could suck them up into the tube. Excitement ran high. With a rattling rush of sound, a powerful stream of debris-filled water burst from the air lift's mouth. For several days not much more than mud and gravel plunked out on the barge deck.

WE MOVED SEA DIVER close to the east wall of Fort James; almost immediately the lift began to spew out bricks, bits of old wine bottles, sections of clay pipes. Divers fished out a long-handled brass ladle, broken pewter spoons, a corroded plate, and many greenish-black 17th-century rum bottles, known as "onion" bottles because of their shape. We had really struck pay dirt.

I decided to have a look. Guided downward by the pale gleam of the tube, feet floating upward to avoid kicking up silt clouds, I glimpsed a small section of brick wall. But I could make out nothing more in this utter obscurity. It was the most difficult diving we had ever experienced. The diver worked in a world by himself, unseeing and unseen, amid the constant danger of cave-ins and the threat of stingrays, scorpion fish, sharks, and barracuda.

The air lift, with its powerful suction, was an ally to be respected. Many times it seized divers' gloves in its greedy maw and shot them out onto the barge above. We almost expected some day to see the elongated form of a diver erupt from the pipe's upper end.

One morning the divers handed up a battered copper pot. As Ed scooped out the sticky mud, he discovered bleached white beef and turtle bones. "Why, a stew must have been cooking for dinner when the earthquake struck," he said. "You can see the marks of the meat cleaver on the bones." Charred bricks, a fireplace grill,

207

a mortar, and more pots piled up evidence that we were digging in a kitchen. It would be hard to find another kitchen in the world today with everything just as it was 300 years ago. That's the advantage of underwater archeology.

When a sealed onion bottle came up, we inserted a hypodermic needle through the cork and squirted the yellowish fluid into a cup. Ed grimaced as he sipped it. "Horrible," he sputtered. "Tastes like strongly salted vinegar. I guess 1692 must have been a bad vintage year."

Al Banasky, one of the crack Navy divers working with us, glimpsed a flash of bright metal hurtling out of the air lift one day. "How would you like a gold watch?" he inquired moments later.

I thought he was spoofing, but it was indeed a watch. A heavy black crust covered the face. The Roman numeral hours were distinctly visible on the face, and repeated in reverse on the coral crust. The hands had vanished. Had they disintegrated against the coral? A Kingston dentist X-rayed it. The negatives showed a faint trace of hands on the crust pointing close to the eight and the twelve. Ed matched the coral against the face.

"It stopped at 17 minutes to twelve," he said in amazement. All accounts put the earthquake at shortly before noon. Either the first heavy shock or the plunge into the sea had halted the watch forever.

In ten weeks of work we had drafted the most accurate existing chart of pre-earthquake Port Royal, had brought up hundreds of artifacts depicting its life, and had ascertained the instant of its doom.

Here Lyes the Body of LEWIS GALDY who departed this Life at Port Royal the 22. December 1739 Aged 80 He was Born at Montpelier in France but left that Country for his Religion & came to settle in this Island where He was Swallowed up in the Great Earth-quake in the Year 1692 & By the Providence of God was by another Shock thrown into the Sea & Miraculously saved By Swimming until a Boat took him up H Lived many Years after in great Reputat Beloved by all that knew him and m Lamented at his Death

LUIS MARDEN, NATIONAL GEOGRAPHIC STAFF. OPPOSITE ABOVE: W. D. VAUGHN

X-RAY TRACES *vanished watch hands (arrows), stopped at 11:43, the time the temblors hit. Lewis Galdy's tombstone tells how he was "swallowed" by the quake, tossed into the sea, and saved "miraculously" by swimming. Decorated comb of 1690 mirrors pre-earthquake wealth. National Geographic research team and the Links—from left, Dr. Remington Kellogg, Dr. Lyman Briggs, the author and her husband, Dr. Melvin Payne, Dr. Alexander Wetmore, and Rear Adm. L. O. Colbert—study other relics.*

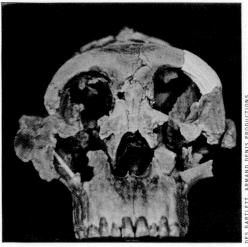

DES BARTLETT, ARMAND DENIS PRODUCTIONS

Search for the World's Earliest Man

Archeologist L. S. B. Leakey's momentous discoveries in East Africa have revolutionized man's knowledge of prehistory

SUNBAKED SEARCH IN OLDUVAI GORGE UNCOVERED 400 SKULL FRAGMENTS OF

"I'VE GOT HIM! I've got him! I've got him!" Mary's voice called it over and over as the Land-Rover rattled up to our African camp and she jumped out. "Got what? Are you hurt?" I asked my wife.

"Him, the man. *Our* man!" Mary said. "The one we've been looking for. Come quick. I've found his teeth!"

The headache that had kept me in camp that morning of July 17, 1959, departed magically. We bounced down the gorge trail in the car, then covered the last half

mile at a run. Mary led me to a cairn, and we knelt to examine her treasure.

The teeth projected from a rock face. To us these shining bits of fossilized matter represented the end of a 28-year search. For there, in Tanganyika's remote Olduvai Gorge, lay the remains of the earliest man ever found.

We almost cried with joy. After all our hoping and hardship and sacrifice, we had reached our goal.

Gingerly we began the work of uncov-

ering the find. Our method of search is simple and, to say the least, uncomfortable. It consists of crawling up and down the slopes of the gorge with eyes barely inches from the ground, stopping at the slightest fragment of a fossil bone and delicately investigating the clue with a fine brush or a dental pick. All this in heat that sometimes reaches 110° F.

We found that expansion and contraction of the soft rock had cracked our new-found skull into 400 fragments. In order not to lose a single precious scrap we sifted tons of scree below the find. After 19 days we recovered the nearly complete skull, minus only the lower jaw. From the fact that the wisdom teeth, the third molars, show no wear, I put the age of our specimen at 18. I call him *Zinjanthropus*, or "East Africa Man."

What does the Zinjanthropus skull tell us? Its flat cranium housed a brain probably less than half the size of ours. There is also a bony ridge crowning the skull

UGANDA
Victoria Nile
Rusinga Island
Fort Ternan □ + Mt. Kenya
KENYA
Lake Victoria
Nairobi ●
SERENGETI PLAIN
Olduvai Gorge □   Kilimanjaro
Ngorongoro Crater ○   +
TANGANYIKA
0 ————— 150
STATUTE MILES

OLDUVAI GORGE, *peephole into prehistory, slices 300 feet through volcanic ash and clay beside Tanganyika's Serengeti Plain.*

Here a silted lake buried Zinjanthropus 1,750,000 years ago. Quakes formed a chasm sand choked it, rain scoured it, exposing

the fossils. Fort Ternan (map) yielded 14-million-year-old Kenyapithecus. *Rusinga produced* Proconsul, *25 million years old.*

which is found in some near-men. Clearly, Zinjanthropus stands a long way from the state of development seen in *Homo sapiens* of the present day. But I have counted at least 20 features in which he is more like modern man than are the near-men discovered in South Africa.

Man—what does the word really mean? To me it suggests no mere primeval ape-like creature that walked erect and had hands. To be truly like man, he must have had the power to reason and the ability to fashion crude tools to do his work.

There is the key—the ability to make tools, as distinct from merely using the pointed sticks or sharp stones that lay readily at hand.

On the ancient "living floor"—the actual site where Zinjanthropus made his rude home—we found tools years before the skull came to light. There were crude stone utensils used for skinning and cutting up carcasses. There were hammerlike stones for cracking bones to get at the marrow. Zinjanthropus clearly fashioned his own tools.

The key to our man's development as a tool-maker lies in his teeth. He has the largest molars ever found in a human skull, but his incisors and canines are relatively small and blunt. They could never have torn the skin or fur from creatures the size of rabbits. Yet we know from bones strewn on his living floor that he ate small animals. There is only one answer: Zinjanthropus must have begun making tools when he added meat to his diet.

OLDUVAI is a fossil hunter's dream, for the gorge shears 300 feet through stratum after stratum of earth's history as through a gigantic layer cake. Here lie countless fossils and artifacts.

Before the road was improved, the 347-mile trip from Nairobi to the gorge took 13 hours, with luck. I say with luck, for during the rainy season, parts of the road became a mud wallow. Now the trip over an all-weather road takes 9 or 10 hours.

My first trek to Olduvai in 1931 took seven days. There was no lack of wildlife along the way; I saw elephants, zebras, rhinoceroses, giraffes, wildebeests, and smaller game such as Thomson's gazelles and dik-diks, delightful little antelopes

213

DES BARTLETT, ARMAND DENIS PRODUCTIONS

about 14 inches tall. Most of the animals showed scant fear; I often approached as close as 20 feet.

That first night, while we were camped at the edge of the gorge, our new neighbors came to visit us. I went out to see what was moving about the camp. In the blackness I picked out the green eyes of 11 lions, some near, some far. They were investigating this invasion of their territory, for these animals are the most curious of all the cat family. They always greet us on our return to Olduvai; they never bother us. Needless to say, we extend the same courtesy to them.

Not all the animals that visited us over the years were as unobtrusive as our lion neighbors. Giraffes, hyenas, even rhinos have wandered into our camp. The explanation is simple: water.

Lack of water has been the great hardship at Olduvai. When the rainy season ends, water simply vanishes. For years we had to haul every precious drop from a spring 35 miles away on the rim of the Ngorongoro Crater. The cost of hauling water limited us to a working season of about seven weeks.

One year Mary and I decided to visit the gorge toward the end of the rainy season. For a week we even had running water for a daily bath. Then we found ourselves reduced to a single water hole which, unfortunately, two rhinos discovered and turned into a wallow. To those who have never lived on rhino bath water, I can only offer my congratulations. The taste stayed with Mary and me for months.

Another time, as our cook was preparing a meal, he was interrupted by a faint growl. He glanced up, expecting to see the usual timid hyena sniffing for scraps, and found himself face to face with a leopard! It is hard to say which bolted faster. Supper that evening was sketchy.

Our Dalmatians are our best protection against animals and snakes. They sense danger long before we do, and this saves us the bother of carrying guns. Once Mary looked up at the sound of furious barking

CURIOUS CATS *often come calling at Olduvai. These two lionesses, fresh from a wildebeest feast, prowl Kenya's Amboseli National Reserve.*

Lions have never bothered the Leakeys, but rhinos, desperate for water during the dry season, have rumbled right into the fossil hunters' camp. Two of the nearsighted brutes almost stumbled over a camp helper; Jonathan Leakey had to detour around several while he was out hunting rain-filled pools one night. Best protection is provided by the Leakeys' dogs; they terrify the beasts.

Wallowing in dust (below), rhinos wear away hide, exposing patches of pink skin.

CAMPED IN SEMIDESERT, *the Leakeys must haul water in tank trailers from a spring near Ngorongoro Crater, 35 miles away. As supplies are used, empty crates are filled with prehistoric treasures—fossil bones and the tools of Stone Age men.*

215

LAYER-CAKE LEVELS *of prehistoric campsites run through Olduvai's walls. Kneeling on the living floor of the pre-Zinj child, Dr. Leakey points out the stratum which yielded Zinjanthropus. Dr. Thomas W. McKnew, Vice Chairman of the Society's Board of Trustees, and Dr. Leonard Carmichael, Research Committee Chairman, examine the site.*

to see the dogs chasing a huge black-maned lion down the gorge.

Dr. Matthew W. Stirling, a member of the National Geographic Society's Committee for Research and Exploration, can testify to our animal guest list. We were at lunch one day during Matt's visit when I happened to glance above his head. A black-and-white checked form slithered along the rafters.

"Boomslang," I announced, and to Matt's credit he never stirred, though he must have had a bad moment. My son Jonathan, our snake expert, casually took the visitor

by the tail and marched it outside into a collecting bag. The innocuous-looking boomslang is one of Africa's deadliest reptiles. Strangely, the highly lethal quality of its venom was not recognized until early in this century. I can remember playing with boomslangs as a boy of ten. I do not play with them anymore.

In 1960 a generous grant from the National Geographic Society enabled us to work right through the year. Among our first purchases was a larger water trailer. The day we got it, Mary and I deeded all our water-hole rights to the rhinos.

"Leakey Luck," my colleagues tease, when we make an important discovery. I readily admit that luck often plays a part. But then so has 35 years' striving and digging and never giving up.

We had cleared more than a hundred sites on Rusinga Island in Lake Victoria before Mary made her great discovery there in 1948. We were scanning a slope when she suddenly spotted a tooth, just a speck of gray fossilized matter. As we cleared the rock we found another tooth,

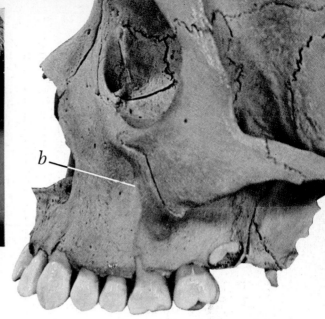

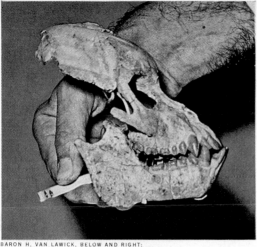

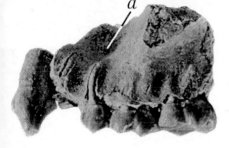

UPPER JAW *of Kenyapithecus (left) suggests a step in the ancestry of man, with its small canine tooth and canine fossa (a), resembling that in a human skull (b). This bone depression anchors a muscle which modern man uses in speech. Older Proconsul (above left) has much larger, apelike canine teeth.*

and something more. After several days we put our jigsaw puzzle together. It was a nearly complete skull of *Proconsul africanus*, a creature some 25 million years old! Many scientists believe it represents the common stock leading to both man and the apes. It was the first time anyone had found so nearly complete a specimen of an early fossil apelike skull. A new door in the study of man's past had opened.

The find was of such great importance we decided to fly it at once to England. I put Mary on the plane at Nairobi with the fragile skull wrapped in a padded box on her lap. Newsreel cameramen and reporters were waiting in London. "I had to go up and down that plane's ladder several times with Proconsul before they were satisfied," she told me later. At the airport press conference two detectives never let the skull out of their sight.

Proconsul and Zinjanthropus were the fruit of slow, hard years. Then, with the Society's help, in a 13-month period our staff put in 92,000 man-hours of excavating more than twice what Mary and I were able to do in the previous 30 years. What did we find in those 13 months? So much it is hard to know where to begin!

I was home at Nairobi one day when the radiophone crackled from Olduvai. It was Mary. "We found a foot. Yes, I said a foot — we may have another discovery as exciting as Zinjanthropus. Over."

"Wonderful news!" I replied. "How much have you got?"

"Quite a large part. The heel and ankle bones and a number of others. When are you coming to see them?"

"I'm on my way. Over and out."

And that is how I learned of the discovery of fossil bones belonging to the world's oldest known hominid, a member of the scientific family that includes man and near-men.

Weeks before, working on the lowest stratum of the gorge, Jonathan had picked up the fossil jawbone of the first saber-toothed tiger ever found in East Africa. Combing the slope for more sabertooth, our party discovered a tooth all right, but it had never belonged to a tiger.

217

"Primate!" Mary exclaimed. From a trench beneath the surface came a collarbone, tiny bits of skull, finger bones, the precious foot bones that brought me racing to the gorge, and at last a large section of lower jaw with beautifully preserved teeth. The great find was some 250 yards from the spot where we had found Zinjanthropus but at an even lower level.

Worn first molars, second molars showing little wear, no sign of third molars—these tell us that our pre-Zinj fossil was a child of 11 or 12. And the parietals, bones that form the dome of the skull, suggest that the child died by violence. The left parietal shows a point of impact, a break in the skull that reaches to the inner wall, and fractures that radiate from the break.

The child could not have fallen on a rock, for there were no rocks on the mud flats where it lived that could have caused such a massive fracture. I think it reasonable to say that the child died from what in modern police parlance is known as "a blow from a blunt instrument."

W E DO NOT KNOW enough yet about the pre-Zinj child to describe it as man. I suspect that it was a different type of hominid from Zinjanthropus. But in the child's living floor we found tools of simple though regular design.

We also found great quantities of the remains of tortoises, catfish, and the relatively easily caught aquatic birds. This suggests that our pre-Zinj being was such a poor hunter that he found slow-moving and shallow-water creatures a better prospect to catch and kill than other animals.

How old are Zinjanthropus and the child? Pending exhaustive tests, Mary and I could only say that Zinjanthropus lived more than 600,000 years ago, though we believed he would prove to be far older. Then in the spring of 1961 came staggering news from Dr. Garniss H. Curtis of the University of California's Department of Geology. Potassium-argon dating placed Zinjanthropus and the pre-Zinj child an incredible 1,750,000 years in the past!

The subject of hunting brings up a recent find at Olduvai that puts Zinjanthropus and the tortoise-eating child to shame. To understand the importance of this discovery we must go back to 1846, when the existence of a Stone Age culture was first reported. It was called Chellean after Chelles, the site in France where the first remains were found.

The amazing thing about this culture—typified by easily recognized stone tools—is that although evidence of it has since been discovered over much of Africa, Asia, and southwestern Europe, no one had ever found the skull of a Chellean man. From our earliest days at Olduvai we had unearthed Chellean tools in Bed II, the stratum just above Bed I. In 1960 we found a Chellean living floor, but not one fossil to tell us what the man had looked like.

MASSIVE MOLARS *reveal remains of the ancient*

218

I sometimes think fate plays a game with us, for no sooner had we stopped looking for our prehistoric mystery man than he made his appearance.

While touring the gorge one day with Ray Pickering, a geologist working with us, I spotted an area of exposed Bed II deposits that I had never noticed before. Early next morning my youngest son Philip and I hacked our way through the bush to the spot.

"This is the sort of place where we'll find a skull," I said, half laughingly. I had scarcely finished speaking when my eyes happened to fall on some bone fragments in an eroded gully. It was a skull!

I fell on my knees beside the spot. It *was* a skull, a human skull. I could not speak coherently. At last we had found what countless prehistorians had sought for more than a century.

We already know a great deal about how Chellean man lived some 400,000 years ago, as I have said. It seems certain that he hunted with a bola, a weapon made of weights connected by thongs. It is still occasionally used by the gauchos of South America and by some Eskimos.

We cannot, of course, find a complete Chellean bola, for the leather thongs have

tool-maker, Zinjanthropus. His broken palate appears just as it was uncovered.

DES BARTLETT, ARMAND DENIS PRODUCTIONS

CHELLEAN HUNTERS GORGE *on an elephantlike* Dinotherium, *mired in a swamp. Sated, th*

long since perished. But we have many bola stones from Chellean living floors. We may guess that he used the bola as it is still used, hurling it at an animal to entangle its legs and hobble it so as to make a kill possible.

Olduvai is a fabulously rich storehouse of manlike fossils, but the animals have by no means been absent. Over the years we have found remains of *Afrochoerus*, a pig as big as a rhinoceros; *Pelorovis*, a sheep that towered six feet at the shoulders and had a horn span of four or five yards; and an enormous fossil rhinoceros nearly twice as large as today's East African black rhino. Then there was the giant

t their cutting tools of stone, which the Leakeys discovered with the skeleton at Olduvai.

baboon *Simopithecus jonathani*—Jonathan found its jaw—which dwarfed any primate known until we found another, even larger baboon in 1962.

One of the most surprising finds is our *Dinotherium*—a strange type of extinct elephant with tusks set in the lower jaw. Scientists have labeled its giant forms *Dinotherium maximus* and *Dinotherium gigantissimus*. Science has a real problem now, for our fossil puts gigantissimus to shame—its tusks alone measure five feet on the curve. Perhaps Dr. Stirling has the answer. He suggests *mirabilis*, Latin for "marvelous." Mirabilis apparently died in a swamp where Chellean man seems to have found it and cut up the carcass with stone tools.

Olduvai's fossils are as varied as they are rich, and if we have giants, we also have dwarfs. We have collected thousands of minute creatures, such as mice, birds, shrews, and lizards. Some are so tiny that six jawbones fit on my thumbnail.

The only resemblance between flat, canyon-sliced Olduvai and lush Fort Ternan, in Kenya, is in the richness of fossil remains. During two months' work at Fort Ternan in 1961 we found no fewer than 1,200 fossils. For the most part they are creatures new to science.

One was a tiny giraffe about the size of a calf. Fossil giraffes found in Europe and Asia were short-legged and thickset. But our find closely resembles the modern giraffe, and may be a direct ancestor.

Our most exciting find in the grassy lowlands of Fort Ternan, however, was part of the jaw of a 14-million-year-old creature that helps bridge the enormous gap in man's development between Proconsul and Zinjanthropus, a gap of more than 20 million years. We called him *Kenyapithecus wickeri*. Pithecus is one of the endings used in describing the higher prehistoric primates. Wickeri honors my friend Fred Wicker, who found the first fossils at the site.

Kenyapithecus was not—emphatically not—a man, but he leads straight in man's direction. His upper jaw has a depression which is an essential characteristic of man. It serves as anchor for a muscle which controls the movement of the upper lip, and gives humans the potential of speech, as distinct from mere sound. In addition, where Proconsul had the long, pointed canine teeth of the apes, Kenyapithecus's were small, closer to man's.

What other characteristics does Kenyapithecus have in common with man? We cannot yet say. But once we have more material, we may begin to paint a more detailed picture, as we have done with Proconsul, Zinjanthropus, and Chellean man.

If Fort Ternan promises to be one of the most important fossil sites Mary and I have explored, Rusinga Island is surely the most mysterious. The riddle of Rusinga lies in its fossils of beautifully preserved insects, fruits, and flowers.

Dr. Leakey's "do it yourself" archeology

SHOW ME! *Skeptical staff members gather round to see whether the simple stone implements they dig up at Olduvai can really be used.*

Preparing a ram for a Christmas feast, Leakey cracks one rock against another to make a Stone Age butcher knife. With it he skins and disjoints the ram in less than 20 minutes. Sharpened stones (lower right) served a similar purpose for Zinjanthropus 1,750,000 years ago. Five-foot tusks (lower left) of the giant Dinotherium were part of a carcass hacked up by Chellean hunters 400,000 years ago.

In science Leakey takes nothing for granted. "I first began making stone tools some 35 years ago," he says, "in the belief that I would never fully comprehend the prehistoric tool-makers until I could handle their implements as effectively as they did." He once stalked a Thomson's gazelle, killed it with his hands, and skinned it. He tried skinning animals with his teeth. It couldn't be done. Hence, he surmised, the early invention of stone tools.

The Cambridge-educated archeologist was born in a wattle hut. His parents were among the first missionaries to the Kikuyu tribe, and he was the first white baby these East Africans had ever seen. They came from miles around to spit on him, to show respect. He learned their language, eventually became an elder in the Kikuyu tribe. He served for years as curator of the Coryndon Museum in Nairobi. For their great finds he and his wife Mary won the Society's Hubbard Medal in 1962.

After visiting the Leakeys at Olduvai, Dr. Matthew W. Stirling reported to the Society's Research Committee: "I talked to many people who consider Dr. Leakey the greatest figure in East Africa today."

ROBERT F. SISSON, NATIONAL GEOGRAPHIC PHOTOGRAPHER. BELOW RIGHT: KATHLEEN REVIS JUDGE. LEFT: DES BARTLETT, ARMAND DENIS PRODUCTIONS

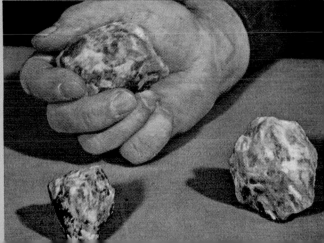

When we pick up a fossil, what we hold is not the actual bone or tusk. The originals have been replaced—to the last detail—by minerals. The process is immensely slow, and normally tissue and muscle do not hold their form long enough for the minerals to do their work.

That is why, when we found our first stone beetle, Mary said, "I'm sorry, but it's just not possible." Later we collected many of these stone wonders of nature—caterpillars, flies, a grub, a worm, and even the head of a large lizard, tongue still sticking out of its mouth.

Even more fantastic are the fossilized flower buds, nuts, and fruits we found. It took a diamond cutter to get through some of the fruits to show us the insides. Preserved in stone were the whole inner structures and seeds, just as you find them today when you cut into a fresh apple!

One other mystery appeared at Olduvai in 1962, and to me it is the most intriguing of all. In the very lowest level, well below the site of Zinjanthropus, we unearthed wide circles made of stones, some actually resting on top of others. No such stones existed on the site naturally when it was lakeshore two million years ago.

How did they get there? What forces arranged them in those unmistakable circles, and why? Could they be the remains of primitive dwellings or windbreaks?

Somewhere in Olduvai, the answers to such questions await us. It is this kind of detective work that makes our job so fascinating. I have often heard archeology referred to as a dry and boring science. Mary and I can tell you that it is nothing of the kind. The cleverest mystery story ever written cannot match our job for sheer excitement and suspense.

DEEP-JAWED, FLAT-SKULLED
Zinjanthropus stares from an artist's canvas. Peter Bianchi fleshed out the ancient bones from Dr. Leakey's clues.

University of California geologists dated Olduvai volcanic ash with an "atomic clock," measuring the change of potassium 40 atoms into argon 40. A coiled furnace (below) heated the samples to 2,200° F., releasing argon atoms. Dr. Garniss Curtis called the result "a giant step toward the solution of one of earth's mysteries." He wrote the author that "Olduvai man is old, old, old!"

UNIVERSITY OF CALIFORNIA

DEPARTMENT OF GEOLOGY
BERKELEY 4, CALIFORNIA

May 20, 1961

Dr. Louis S.B. Leakey, Curator,
Coryndon Museum
Nairobi, Kenya,
East Africa

Dear Dr. Leakey:

The potassium-argon dating of the Olduvai fossils is progressing well, and though much remains to be done, the early results are so startling I thought you should know them at once.

Zinjanthropus and the "pre-Zinj" child are much, much older than anyone had suspected, except perhaps you and Mrs. Leakey. The average age of the samples my partner Dr. Jack Evernden and I have dated so far is 1,750,000 years.

Dr. Evernden and I believe that this date is close to the true age of Olduvai's early men, but that if anything it is slightly conservative.

One thing is certain -- Olduvai man is old, old, old!

Sincerely yours,

Garniss H. Curtis

Garniss H. Curtis

SAN FRANCISCANS *look down from Nob Hill on a shattered, burning city. The 1906 quake struck with a "deep and terrible" rumble; pavement undulated "as waves of the ocean."*

Beholding Nature's Phenomena

"DARKNESS HAD FALLEN over the upper Luhit Valley in rugged, far-eastern Tibet. Suddenly the earth began to shudder. The ominous rumble swelled to a deafening roar. A dark ridge silhouetted against the sky became fuzzy. The whole forest was shaking violently. All four of us held hands and lay flat, waiting for the end."

Thus botanist F. Kingdon-Ward described in *National Geographic* an earthquake that "ripped to pieces" mountains over thousands of square miles and killed 5,000 people. His words convey man's eternal awe at nature's rampages.

"Here I am! Here I am!" cried ancient Peruvians when the earth shook, convinced the tremors were a summons from their creator who had returned to earth for an inspection. Hawaiians climbed dark slopes to toss offerings of pigs and wild berries into the crater where the goddess Pele lurked. Romans built temples to Volcanus, god of earth fire. But nature paid no heed.

The earth trembled, and Vesuvius buried Pompeii and her people beneath tons of ashes. The earth trembled, and mighty Krakatau exploded with a roar heard 3,000 miles away, blowing to bits a fertile East Indian island. The earth trembled, and Mont Pelée incinerated a West Indian city. Scientists of the National

A **FOUNTAIN** *of incandescent rock spurts 400 feet in the air during an eruption of Kilauea, in Hawaii. Surging up from miles below the earth's surface, it fed a river of lava three miles long, 20 feet deep.*

PLUMES OF STEAM *hiss through hot volcanic ash as a National Geographic expedition explores its great discovery—Alaska's Valley of Ten Thousand Smokes.*

Geographic Society beheld Pelée's grim work. "In silent streets," wrote Israel C. Russell, "shriveled corpses lay beneath a universal sheet of gray volcanic dust." Angelo Heilprin ascended the volcano "amid a thousand dangers" to study its crater. "One violent explosion of mud covered the professor from head to toe with the hideous viscid and semi-solid matter. He still persisted."

Since its founding, the National Geographic Society has persisted in its study and reporting of nature's great spectacles. "I can never forget my sensations at the sight," wrote expedition leader Robert F. Griggs of the moment he discovered the Valley of Ten Thousand Smokes in Alaska. "Stretching as far as the eye could reach ... were hundreds—no, thousands, literally tens of thousands —of smokes curling up from its fissured floor. It was as though all the steam engines in the world had popped their safety valves at once."

National Geographic's John Scofield rushed to the Azores to witness the birth of an island, Ilha Nova: "A steady half-mile-high jet of incandescent boulders, some the size of small automobiles, soared into the air and slammed down onto the ash-covered slope, to lie glowing there like angry red fireflies." Hawaii's Kilauea Iki spat a torrent of fiery lava, and Frederick Simpich, Jr., reported:

ANTARCTICA *spawns much of the world's weather. Scientists seek to read its fickle mind with instruments carried aloft by weather balloons.*

W. D. VAUGHN. LEFT: W. ROBERT MOORE, NATIONAL GEOGRAPHIC STAFF

SECONDS BEFORE AN ECLIPSE,
George Van Biesbroeck readies his telescope on the sands of the Sudan. His field study, backed by the Society, contributed new proof of Einstein's theory that starlight is bent by the gravitational pull of the sun.

"The berserk fountain played ever upward, tossing its body in wild patterns with the abandon of a demented being. To 1,500, then 1,600 feet it towered. I was on the rim as it pumped to 1,700 feet, then a record for Hawaii."

In gentler mood, nature is a patient sculptor, carving with wind and water. Among Utah's mesas, Byron Cummings found an enormous natural bridge stretching "out across the canyon like a rainbow." His words in *National Geographic*, published with the first photographs of the great arch, helped make Rainbow Bridge a national monument. Struggling "like a train of ants," a Society expedition led by Willis T. Lee mapped New Mexico's Carlsbad Caverns. Lee slipped through one small hole to discover a wall hung with "thin sheets of delicately colored onyx looped in graceful folds. . . . One is impelled to touch them before he is convinced they are cold, hard stone." His reports won world attention for the caverns. Today they form the heart of a national park.

A "Gargantuan punch bowl" is discovered in northern Quebec, and a Society expedition flies in to determine what carved so huge a crater. In howling wastes like those of "some deserted planet," the scientists find evidence that a mighty meteor, hurtling perhaps 150,000 miles an hour, blasted a hole 1,300 feet

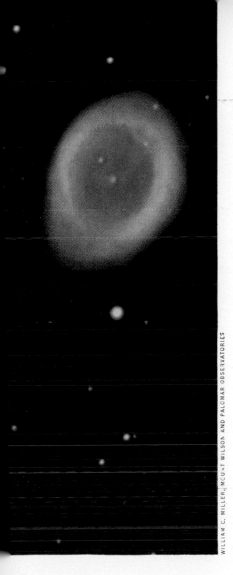

THE **MONUMENTAL** *Sky Survey,*
cosponsored by the Society
and directed by Palomar's
Ira Sprague Bowen (right),
disclosed billions of stars.
First color portraits of the
heavens — recording marvels
like the Ring Nebula in
Lyra (left) — were presented
in National Geographic.

NORTHERN LIGHTS *yield*
shimmering secrets to
Carl W. Gartlein.
Society grants aided the
Cornell scientist's work.

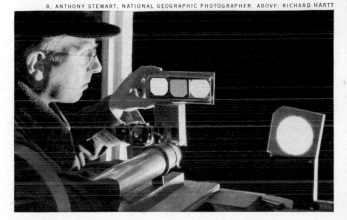

deep, strewing five billion tons of shattered granite around the seven-mile rim.

On California's Mount Palomar, astronomers aim the 48-inch Big Schmidt telescope into the night sky, snap the shutter — and a photographic plate begins to soak up light from heavenly bodies 6,000,000,000,000,000,000,000 miles away! In the seven-year Sky Survey, sponsored by the National Geographic Society and California Institute of Technology, scientists discovered and charted billions of new stars. So distant are some that "their light, arriving at Palomar that night, had started on its journey 300 million years before." One newly found baby planet bears the name *Geographos.*

In 1900 an excursion party — the ladies in Gibson Girl hairdos, the men in caps and derbies — sailed from Washington, D. C., to Norfolk, Virginia, for "a perfect view" of an eclipse. This was the Society's first eclipse expedition. In later years teams of astronomers set up eclipse stations across the Pacific, in Brazil, and in the Sudan. In 1963 a jet plane raced sun and moon across Canada's skies, its great speed "stretching" the period of eclipse by 44 seconds. Aboard was a National Geographic team. When nature puts on a show, the Society's scientists answer in the words of the ancient Peruvians: "Here I am!"

Mont Pelée:
Volcano that Killed a City

Sifting the smoldering ashes of St. Pierre, Robert T. Hill
uncovers a chilling tale of extinction

ST. PIERRE BEFORE 1902, PELÉE LOOMING IN DISTANCE; C. W. BLACKBURNE

many pleasant cafes. Its people, Negro and European, were happy and prosperous. Admirers sometimes called it "little Paris of the Antilles."

On the morning of May 8, 1902, St. Pierre ceased to exist. At precisely 7:50 Mont Pelée exploded with a roar heard hundreds of miles away. An awesome blast of flaming gases and superheated steam raced down its flanks with incredible speed. *In less than three minutes* the beautiful city, its 30,000 people, all nearby country homes, and 17 out of 18 ships in the anchorage were annihilated.

The frightful news reached the United States on May 9. Four days later officers of the National Geographic Society asked me to accompany a relief expedition to Martinique and report on the disaster. For ten days I probed the still-smoking ruins of St. Pierre, studying the physiographic results of the eruption, talking to eyewitnesses. From my findings I have pieced together this account of the catastrophe.

For several weeks Pelée had hinted at the dreadful secret within her heart. But she had fumed and rumbled in 1839 and 1851, and nothing had come of it. Most geographers labeled her extinct, and so the people of St. Pierre believed. Here is the record of their last days.

APRIL 23 – MAY 1: THE WARNINGS

Mrs. Thomas T. Prentiss, wife of the American Consul, wrote to her sister that three shocks on the 23d hurled the dishes from her shelves. On the 25th a great cloud of smoke wreathed Pelée. Julien Romaine climbed up for a look and saw a remarkable black mixture bubbling in the summit crater. On the 27th *L'Colonie* reported what should have been an alarming fact — a new hole in La Soufrière, a sulphurous crater below the summit. Jets of steam fumed in the air.

On the 28th ominous rumblings began echoing through St. Pierre. Ashes showered down. Mrs. Prentiss wrote again: "The smell of sulphur is so strong that horses on the street stop and snort, and some of them drop in their harness and die from suffocation. Many of the people are obliged to wear wet handkerchiefs to protect them from the fumes." The earth trembled three times on the 30th. Streams

THE ST. PIERRE I had known from previous geological trips to Martinique was a gracious French colonial city of red-tiled roofs, quaint narrow streets, and the fairest gardens in the West Indies. It nestled at the base of long-dormant Mont Pelée, green-clad slopes climbing above, blue Caribbean waters sparkling below. Cultural and commercial center of the island, it boasted two banks, an excellent *lycée*, a cathedral, theaters, and

7:50 A.M., MAY 8, 1902: *Blotting out the sky, churning down Pelée's slope at 100 miles an hour, superheated steam and ash from the volcano's belly smash the city, snuff out its life, roar across ships in the harbor where terrified seamen leap for cover. Only one vessel in 18 stays afloat as the wall of death engulfs them.*

PAINTING BY PAUL CALLE FOR NATIONAL GEOGRAPHIC

swelled into raging torrents, carrying debris and dead fish through the city.

MAY 2–6: THE FIRST ERUPTIONS

Dense yellow-brown fumes and boiling mud spumed from the volcano on May 2 and 3. Birds died of asphyxiation in a rain of hot cinders which covered the city an inch thick. The Rivière Blanche became a torrent of mud and pumice. The telegraphic cable north of Martinique broke at an unknown distance from shore. At midnight on the 3d flames lit the sky over Pelée, causing widespread terror. Some citizens prepared to flee.

By 5 A.M., May 5, the eruptions seemed at an end. But shortly after noon an avalanche of volcanic mud rushed down the mountainside, sweeping up buildings, cattle, and people over a half-mile-wide belt. At the mouth of the Rivière Blanche the seething mass engulfed the Guerin sugar factory, entombing 150 souls in a mud mausoleum 200 feet high. Minutes later, all along the west coast, the sea suddenly receded about 100 yards, then swirled back, climbing as high as the houses on Place Bertin. People fled to higher ground. The sea soon retired again.

Terrible detonations now began bursting from the mountain at short intervals, accompanied by thick smoke and lurid flashes—awful by daylight, worse when darkness fell. People in nightclothes, carrying children, ran aimlessly about the dark streets, wailing and screaming. Churches were filled with weeping men and women, pleading for the weary priests to hear their confessions.

On May 6 Pelée was apparently in full eruption. Its detonations were heard in Guadeloupe, 100 miles away. Thick clouds overshadowed the summit. Cattle were dying for lack of water, trees breaking under the weight of cinders. Frightened families fled south to Fort de France, the capital, and to the neighboring island of St. Lucia. But refugees from the countryside were streaming into St. Pierre. Its population increased rather than diminished.

MAY 7: THE DAY BEFORE THE END

A day of horror in St. Pierre. Explosions crashed incessantly; the mental strain became unbearable. A jagged crevasse,

BONES OF ST. PIERRE *jut through the ash. "At*

100 meters long and 40 wide, cracked open at the base of Morne La Croix, a round-topped hill south of Pelée. Rumors flew that the volcano was being undermined. Before noon the cable office at St. Lucia received a message from the operator at St. Pierre: "Red hot stones falling here; don't know how long I can hold out." At 2 P.M. American Consul Louis Ayme at Guadeloupe tried to contact St. Pierre. He

ıy feet lay the dead city, silent and gray," wrote geologist Israel Russell, who joined Hill.

was informed that all cables to Martinique were broken. By nightfall the detonations had ceased and fine ashes were falling over St. Pierre like rain.

The governor at Fort de France, M. Mouttet, told by a committee of experts that there was no need for a mass evacuation of St. Pierre, sent a detachment of soldiers to the city to prevent an exodus of officials. In a brave attempt to quell the panic, he took up residence there himself with his wife. It was his last official act.

MAY 8: DEATH OF A CITY

At 6:30 A.M. the steamer *Roraima* anchored off St. Pierre, ashes blanketing her like dirty snow. On deck, fascinated by the sight of the fuming volcano, was second engineer Charles Evans. Unlike so many, he lived to give an account of what he saw. At 7, Ferdinand Clerc, chief planter of the island, took one look at the violently fluctuating needle of his barometer and fled. He, too, lived to tell the tale.

Early morning worshipers hurried to mass, for this was Ascension Day. At 7:50, as church bells were ringing, Pelée erupted with a stupefying roar, vomiting death upon the helpless city.

I HAVE INTERVIEWED more than a dozen witnesses and carefully analyzed the printed reports of others. Two have given unusually intelligible and accurate accounts—second engineer Evans and Father Alte Roché, a priest from Mont Verte, two miles south of St. Pierre. Here is what they told me.

Evans: "I was standing at the ship's rail, looking at the mountain. Suddenly it seemed to explode. An immense dark cloud shot up, blacking out the sky. Then a second cloud, even larger than the first, burst from the side of the volcano and rushed down on the city. Its speed was unbelievable. Flames spurted up wherever it touched. A huge wall of hot ashes filled the air, coming toward us *against the wind.* [I cannot interpret this phenomenon. Was there an indraft?]

"Rope and bedding on the *Roraima* caught fire. I turned to run below and was burned on the back. The shock of the explosion hit like a hurricane; I could get no air to breathe. Then an enormous wave struck our port quarter. We keeled over so far the bridge went under and water poured into the hold through the fiddlers."

Father Roché: "From high up on Mont Verte I had a clear view of the mountain, but not of the city or the lower vent. I saw a dense column of smoke and steam shoot up from the summit and spread out like the leaves of a palm tree. I ran from it for about 200 yards, then was knocked down, gasping for air, by a tremendous force. As I got up I saw a blinding flash of fire. It was the whole beautiful city going up in

flames. As the houses were of stone, with tin or tile roofing, the temperature must have been intense to cause such sudden and violent inflammation."

All who glimpsed this terrible moment agreed that the cloud of aerial volcanic ejecta which overwhelmed St. Pierre was brownish-black in color, and of a density so great as to cause total darkness. In addition to hot ashes, it contained an invisible substance—superheated steam—which penetrated clothing without firing it and burned the skin beneath. Nearly all those burned on the ships, according to one of the harried doctors I talked to, suffered only first-degree burns; their eyes were unaffected and their eyelashes intact. Remains on shore, however, were horribly burned to the quick.

Bolts of lightning leaped incessantly from the cloud during the eruptions. M. Clerc found the iron cross formerly surmounting Morne La Croix melted down to its stone pedestal. The correspondent

237

LONE SURVIVOR *of the city of death, Ludger Sylbaris*
had been jailed in solitary confinement.
His thick-walled cell, door facing away from the blast,
sheltered Sylbaris so effectively that
he learned of the catastrophe from rescuers.
The partially buried door shows the depth of the ash.
Sylbaris emerged into a rubble-filled shell of a city
littering the foot of shattered Mont Pelée (left).
Two other residents were found alive in the ruins.
Both soon died of their injuries.

Fused bottle and melted tableware bear grim witness
to the wave of incredible heat that swept the area.
Sulphur fumes blackened the utensils.
The gas still lingered when Professor Hill arrived
on May 21. He sniffed it again during
another violent eruption on May 25.

of the *Sun* of May 13 says many bodies looked as though they had been struck by lightning; but this is not proven.

The force of the blast uprooted trees, shattered buildings, overturned ships. The stones of the lighthouse were torn asunder and hurled great distances. An iron statue of the Virgin, 11 feet high and weighing several tons, was swept 45 feet from its pedestal. Not a vestige was left of the little village of Fond de Core, north of the city. Not a piece could be found of the great rum factory, with its heavy iron machinery and castings.

Every metal relic in the ruins susceptible to sulphur discoloration showed the presence of the gas. A bucket of silver plate rescued from the Prentiss home by Consul Ayme resembled old black junk. Deputy Mayor Labat told me that the captain of the French cruiser *Suchet* picked up pieces of pure sulphur in the ruined streets of St. Pierre. A newspaperman described splotches of flame on the ships, which might have been sulphur. I myself smelled the lingering fumes when poking among the grisly ashes.

There were no flows of lava whatsoever. But immediately following the fiery holocaust a deluge of mud cascaded down from the wrathful heavens. "Wet met the ashes in the sky," is how one Negro witness described it. Everything—houses, ships, human beings—was encased in it. Accompanying the mud was a shower of pumice stones which, rolling down the hillsides, striped the plaster as if it had been raked with a coarse comb.

Torrents of viscous volcanic mud, thick with pumice, continue to spew from the fissures in Pelée's fractured flanks. The magnificent highway on the bluffs above St. Pierre is buried; cemented to it are the bodies of cattle, horses, donkeys, and people. The mud has so choked the coastal streams that they are practically obliterated. The inky rivers do not run freely but pulsate, surging foward as pressure increases with horrible gulping noises.

As terrible as are volcanic disasters, we are loath to believe that 30,000 people could have been swept into eternity at a single moment. But death was the inevitable accompaniment of the horrors visited upon St. Pierre. Some were burned

to death by steam or flames; others were buried in mud or crushed by the blast; many were killed by inhaling hot ashes.

Not everyone died instantly. Officer Scott of the *Roraima* tells of children who moaned for water, "unable to swallow because of the ashes which clogged their throats." Captain Freeman of the *Roddam*, the only ship in the anchorage to survive, told me he saw people running about the water's edge for several minutes. Another witness told me he found a man holding a struggling, frightened horse, both dead in this posture. The man running the *Roraima*'s donkey engine was killed where he was sitting; yet nearby a child and nurse were only burned.

The volcano continued working after the deadly eruptions of May 8. On the 12th a great black canopy of smoke caused darkness even in the middle of the day. On the 20th Pelée blew up again, and hot stones the size of hens' eggs fell like hail, leveling what was left of the ruined city and burying the dead where they had been gathered in the streets. On May 25, I witnessed a frightful eruption accompanied by lightning and what I believe to be the ignition of gases. On the 30th the cable via Puerto Plata broke again, and almost simultaneously vast rivers of mud spilled out of the north crater. This was the last news I received as we weighed anchor for the United States.

IT IS NOW EVIDENT that the eruption of Mont Pelée, measured strictly by geological standards, was not one of history's major volcanic disturbances. No new craters have been formed, only old ones reopened. The topography of the island shows no serious alteration. All the homes of St. Pierre and the surrounding area have been destroyed, and what once was a green carpet of cane and wood is now a dreary, weird landscape of cooling ash heaps, stiffening plains of mud, and dozens of fumaroles puffing out wreaths of noisome, yellowish steam. Yet this amphitheater of death covers only 12½ square miles; the rest of Martinique is as green and beautiful as ever.

Has nothing happened, then? Ask the 30,000 dead who lie moldering beneath the ashes of St. Pierre.

A **GHOST TOWN REBORN**, *St. Pierre lies in the shadow of its slayer, Mont Pcléc. For two and a half centuries the city flourished as financial and cultural center of Martinique. Today it is a sleepy town with memories—perhaps nightmares.*

San Francisco Earthquake

AT 5:12 A.M. *on April 18, 1906, horses in the city's produce district whinnied a warning. At 5:13, while 400,000 residents slept, the earthquake struck. Brick buildings crumbled. Chinatown's shacks splintered. Old Long Wharf disintegrated. Legend says Caruso stumbled from the Palace Hotel shouting, "Give me Vesuvius!" People jammed the shaking streets, in their ears the screams of the hurt and dying, the clanging of church bells.*

Fires broke out all over the city. For years Fire Chief Dennis Sullivan had been denied an efficient water system. Now, as he lay dying, the ancient cisterns and pipes bubbled out only a pitiful dribble. Fire fighters tried sand and dynamite— to no avail. Flames raged for three days. The toll: 450 dead.

What caused the quake? Thousands of years before, forces within the earth stretched and squeezed layers of surface rock until a deep, 600-mile-long fracture rent the face of California—the San Andreas Fault. Great pressures continued. Suddenly the land masses on each side of the fault lurched in opposite directions as much as 21 feet.

So great was the shock that in Washington, D. C., the arm of a seismograph swung off the edge of its recording sheet. "The time taken for these waves to cross the continent was 6 minutes 46 seconds," reported the May issue of National Geographic, *which devoted three scientific articles to the earthquake. In one, geologist Frederick Leslie Ransome analyzed the causes of the disaster, then looked clearly into the future: "That San Francisco will rise beautiful and triumphant from ruin no one who knows California can doubt."*

Into the Valley of Ten Thousand Smokes

*Robert F. Griggs took the Society flag
to Alaska to study a volcanic explosion—
and found a new wonder of the world*

THE ERUPTION of a volcano in the Mount Katmai region of Alaska in June, 1912, was one of the most tremendous explosions ever recorded. Some seven cubic miles of ash and pumice were hurled into the air. The fall buried an area almost as large as Connecticut ten inches to ten feet deep, and some of the ash drifted 1,500 miles. Dust was thrown into the atmosphere and spread around the world, profoundly affecting its weather.

To study effects of this gigantic ashfall for the National Geographic Society, I went to the Alaska Peninsula in 1915 and again in 1916. I never dreamed I would stumble onto one of the most amazing visions ever beheld by mortal eye.

With me on the first expedition were B. B. Fulton, an entomologist from New York, and Lucius G. Folsom, a teacher from near Kodiak. Only desolation confronted us when we landed at pumice-clogged Katmai Bay. The shore was barren of vegetation. There were signs of flooding

243

everywhere. Ankle-deep mud covered the flats. Boulders crashed down the slopes every few minutes. The sun glowed wanly through a pall of volcanic dust. We camped on a bed of pumice, in constant fear the water would rise and drive us out.

We pushed up the valley of the Katmai River toward the volcanic area, 15 miles to the north (map, page 259). Houses in the deserted village of Katmai were packed to the eaves with pumice. The Russian church had been wrenched from its foundations and stood in a sea of mud. The river, choked with ash, was five miles wide and only five inches deep, except where shifting currents raced. We tried to slosh across but found ourselves in a maze of quicksands and had to turn back.

Cutting our gear to the minimum, camping where we could, we struggled north. We awoke one morning to a blinding dust storm of glass-sharp volcanic particles so much like snow that I started with surprise to realize it was not cold. We groped through it along a well-worn bear trail, pondering the thought of coming face to face with a huge Alaska brown bear.

At last, on a clear day, we sighted the magnificent three-peaked snowcap of Mount Mageik. West of it, where nothing

A BLIZZARD OF ASH *from the eruption swirled down on Kodiak, 100 miles away. First, people swept it up as a souvenir. But after three days of awful darkness, ten packed inches smothered the town, and 400 terrified souls jammed aboard the cutter* Manning *(below). Earlier, her captain had declaimed, "This is a time to keep minds clear!" — and closed the village bars.*

Probing the volcanic region for National Geographic, Professor Griggs (right) found that ash still choked the shattered land three years later and had paved the bed of the flooded Katmai River with shoals of quicksand.

showed on our charts, a 6,100-foot peak poured out an immense column of steam. We were anxious for a sight of Mount Katmai, still hidden beyond a bend in the valley to the east. We believed Katmai to have been the seat of the great eruption. Now we were not sure. Perhaps this new volcano had been the one that exploded.*

We continued up the Katmai valley, fording tributaries across the quicksands, where our six-foot alpenstocks could find no bottom. On the shoulder of a mountain beside one stream we found ourselves on a treadmill of ashes, slipping back two strides for every one forward. Suddenly the whole body of ash started to slide. We dropped on all fours and scrambled to the top. The pumice cut our fingertips and wore our fingernails to the quick.

Ironically, with streams all around us, we had a water problem. Trying to bathe in creeks clouded with pumice was like scrubbing ourselves with sandpaper. We strained out the coarsest grit, but the mud

*Studies in the 1950's indicate the eruption did not center at this volcano, Martin Mountain, but at Novarupta, lying between Martin and Katmai. The ejecta, thickest at Novarupta, thinned toward Katmai, six miles away.

that remained was barely potable. Folsom once refused to wash his face for three days because he "did not want to dirty it with the water we had to drink."

We hastened on, since the fine weather could not last much longer. Our provisions were getting short. But we were continually balked in our efforts to reach Mount Katmai and inspect its crater. Climbing a pass, I stamped my cold feet and was astonished to hear the ground ring hollow. Gingerly we probed with our staffs — we were standing on a one-foot-thick ash arch over a black cavern that could have been 5 feet deep or 50!

Turning back to go around the mountains, we entered the most oppressive country we had seen. Gaunt white bones of the dead forest stuck out of the ashes. We traveled all day without hearing a sound but the crunch of our own footsteps and the plunge of rushing water. The bear trails disappeared; we saw no signs of life but a pair of bald eagles flying over at a great height, a few mosquitoes, and a single hummingbird moth, strangely out of place in this valley of death.

We camped under clouds so low we could not tell where we were. But after two days the sky cleared, and before us

245

B. B. FULTON, OPPOSITE: J. F. HAHN, UPPER: W. J. ERSKINE

MACBETH'S WITCHES, *bent over their pot, had nothing on Katmai's explorers probing nature's bubbling caldron. Griggs led five Geographic surveys of what is now Katmai National Monument. His men stood on quaking glaciers of jelled volcanic mud (left) to peer at 60-foot water-cut canyons. They shivered on the caldera rim (right), their hooded camera poised to capture through a moment's rift in the steam the lake spread 3,700 feet below. They sidestepped white-hot vents in the Valley of Ten Thousand Smokes (below) to trap noxious gases for analysis. They even played Samson, tossing about huge boulders of bubble-filled pumice so light they would float.*

towered the glacier-covered volcanoes— Mageik, Trident, and finally Katmai, dirty with ash, a mere disemboweled stump of its former self. We would never be able to explore it this year. Its flanks were pitted with yawning crevasses, and we had no alpine ropes. We had to be satisfied with some long-range photographs. But we were determined to return.

We organized our next journey to Katmai with two changes. D. B. Church took the place of Fulton, and this time we sought the services of a packer. Finding one proved difficult, for the Indians were

afraid of the volcano. One chief told us, "Me no Katmai," and advised his people, "Life is better than money."

Then we thought of Walter Metrokin, the celebrated one-handed bear hunter of Kodiak, and happily he agreed to go with us. He had lost his right hand in a boyhood hunting accident, but could do more with one hand than most men with two—tie knots, roll a cigarette, even row a boat by lashing one oar to his stub.

As we plodded up the Katmai valley this time, we found the mountains greener, with seedlings beginning to sprout on the

F. I. JONES, TOP AND BOTTOM; L. G. FOLSOM, OPPOSITE: ROBERT F. GRIGGS

flats. But crossing the creeks was just as bad as before. I never got used to the danger of quicksand, the fear that next time it would get one of us.

Near the head of the valley we saw the mountains—a whole chain of glacier-bearing volcanoes broken only by Katmai Pass. They were steaming more than ever, and beyond the pass we saw two large clouds, inconstant and elusive, that puzzled us. Had we known then what lay below them....

But we were intent upon climbing Katmai at last. We left the valley and took a long ridge leading toward it. Roping up, we tackled the slope.

From the outset we found ourselves on dangerous ground. The ash crust had cracked open as snow melted beneath it, and boiling torrents issued from the cavernous depths. Higher up we came to mud—slippery, sticky, and in spots nearly knee-deep. At times we needed all our strength to extricate ourselves.

At 5,500 feet we reached the rim of Katmai's crater—so suddenly we almost went right over it. The edge was unbelievably sharp and invisible in roiling clouds of steam. We dropped to our knees and leaned forward. For long, suspenseful minutes we could see nothing. Then the curtain of steam blew away abruptly. We were struck speechless by the scene.

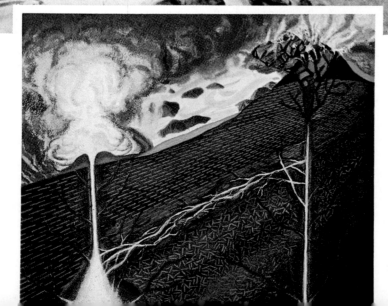

NOVARUPTA EXPLODES,
*and underground conduits
siphon molten rock
from beneath Mount Katmai,
six miles to the east.
Undermined, Katmai's
summit collapses with a roar
that is lost in the awesome
voice of the eruption.
A billowing mushroom cloud,*

OF 1912; ROBERT C. MAGIS AND (ABOVE) WINFIELD PARKS, BOTH NATIONAL GEOGRAPHIC STAFF

spotted from a ship 55 miles away,
seems to pinpoint Katmai as its source.

Now cooled and lined by snow,
Mount Katmai (above) reveals its vast
caldera—two and a half miles across—
cupping, as if it were a precious jade,
that lake which Griggs glimpsed only
through the parting clouds.
Tinted by minerals, made milky
by the melt of many glaciers,

the still water rises and falls eerily.

Beyond looms Mount Griggs, second
highest peak in the national monument,
a 7,589-foot tribute to the author.
Though streaked with snow this cone
has not lost its steam, and rumbles
sometimes deep within its furnace.

To its left, receding into mist,
spreads the great discovery—silent now—
the Valley of Ten Thousand Smokes.

249

We were hanging over the brink of an immense abyss. Far below stretched a wonderful blue-green lake with a horse-shoe island of cinder near the middle. Around the margin a thousand steam jets hissed and roared. On the far side were two yellow spots of sulphur.

The perpendicular sides near us were composed of frozen mud and fragments of lava. The opposite wall had a stratified look where successive flows had cooled.

We just knelt there, gaping, until the clouds closed in again and robbed us of a chance to set up our camera tripod. On a later expedition, when we were recording this impressive sight on film, one man took a long first look at the crater, then turned to the photographer. "Tear up your damn pictures," he said. "They'll never help anybody imagine what this is like!"

KATMAI CRATER, we thought, was the supreme wonder of the area. A few days later we discovered how wrong we were. We had climbed to the crater lip for a second look and had noticed again the strange cloud activity beyond Katmai Pass. We mounted the pass and gained a view of the other side. But not a puff of steam could we see, though the sun was shining directly down the pass.

I concluded that all we had seen before had been ordinary clouds. But with Folsom I went on a little farther. Church rested below with the packs.

Just as I was about to suggest turning back, I caught sight of a tiny ribbon of vapor. I rubbed my eyes and looked again. Far away beyond a hill, a much larger steam puff billowed into the air.

Late as it was, we had to have a look. The sight that flashed into view as we surmounted the hillock and looked down the valley was unbelievable. Stretching as far as the eye could reach, till the valley turned behind a blue mountain in the distance, were hundreds — no, thousands, literally tens of thousands — of smokes curling up from its fissured floor. It was as though all the steam engines in the world had popped their safety valves at once.

Many of these little volcanoes were sending up columns of steam which rose a thousand feet before dissolving. We judged there must be a thousand with plumes exceeding 500 feet. The biggest of all, whose steam had first caught my eye, stood well up on a mountainside in a nest of fissures which looked like the crevasses of a glacier. We had stumbled into another Yellowstone — unsuspected by man until this hour. Ten Thousand Smokes! The valley named itself.

I tried to keep my head, yet wasted two shots from the one precious roll of film I had with me, trying for pictures I knew were impossible.

We plunged down to get a better look. The ground was hot beneath our feet, and foul odors assailed our nostrils — sulphurous gases and strangely organic smells recalling burning wool, decay, and the musk of a fox den. If a strong wind had not been blowing the fumes down the valley, we might not have dared to go on.

We had time for only the most hurried observations, for it was getting late and we did not want to fall into one of those seething caldrons in the dark. We returned to camp, intending to come back equipped for more extensive exploration. But the river was rising so fast from melting snow we knew we had to leave immediately.

Sleep that night was impossible. We had discovered one of the great wonders of the world, but as proof we had only one partial roll of undeveloped pictures. Would our story be believed, or would we be regarded as modern Munchausens?

Since that night I have had occasion many times to be grateful to the National Geographic Society. With only that single roll of film as evidence, the Society gave us both credence and publicity and sent us back to Alaska to complete our explorations. As a direct result of its magazine reports on our findings, a proclamation signed by President Wilson on September 16, 1918, turned more than a million acres of Alaskan volcanic wonderland into Katmai National Monument.

GHOST FORESTS *still haunt the Katmai region. The explosion carbonized forests and buried 42 square miles of valley up to 700 feet deep in hot sandflow. Senator Ernest Gruening (left) inspects the scene for a report in the* Geographic.

WINFIELD PARKS, NATIONAL GEOGRAPHIC PHOTOGRAPHER

MAGNETOMETER SURVEY TEAM SCOURS THE CRATER'S BLUSTERY RIM FOR SIGNS OF METEOR FRAGMENTS; RICHARD H. STEWART, NATIONAL GEOGRAPHIC STAFF

The Mystery of Chubb Crater

What mighty force gouged a hole two miles wide in the wastes of northern Quebec? V. Ben Meen leads a team of scientists to find out.

IN ALL THE VAST and lonely reaches of the Far North I doubt that there was a more disappointed man than I that Sunday evening, August 19, 1951.

The Royal Ontario Museum of Toronto and the National Geographic Society had sent us to the subarctic tip of Quebec to solve the mystery of two-mile-wide Chubb Crater. Was it the throat of some long-extinct volcano? Was it a sinkhole formed after the retreat of a glacier? Or, as I thought most likely, had it been blasted out by a giant meteor?

Seeking the answer, six of us had been working our hearts out for almost a month against cold, rain, and the everlasting wind that sweeps this desolate land. Now time was running out. The first snows of the oncoming winter were upon us, and a drop in temperature would ice up nearby Museum Lake, the only landing place for our plane. We had to get out.

Although I believed I knew what had *not* caused the crater, I still lacked ac-

ceptable evidence as to what *had*. Chubb Crater stubbornly held its secret.

The Catalina flying boat had landed us on July 25, the start of craterland's short summer at its best. My team was hand-picked: Fred Chubb, sturdy prospector and frontiersman after whom I had named the crater; Len Cowan and "Long John" Keefe, my geological assistants; biologist Nick Martin, and National Geographic photographer Dick Stewart.

Strictly speaking, Dick's only job was to make a photographic record of the expedition. But he volunteered to serve as *chef de cuisine*, with this ultimatum: "The first man who complains about the food replaces me as cook immediately!" Dick held his job until we struck camp.

We got on with our work in a boulder-choked world that could have been the landscape of a deserted planet. But from the beginning, progress was discouraging.

Rain and snow often made the boulders on the crater's rim too slippery for Keefe and Cowan to work. Even in fair weather, magnetic storms plagued their operation, jumbling the magnetometer readings. And the mine detectors failed to find meteoritic material. They "sang" continuously because almost all the rocks held traces of metallic minerals.

Martin and Chubb labored for days to lug our equipment the two miles from Museum Lake to the crater and down its rocky slope. But we had only two days during our stay when the crater lake surface was calm enough to take soundings.

As expedition geologist, I studied the region's rock formation and the fracture pattern which indicated that a terrific explosion had produced the crater. I also assumed the task of seeking traces of the meteor. Over and over I asked myself, "Where are the fragments?" Surely there must be *some* evidence that would tie the crater to a meteoritic origin.

TOPPING OFF our frustrations was the nightly tragedy of Meen at the microphone. After some preliminary instruction by experts, I had volunteered as radio operator. But no matter how often I checked my notes and manuals, my calls failed to bring a reply. This failure filled me with uneasiness. What if an emergency should occur?

Then one night, for no reason at all, I cut in both our microphones instead of one and blurted out our call letters. The two "mikes" worked a miracle.

"You wouldn't be the crater, would you?" Fort McKenzie's operator inquired from 350 miles away.

The shout of "Yes!" that I hurled back across the ether must have set the other chap's ears ringing.

Our luck with the radio failed to alter our fortunes in the field, however. Days dwindled. Sunday, August 19, arrived. I had sent word to the magnetometer team on the crater rim to return to base and pack up for our departure. But now Keefe came striding up, almost beside himself with excitement. "Doc!" he shouted. "I've got it! I've found the anomaly! But I need more time to study it. How much longer have I got?"

My hopes soared, then ebbed. Even if he had found a magnetic anomaly—an area in which a foreign subsurface mass has changed the earth's magnetic force—we still lacked time to establish positive evidence. Our plane was due the next day.

If only we had more time! I felt cheated by clock, calendar, and weather.

But overnight, bad weather, our implacable foe, intervened to give us more time. Driving sleet and snow squalls—no amphibian could come through in *that*.

The boys went scrambling back to the crater. I had to monitor the radio for news of the plane. Reception could not have been worse. We were in the midst of a magnetic storm which was playing havoc with the magnetometer readings.

About 5 P.M. the storm passed, leaving crystal-clear radio reception. Soon Fort McKenzie called; the plane had arrived. Then came the climax of the day—of the entire expedition.

At 9 P.M. Keefe and Cowan staggered into camp, spent with fatigue. Their happy faces told the story. They had defined the anomaly as an elliptical area, elongated between the two highest peaks on the crater's rim. The shape of the underground mass and character of the magnetometer readings strongly indicated a concentration of exploded meteor fragments buried deep in the granite rim.

Here at last was something to go on.

Eventually someone may find meteor fragments on Chubb's wide plain. Until then, we must rely on the magnetometer data, the crater's similarity to proven meteor scars, and the absence of clues pointing to any other origin.

Six happy men flew out the next morning with evidence of a new giant among the world's meteor craters.

AMID A NIGHTMARE *of rocks, the crater's lake sparkles so clear that Nick Martin spotted his Secchi disk 115 feet down. But portaging his canoe down the slope proved an ankle-twisting chore.*

Misshapen Arctic char (center right) puzzled the scientists: How did they get there, and what do they eat?

Examining ore (lower right), Dr. Meen found many signs of terrestrial metals. Meteor fragments may lie far below.

Operation Eclipse

From Burma to the Aleutians astronomers mark the moon's progress across the sun's face. William A. Kinney reports.

E-DAY DAWNED CLEAR and sunny in Washington, D. C. The Bureau of Standards reported a slackening in the sunspot activity and radio static that threatened the project. Time signals were given a good chance of getting through. Final weather forecasts began to trickle in. Now there was nothing to do but wait—sweat it out, as GI's say.

On May 8, 1948, "Operation Eclipse," the National Geographic Society's study of solar phenomena, was underway. Observation teams were on station at meticulously plotted sites in Burma, Siam, China, Korea, Japan, and the Aleutians. Two Aleutian-based B-29 Superforts were ready to take off to test an unproven technique in astronomical research.

As the moon blacked out the sun along this 5,320-mile path, the teams were to take motion pictures of the eclipse. A sound track would record the one-per-second ticks of chronometers checked for

FLAMING HYDROGEN ERUPTS 150,000 MILES FROM SUN'S SURFACE IN THIS CORONAGRAPHIC SHOT OF A PROMINENCE; COURTESY OF THE HIGH ALTITUDE OBSERVATORY, CLIMAX, COLORADO, AND HUMBLE OIL & REFINING COMPANY

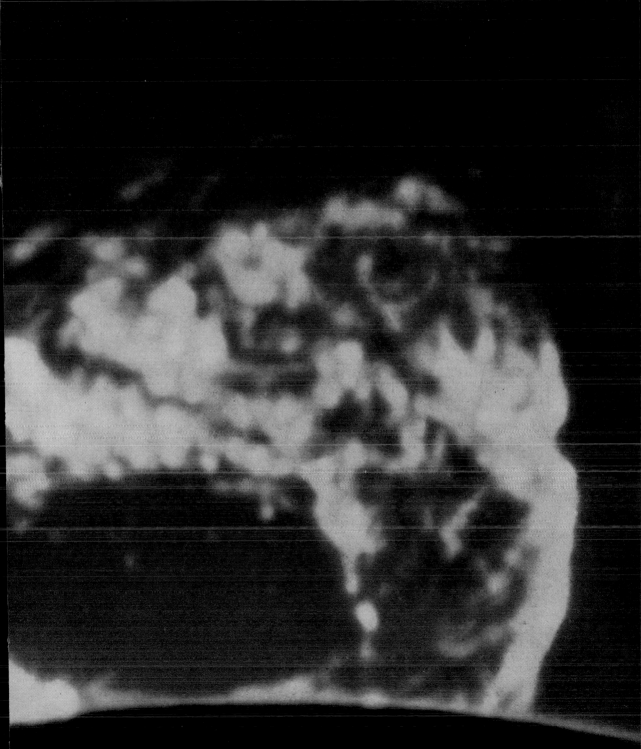

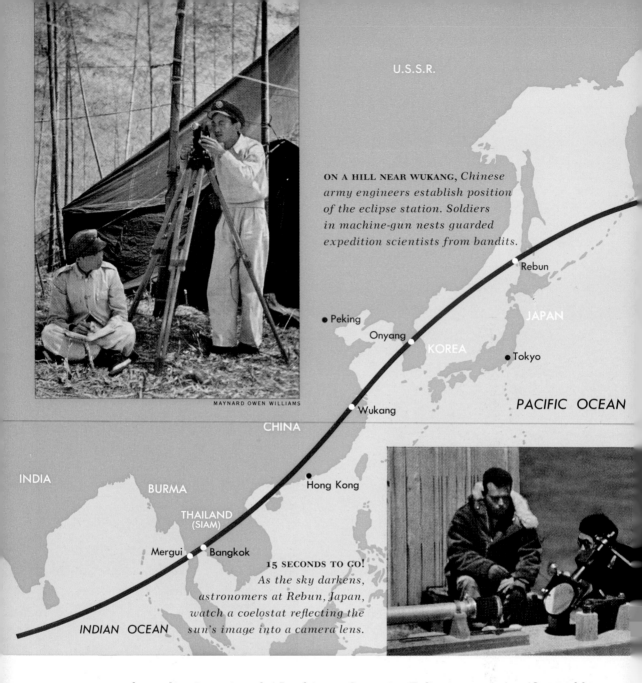

ON A HILL NEAR WUKANG, *Chinese army engineers establish position of the eclipse station. Soldiers in machine-gun nests guarded expedition scientists from bandits.*

MAYNARD OWEN WILLIAMS

U.S.S.R.

Rebun

• Peking

Onyang

KOREA

JAPAN

• Tokyo

Wukang

PACIFIC OCEAN

CHINA

INDIA

BURMA

Hong Kong

THAILAND
(SIAM)

Mergui   Bangkok

15 SECONDS TO GO! *As the sky darkens, astronomers at Rebun, Japan, watch a coelostat reflecting the sun's image into a camera lens.*

INDIAN OCEAN

accuracy by radio time signals. In this way the scientists would be able to measure the split-second time of the eclipse from exact geographical locations.

If these observations were successful, scientists could use the eclipse as an enormous measuring instrument to tell the size of the earth and the relative positions of points on its surface. Adverse weather, however, could defeat the observers and wipe out the 11-month preparations of Gilbert Grosvenor, President of the Society, Lyman J. Briggs, Research Committee Chairman, and a host of experts.

Operation Eclipse was a scientific gamble.

At Society headquarters in Washington, Dr. Briggs knew he was in for a long day. The first contact was due in Mergui, Burma, at 6:53 P.M. (Eastern Standard Time), the last in the Aleutians five hours later.

Morning and afternoon waned; 6:53 came and passed. No news. Evening wore on. Midnight and still no word. But soon after came the break. Siam reporting: *Despite massing monsoon clouds first contact . . . second contact and most annularity recorded but third contact problematical. . . . Party jubilant.*

SUNDAY DATE LINE SATURDAY

Alaska

+Mt. McKinley

+Mt. Logan
+Mt. St. Elias

BERING SEA

+Mt. Katmai

Kodiak

CANADA

Shemya

ALEUTIAN ISLANDS

Kiska   Adak
Amchitka

Vancouver ●

UNITED
STATES

FROM BOXLIKE TURRET *behind B-29's nose,*
camera recorded eclipse above the clouds.
The plane got position signals from
the Aleutians, time signals from Hawaii.

San Francisco ●

J. BAYLOR ROBERTS, NATIONAL GEOGRAPHIC STAFF. BELOW: JUSTIN LOCKE

CAMERA TRIALS *ran smoothly, but clouds*
over the Aleutians on E-Day socked in
this site on Adak. Elsewhere on the
island another team, turned back from
Kiska by World War II land mines, got
limited coverage through swirling snow.

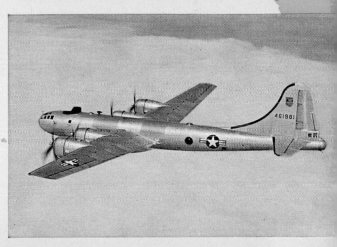

NATIONAL GEOGRAPHIC MAP
BY JOHN LOTHERS

ANXIOUS HOURS *weighed*
on Dr. Lyman J. Briggs,
Director of Operation
Eclipse, in Washington,
D. C., until belated
radiograms from the field
signaled success. The
1948 eclipse crossed the
Date Line and lost a day,
ending in the Aleutians
the afternoon of May 8
before starting in Burma
the morning of May 9!

Eclipse hunting in Brazil

Tracking *the eclipse of May 20, 1947,*
Father Francis J. Heyden (with cap)
and his aides photographed the sun
every 15 seconds for 2½ hours,
then dropped, exhausted, on their cots.

They were part of a 76-man expedition,
one of a long line of eclipse studies
by the National Geographic Society.
They studied cosmic rays, compiled
an atlas of the southern Milky Way,
and measured the bending of starlight
to test Einstein's theory of relativity.

Cosponsored by the Army Air Forces,
the 1947 expedition flew men and
supplies to its camp at Bocaiúva
(map, page 108), so deep in the wilds of
Brazil that locals dubbed it "Extrema."

Project Officer Melvin M. Payne,
now Executive Vice President and
Secretary of the Society, made the
400-mile trip north from Rio de Janeiro
in a battered transport that sagged
under the weight of a generator. No need
to worry, a crewman assured him:
"The plane is condemned, anyhow."

These were heartening tidings. An annular eclipse (when a ring of sunlight shines around the moon's dark edges) has four critical phases which yield useful facts: When the moon makes contact with the sun's rim; when it lies within the sun's disk but not concentric to it; when it starts moving off the sun's face; and when the two are about to part. The Siam team had photographed at least two of the phases. What of the other stations?

The small hours plodded on, dawn came, the clock edged toward noon. Then, with a rush, came an unwelcome story.

Wukang, China: On a bamboo-thicketed hill dubbed "Camp One Long Climb," Father Francis J. Heyden of Georgetown College Observatory stared helplessly at the sky. An unbroken stretch of cloud darkened, then lightened, as the eclipse passed. The sun never appeared. The last straw: Lt. N. J. Fay, hoarding a bottle of champagne to celebrate success, opened it now for solace. It was flat.

Onyang, Korea: Dr. George Van Biesbroeck, a grand old man of American astronomy, had given a lecture on the eclipse to school children. Now many of them crowded about to watch the scientific work. But no one saw the eclipse. "It was tantalizing," said Van Biesbroeck, "to be able to distinguish faintly the narrowing crescent of the sun when the clouds were a little less heavy."

Adak Island, the Aleutians: Lt. Comdr. George R. Shelton's group on Mount Moffett got usable footage at first contact—then snow. They kept cameras grinding, but heavy clouds rolled over at critical moments. On nearby Mount Adagdak, Clarence Shelton's party reported "zero."

In a Washington office cluttered with radiograms, Dr. Briggs checked the scorecard. Disappointment lined his face. "It looks as if we are going to lose out."

Then came bell-ringing news from Rebun, Japan: *Contacts one, two, three perfect weather. Minor cloud interference fourth contact.... Well satisfied.*

Operation Eclipse was not a complete failure after all! Now if Burma and the B-29's could come through....

After many hours' delay Burma reported

qualified success. But still no news from the B-29's, though their bases were peppered with urgent messages.

Four days later their project officer showed up in Washington to explain the confusion and tell an exciting story.

On E-Day, layers of haze had swirled at 10,000 feet, the planned working level. The Superforts groped higher. Three miles. Four. Five. Still the "soup" persisted. Finally they broke into the clear. At an altitude of 29,000 feet, outside thermometers registered 50° below zero centigrade and crewmen commented on the strange brightness of the atmosphere. Then the moon bit into the edge of the resplendent sun. Brightness gave way to eerie twilight, then darkness.

Suddenly, ribs in the specially built optical-glass camera turrets began to crack under the planes' pressurization. The photographers were lashed in, but should the turrets give way.... Similar accidents had sucked men out of high-flying planes to certain death.

The photographers worked feverishly. The ribs cracked and groaned—but held. Light returned to the sky. The B-29 crews landed, sent "Mission Accomplished" reports. Because of radio interference, the messages were never received.

Happily, Dr. Briggs revised his estimate. With a linkup from Burma to the Aleutians, new data had been obtained on distances between North America and Asia. Some 100,000 eclipse pictures had been collected. The revolutionary use of airplanes had proved itself, giving astronomers a veto over bad weather.

ECLIPSE WATCHERS *squint through film or smoked glass in Japan (above), where the sky spectacle stalls traffic and disrupts baseball games. In Korea (below), Dr. Van Biesbroeck takes time out to share his vast knowledge of eclipses with the school children of Onyang.*

Avalanche!

An Andean glacier snaps, and in minutes 3,500 Peruvians perish. In the aftermath Bart McDowell finds grief—and courage.

FACES REFLECT THE TRAGEDY OF BURIED YANAMACHICO (OPPOSITE) AND SEVEN OTHER RAVAGED SETTLEMENTS; JOHN E. FLETCHER, NATIONAL GEOGRAPHIC PHOTOGRAPHER

O N THE NORTHWEST FACE of 22,205-foot Huascarán, Peru's tallest mountain, Glacier 511 absorbed the amber warmth of the setting sun. The mass of ice was huge. Droplets of melt seeped into its cracked surface, and the water lubricated its footing. Heat, cold, and gravity were forming a fatal equation.

It was 6 P.M., January 10, 1962. Violence was still 13 minutes away.

Beneath the mountain's glacial grandeur shepherds hurried to finish the day's chores. In the valley village of Calla, 11 miles from the peak, Señora Montoro de Narcisa found she would need more bread for supper. "Watch the baby until I return," she instructed her older daughter. Then she walked briskly to Ranrahirca, two miles away.

In that prosperous town, Alberto Méndez, wealthy owner of a trucking line, had just arrived home from Lima and was resting. Over cobbled streets Lamberto Guzmán Tapia, barrel-chested mountain climber of 26, walked with happy impatience to a family party. In the school-yard, teen-age sisters Lira and Wanda Giraldo gossiped and giggled.

At the stroke of six Ricardo Olivera arrived at the power station for his evening ritual: throwing the switch to give Ranrahirca five hours of electricity. Mayor Alfonso Caballero, whose house was across the street, called *"Buenas noches."*

At 6:13, two and a half miles overhead,

Glacier 511 shuddered. A man in nearby Yungay first thought it was a cloud turning golden in the sunset: "But I saw that the cloud was flying downhill."

The first long fall was quiet and quick. Then the ice mass crashed wildly into the gorge of the Callejón de Huailas. A crushing sound echoed down its length. Then came a roar "like that of ten thousand wild beasts," as one man described it.

"I could feel the rumble in the walls of the belly," said another.

Mountaineer Guzmán recognized the noise at once. He had just arrived at his aunt's house. Inside, some 40 guests sang the happy Peruvian songs, *huaynos.*

"¡Alud!" Guzmán cried. "Avalanche!" No one heard him. They only laughed and clapped all the harder. With a final shout of "Save yourselves!" he ran up the street. The happy music receded into the hollow thunder of the avalanche.

Electrician Olivera sprinted down into the center of town, but realized he could not reach his home in time. People were panicking. Scores were running toward the church, a haven for body and spirit. In the crowd Olivera saw the Giraldo sisters. "Here!" he called, seizing each by the wrist to pull them to safety.

JOHN E. FLETCHER, NATIONAL GEOGRAPHIC PHOTOGRAPHER

NINE-MILE AVALANCHE *is traced minute by minute by author Bart McDowell (center) and Col. Humberto Ampuero Pérez, who headed rescue operations from a command post consisting of tent, table, and telephone. To McDowell it was a classic textbook avalanche: Fattened by freak snows, warmed by unseasonal sunshine, the glacier skidded from its 21,834-foot perch on Huascarán (map, page 108) and hurtled down. It smashed through the green valley, killing thousands, wrecking villages, burying fields. It has been called one of the greatest natural disasters of the century.*

C O R

Callejón de Huailas

Yungay

Huarascucho

Shacsha

Ranrahirca

Chuquibamba

Calla

Uchucoto

Río Santa

Matacoto

6:18 P.M.

DEATH SWEEPS DOWN *at 60 miles an hour on Ranrahirca and vicinity, claiming 2,700 lives.*

6:20 P.M.

AVALANCHE *cuts across the Río Santa, after a drop in elevation of more than 2½ miles.*

21,834 **Huascarán** 22,205

Glacier 511

6:13 P.M.

TRIGGERED BY THAW, *snow
pitches headlong from
Huascarán's north summit,
jarring loose 3 million tons
of ice from Glacier 511.*

LLERA   BLANCA

Pacucco
anamachico

6:15 P.M.

CAROMING *off canyon walls,
the lethal barrage devastates
Yanamachico and nearby villages,
leaving 800 dead, 8 alive.*

6:16 P.M.

TITANIC TORRENT, *choked with
boulders, fans onto plain.
Hills banking gorge divert
slide, saving town of Yungay.*

NATIONAL GEOGRAPHIC STAFF ARTIST   JE Barrett

RUBBLE GRAVEYARD, *60 feet thick at center, looms over living remnant of Ranrahirca.*

Mayor Caballero stood speechless before his house. He tried to call his sister but the roar obliterated his words.

In its fall, the ice mass crashed into an uninhabited slope, then bounced — an insane ricochet from the sides of gorges. Surveyors later counted five impact points. The mass carved and collected its own debris: topsoil, boulders, crushed houses from four villages, flocks of sheep. It stirred tempests of shrill wind.

As it approached the valley floor the avalanche flattened to 60 feet in thickness. It slowed to a mile a minute. By this time it had taken nearly a thousand lives. Now it was roaring down on some 2,700 people of Ranrahirca and vicinity.

In a few seconds yellow dust engulfed Olivera and gritted his eyes. "The girls were torn from my hands — by the winds or by a wall of mud," he said. "Electric wires had fallen around me. Somehow, I came free."

The avalanche now reached the valley bottom, nine miles from its mountain perch. It was 6:20. Only seven minutes had passed since the first fall.

The Señora de Narcisa would never return to her children. The party at the Guzmán house, the rich Señor Méndez and his fine home, the church and its refugees — all were gone.

"I regained my senses," said Olivera, "and saw only a waste of mud and ice. I

THIS DOOR saved 12-year-old Jorge
Hilario Vásquez of Huarascucho. At the
roar of the approaching avalanche
Jorge and his Uncle Carlos ran out
of the house. "But Uncle Carlos always
tells me to shut the door when I go out,"
Jorge explained. "I remembered and
hurried back." The frozen flood sliced
the house like cheese but left Jorge and
the door unharmed. Other survivors
(below) cross the slide on a flimsy walkway.

A MILITIAMAN KEEPS LONELY VIGIL *on a dead-end street where children once played.*

was impressed by a profound silence. Realizing that my wife, my children, my parents were all buried under the debris, I suddenly found myself sobbing."

THESE WERE A FEW of the human stories we gathered at the raw white rim of ruin. My National Geographic colleague Jack Fletcher turned his camera upon the mountain's scar. I interviewed the strong and stoic survivors. Together we recorded a disaster that, by official estimate, had taken 3,500 lives. From this valley of deep silence and sorrow, we brought back a burden of impressions.

One was our first glimpse of the avalanche rubble. Neither of us spoke. The scene resembled an Old Testament visitation. White rock and pale mud stretched a mile across the green Andean valley. No ice was visible on the surface. Boulders were mortared together by a crusting mud of granite dust, and streaked by small, disoriented brooks of melt. Following a team of stretcher-bearers to recover the dead, we sank thigh-deep in mire.

We watched the villagers at an outdoor mass for the dead: old women with faces like tooled leather, young ones quieting their infants with milk from the breast, poncho-clad men holding hats in gnarled hands, townsfolk dressed in the decent black of mourning. As the priest intoned the Latin words some women wept, quietly, without sobbing. Their faces seemed numb beyond the curing salt of tears.

For days we shared the life of gradual repair and quiet mourning in this valley of the shadow of death. Yet above all else, one incident typified the special sadness of the avalanche.

Clearing a way for a new road, bulldozers encountered several bodies protected from the full force of the stones. One was a little boy. On the man-size stretcher he seemed pitifully small.

The morgue superintendent ordered the stretcher-bearers to his patio, pointing a hand dusted white with quicklime. Lime was his only disinfectant, his only balm for quick burials. He looked closely into the little face. "Call Señor Jiraldo," he ordered. "Tell him it is one of his sons."

They lifted the body from the stretcher to the floor. Something fell from the boy's pocket. It was a yo-yo.

A crowd entered. In the middle stood a stocky man with a tense, unshaven face.

"The father?" I asked. The morgue-keeper nodded silently.

Señor Jiraldo bent down to the figure of the boy: "It is my son Homero." He repeated carefully the boy's whole name for the morgue records. "Homero Jiraldo Montes. Please bring water."

A woman fetched a pail. Carefully, the father poured water upon the face of his son, washing away the mud in a brusque liturgy of ablution. The man's face showed no emotion, but his voice was hoarse.

"Homero was my youngest," said the father. He held the muddy little shirt and began to undress the child, easing the small arm out of the sleeve. He paused to look at his son's shoulder. It was marked by a purple bruise. The man said nothing; but gently, and only for an instant, he covered the small bruised shoulder with his own square hand.

"Homero was 10 years old," the father said. He continued to undress the child, but more quickly now. He lifted the small body to a bed of boxes. With his own hand he sprinkled the lime.

The stoic Andean Pietà was finished. The yo-yo still lay on the patio floor.

GRIEF AND TERROR *stalked the Peruvian valley in the wake of white death. Above: A bereaved father tenderly washes his dead son's face. Below: "All our people! All our people!" wail mourning women, identifying their kin in the Ranrahirca morgue.*

Nature's Wonders: A Portfolio

CHILD OF COSMIC CHAOS, a nebula blows
its filmy breath across the blue and black
and glitter of the spangled heavens.
Through uncounted ages, brittle fingers of polar winds
weld moisture drop by drop until the land lies dead
and cold beneath a potter's field of ice.
Far beneath the sea a volcano clears its throat:
An island is born.
Earth shudders, and a mountain crumbles.
  Nature diagrams her wonders on the blackboard
of the land in formulas violent, scales majestic.
And man, an apt pupil, crowds close, the more to see.
Some travel far to stand in awe;
some climb and probe and then return,
bringing tales of sights beheld
to jump the pulse and catch the breath of other men.
  To see, to understand—these yearnings
for centuries have lured men to earth's far places.
And now, in the magic of their clicking cameras,
the eyes of one who has seen become the eyes of all.
  Here are moments of wonder,
a sampling to send imaginations vaulting,
captured for *National Geographic*
from nature's vast repertoire of epic scenes.
Man needs to suck his breath in sharply now and then,
to stand with jaw agape and see with childlike eyes.

THE MIGHTY ZAMBEZI STUMBLES *over a precipice and suddenly comes alive, flinging itself from stone to stone, afoam with ecstasy. Miles away its roar still sounds through the Rhodesian countryside. A mile of misty diamonds sparkles in the sun across its brow, and at its feet sweet rainbows arc to charm the leaping waters back to sleep. A sight for "angels in their flight," said Livingstone, and crowned the falls with a queen's name, Victoria.*

MALIGNANT FIRES *flushed from hell*
spurt skyward as a flaming fountain bursts
from Kilauea Iki Crater, Hawaii. In golden
torrents tons of molten rock seethe
across the crater floor, forming a fiery lake
of lava hundreds of feet deep that may take
a century to cool. Trees near the flow explode
like shrapnel and crackle into instant flame.
Great blobs of blazing pumice—devil's popcorn—
catapulted on howling winds, blacken in flight
and submerge the land in crunchy seas of cinder.
The stench of sulphur fouls the air,
a noxious pall of sooted smoke and steam
inflames the sky and chars the fleeing clouds.
By tens of thousands, tourists, drawn like moths
to a colossal candle flame, grope through
the eerie haze to stand spellbound and gaze
into the red-rimmed eye of Dante's netherworld.

275

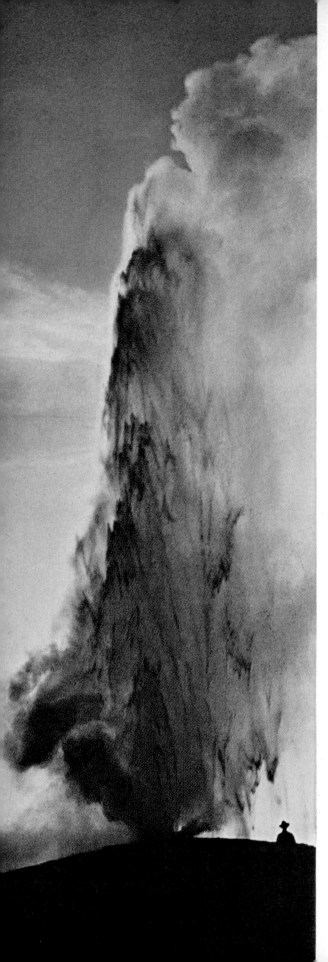

OLD FAITHFUL *plays a landlocked whale in Yellowstone National Park, its hourly spout recalling ancient seas, now gone.*

WRENCHED AND RACKED *by monumental pressures, a mountain in Wyoming grinds its stony ramparts into dust. The earthquake's evil strength soon dies, but gaping wounds remain — for science to catalog, for nature, in her time, to heal.*

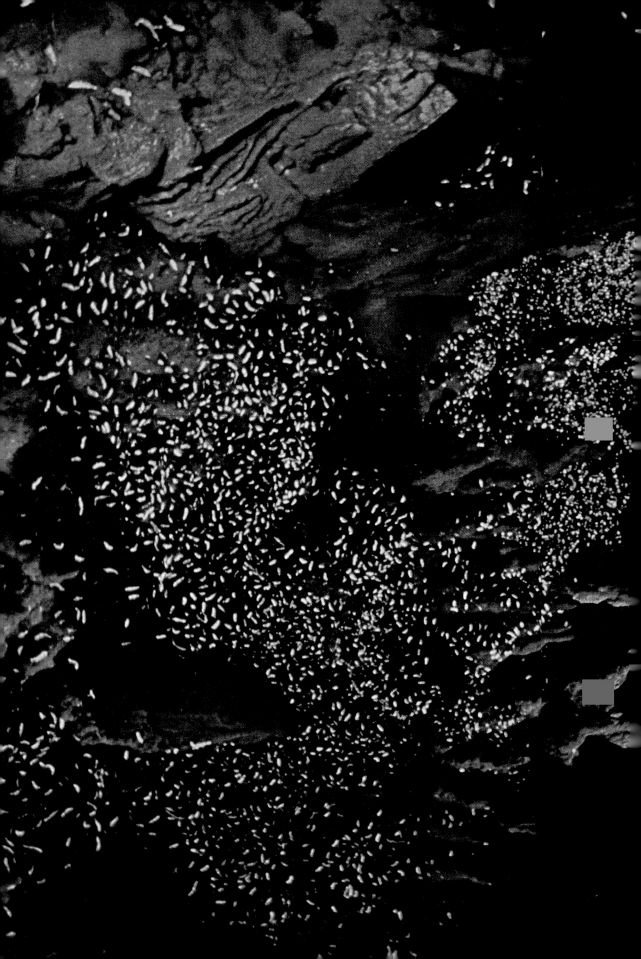

ARACHNOCAMPA LUMINOSA! *What gentle humorist bestowed so grandiloquent a name on a gnat? But in New Zealand's Waitomo Cave the larvae of this lowly glowworm do justice to the name, shining like stars in a dawnless night, luring flies into traps of dangling, sticky threads.*

279

BARREL OF AIR *supplied an 18th century diving bell and skin-helmeted salvager. A pump feeds today's diver (right).*

PETER THROCKMORTON

Probing
the Depths
of the Sea

" THE SEA NEVER CHANGES," wrote Joseph Conrad, "and its works, for all the talk of men, are wrapped in mystery." To fathom this mystery, gill-less man had to find artificial ways of getting to the ocean bottom. It is easy to look back from an age equipped with Aqua-Lungs, submarines, and bathyscaphs and scoff at early efforts. Yet some of them worked. Courageous men dipped below the surface of the sea in such unlikely contrivances as a large wooden chamber linked to a barrel of air by "a Leathern Hose, well liquored with Bees-Wax and Oyl."

Despite centuries of effort, man hardly rippled the vast underwater world. Then, on August 15, 1934, two men huddled in a metal ball as it descended into the abyss off Bermuda. *2,100 feet:* "Now ghostly things in every direction." *2,800 feet:* "Here's a telescope-eyed fish." *3,028 feet:* "Long, lacelike things again." William Beebe and Otis Barton in their bathysphere had taken the National Geographic flag into a realm "almost as unknown as Mars."

The Society has continued to encourage undersea explorers with their fabulous machines. From the lobster-shaped Aquascope on the floor of Chesapeake Bay, Gilbert C. Klingel peers out at an underwater hurricane: "Mangled and

280

AQUA-LUNGERS *take dry-land archeology undersea. With a wire grid, these Society-sponsored scientists plot the position of cargo in a Byzantine ship that sank off Turkey 13 centuries ago.*

BACK FROM THE DEPTHS, *Beebe peers from his bathysphere's quartz window.*

U. S. NAVY'S TRIESTE, *a blimp-shaped bathyscaph, took man on his deepest dive—35,800 feet down to the floor of the Pacific.*

twisted sponges, and tufts of red and purple algae went rolling over and over ... like tumbleweed on a windswept prairie" at the changing of the tide. In a bathyscaph designed on the principle of a free balloon, Jacques Piccard and Lt. Don Walsh, U.S.N., plunge nearly *seven miles* to the bottom of the Pacific. Edwin A. Link invents an aluminum cylinder in which a submerged diver can eat and rest between explorations. Using this "little sea bungalow," a diver spends 24 hours 200 feet down in the Mediterranean.

Since 1952 the Society has supported the explorations of Capt. Jacques-Yves Cousteau, co-inventor of the Aqua-Lung and author of *The Silent World* and *The Living Sea.* Why does he roam the undersea world? "When we are invited to live on this earth, there is no reason why we should not visit the basement."

In the "basement" off Pitcairn Island, National Geographic's Luis Marden glides toward "squiggles" on the sea floor. "I thrust my face closer, almost touching the bottom. My heart jumped." There lay the bones of H.M.S. *Bounty!* In the eastern Mediterranean, George F. Bass of the University of Pennsylvania Museum excavates a 3,200-year-old Bronze Age vessel and a 1,300-year-old Byzantine ship. From the bottom of Stockholm harbor a helmeted diver

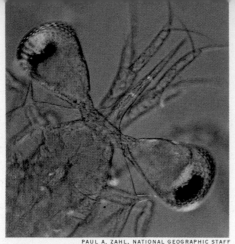

PLANKTON HUNTERS *of the University of Miami (below) net sea creatures like this ghostly crustacean, magnified 30 times.*

DR. EDGERTON *tests his abyssal camera—designed for the world's greatest depths—in M. I. T.'s pool.*

reports: "I just reached out and touched something solid...it feels like a wall of wood." He has found *Vasa!* In *National Geographic* Anders Franzén tells of his recovery of the remarkably preserved 17th century warship.

As world population multiplies, the locker of the sea may become tomorrow's breadbasket. For ten years the Society, in cooperation with the Marine Laboratory of the University of Miami, has studied the spawning grounds and life histories of fish. Off the Bahamas scientists pull aboard a long, silk net. Squirming captives include "three tiny creatures...steel blue in places, transparent elsewhere, with short broad snouts and toothed spines projecting from their heads." Patient laboratory work solves the riddle: Here are progeny of the majestic sailfish. In the open Atlantic the research trawler *Delaware* spins out a fishing line 14 miles long, dangling 700 hooks. The expedition—sponsored by the National Geographic Society, Woods Hole Oceanographic Institution, and the United States Bureau of Commercial Fisheries—seeks life secrets of the tuna, a virtually untapped food source in these waters.

The Society's second president, Alexander Graham Bell, asked in 1914: "Did you ever put your head under water and chuck two stones together to see what

UNDERSEA PIONEER
Jacques-Yves Cousteau receives the Society's Gold Medal from President Kennedy in 1961. Melville Bell Grosvenor (at right) called the Society's support of the French explorer's work "a wonderful example of international cooperation in science."

FISH MAN BATTLES SEA MONSTER? *No, it's Captain Cousteau filming his diving saucer. "To earthbound man he gave the key to the silent world," reads the tribute on his medal.*

the sound is like? Why should we not send down a sound [instead of a sounding line] and listen for an echo from the bottom? Knowing the velocity of sound in water and the time taken for the echo to reach the ear, we should be able to ascertain the depth of the deepest part of the ocean in less than four seconds instead of more than four hours."

Today we call it a sonic depth finder. With such devices pinging away, the research ship *Atlantis*, backed by the Society, crisscrossed the Atlantic charting the peaks and valleys of the 10,000-mile-long Mid-Atlantic Ridge.

To record life in deep-sea wonderlands, Harold E. Edgerton of Massachusetts Institute of Technology, aided by National Geographic grants, has developed ultra-high-speed lights and cameras capable of withstanding pressures of 17,000 pounds per square inch. What does he expect to photograph miles below? "I haven't the least idea. That's why I'm anxious to have a look."

Man has outpaced Jules Verne's imagination. What next? Cousteau predicts "there will be a conscious and deliberate evolution of *Homo aquaticus*" — man living in submerged towns, herding fish, harvesting sea plants, mining the ocean's riches. Fantastic? Such predictions have a way of coming true.

Round Trip to Davy Jones's Locker

Dangling half a mile down, naturalist William Beebe's bathysphere carried the Society flag to a new world, blacker than night, strange as Mars. Here he recounts the wonders he witnessed.

MANY YEARS AGO I spent the best part of an evening with Col. Theodore Roosevelt discussing ways and means of deep-sea diving. From this talk there remains only a smudged bit of paper with a cylinder drawn by myself and a sphere outlined by Colonel Roosevelt, representing our respective preferences.

As the years went by, my yearning for such a deepwater device never slackened. Diving in a copper helmet to a depth of perhaps ten fathoms and drawing hundreds of nets through the sea convinced me that the ocean holds a world almost as unknown as Mars and Venus.

It had lured many before me. Legend has it that Alexander the Great, who sighed for new worlds to conquer, was the first man to go deep in the ocean merely to look at fish. Several versions report that he saw a monster so huge it took three days to swim past his glass cage! In the 18th century the physicist Halley used a diving bell fed by barrels of air to probe to about ten fathoms. And of course, long before man thought of undersea devices, the water spider solved the problem by capturing air bubbles at the surface and storing them under a silken sheet fastened to aquatic plants. Within the air sac the spider ate, courted, and sheltered eggs.

When my dreams took shape, it was the shape suggested by Colonel Roosevelt. I contributed suggestions and unlimited faith. Otis Barton, a restless scientist-adventurer, provided money and a sure knowledge of the mechanical margins of safety. The result was the two-ton steel bathysphere. I coined the name with the hopeful feeling that the Greek prefix, meaning deep, would be appropriate.

Where to "bounce" our great new ball? For years I had been trawling for deep-sea life off Bermuda under the auspices of the New York Zoological Society. The area seemed well adapted to dovetail with attempts to penetrate the depths "in person," as the movies say.

And so, on June 6, 1930, a tug hooked on to the barge *Ready*, a converted British man-of-war and the bathysphere's mother ship. We pulled away from our laboratory at Nonsuch Island off Bermuda. Eight miles out we found a calm sea with only a long, heaving swell. A generous mile of water lay under us. Into the bathysphere went oxygen tanks and racks of chemicals for absorbing moisture and removing excess carbon dioxide. On the barge's deck, crew chief John Tee-Van readied 3,500 feet of 7/8-inch steel cable and half a mile of solid rubber hose containing telephone and light wires.

And now the most painful experience of the whole adventure — getting ourselves into the bathysphere. I looked around at the sea and sky, the boats and my friends. Unable to think of any pithy saying which might echo down the ages, I said nothing and wriggled tortuously over the rough steel bolts of the hatch, fell inside, and curled up on the cold, hard bottom. This

285

aroused me to speech. I yelled for a cushion. Otis climbed in after me. We disentangled our legs and got set.

I had no idea there was so much room in a sphere of only 4½-foot diameter, although the longer we were in it the smaller it seemed. The 400-pound door slammed into place. Giant nuts were screwed down and hammered home. The terrific reverberation almost deafened us. At last we were isolated from the world of sun and air and from human beings—except for the comforting words which slipped up and down the phone line between us and my secretary Gloria Hollister.

I peered through a three-inch-thick window of fused quartz, incredibly strong. Searchlight and oxygen valves checked out perfectly. I remembered Houdini's method for remaining in a closed coffin for a long time, and we both began to regulate our breathing and talk in low tones. But we soon forgot about this.

Now for the most critical moment in our descent—the takeoff. The swing out and over on the winch must be quick and smooth to prevent a crash against *Ready's* bulwarks. Our first try was perfect. I realized for the first time the tremendous weight and strength of the sphere; we struck the surface with a splash which would have crushed a rowboat like an eggshell. Within, we hardly noticed the impact until a froth of foam and bubbles surged up over the glass and the chamber was dimmed to a pleasant green.

At 300 feet Barton suddenly called to me. I turned the flash on the door and saw a slow trickle of water beneath it. I wiped away the meandering stream and still it came. I knew the door would fit tighter the deeper we got, but there remained a shadow of worry as to how much the relaxed pressure of the ascent would allow the door to expand.

Six hundred feet came and passed. The illumination of the ocean at these depths was unimaginable—an undefinable deep blue quite unlike anything I have ever seen in the upper world. It excited our optic nerves in a most confusing manner, for we kept thinking it and calling it brilliant. But when I picked up a book I could not tell the difference between a blank page and a color plate.

"Eight hundred feet" came down the wire. I called a halt. Half a dozen times in my life I have had hunches so vivid that I could not ignore them. This was one of those times. Eight hundred feet spelled bottom and I could not escape the thought.

The slow leak held steady on the way up. Soon we were back on deck listening to the hiss of escaping air and the pounding as the nuts were loosened. I found I was almost paralyzed from the waist down, legs and feet sound asleep. A monkey wrench under me had tattooed itself into my person so deeply that the marks were quite distinct four days later. The cushion I had called for we found reposing in the chemical rack overhead.

Within a week we descended again. Outside our windows hung clusters of luminous baited hooks and bags of ancient squids to lure fish to our hungry eyes.

As we swung just under the surface, the water ceiling looked like a slowly waving, pale green canopy quilted with deep puckers. The sunlight sifted down in long oblique rays as if through some wonderfully beautiful cathedral window.

On this trip a human being was permitted for the first time the sight of living silver hatchetfish. They gleam like tinsel. I called Barton to verify the marvelous sight. At the deepest point, 1,426 feet, there came to me a tremendous wave of emotion, a real appreciation of the whole situation: our barge rolling high overhead in the blazing sunlight like the merest chip in the ocean, the long cobweb of cable leading down to our lonely sphere isolated as a lost planet in outermost space. Within, sealed tight, two conscious human beings sat and peered.

A T CHICAGO's Century of Progress Exposition in 1933 half a million people thrust their heads inside the bathysphere and murmured, "Thank heavens we don't have to go underwater in this!" After the exposition she seemed destined for slow corrosion and rust. But the National Geographic Society offered to sponsor a new dive for scientific observations, with no stipulation of making a record. When I inspected our poor old bathysphere in Bermuda she appeared rather like some ancient Galapagos tor-

DOWN INTO *the abyss
go Beebe, Barton, and
the bathysphere, heading
for depths no living man
has ever penetrated before.
The takeoff makes or breaks
the dive—only a quick,
smooth swing keeps the
two-ton ball from slamming
into its mother ship.
Deck chief John Tee-Van
lends an ear as Gloria
Hollister logs the reports
of eerie wonders
seen by the awed explorers.
"Keep talking," is the
telephone rule—a silence
longer than five seconds
will trigger concern.
When strange fish caught his
eye, Beebe broke the rule.*

toise, scarred and dull, barnacled and stained. Her dark-blue color was sadly marred and scratched, her great eyes closed with wooden lids. We gave her a complete overhaul, refurbished her interior, and put her back into service.

Our first try ended quickly. As soon as the bathysphere hit the water Barton and I got soaked. A feeling of chill around my feet warned me. I glanced at the door. A perfect cataract of water was pouring in. From a depth of four feet I called for an immediate ascent.

For this shallow test dive we thought it would be safe to leave some of the great nuts off the door bolts. The result was a joking matter, but we learned never for an instant to relax precautions.

The incident brought vividly to mind the most serious accident we had experienced in deep-sea diving. Two years earlier we had lowered the empty bathysphere to a great depth to test the soundness of a newly replaced window. When we pulled her up it was apparent that something was very wrong. I saw a needle of water shooting across the face of the window. The sphere was almost full of water.

As I began to unscrew the giant wing bolt in the center of the door, a strange, high singing came forth, then a fine, steamlike mist shot out. I should have sensed it earlier: The contents of the bathysphere were under terrific pressure!

I cleared the deck in front of the door. Carefully, little by little, two of us turned the brass handles. The high, musical tone gradually descended the scale. We leaned back as far as possible from the direct line of fire. Suddenly, and without the slightest warning, the bolt tore out of our hands and the mass of heavy metal shot straight out across the deck like a shell from a gun, shearing out a half-inch notch in a steel winch.

If we had been in the bathysphere when the implosion occurred at 2,000 feet, we should have been crushed into shapeless tissues by nothing more substantial than air and water.

T HE MAGIC CIRCLE off Nonsuch Island —our regular diving area—never failed to produce new wonders. I marveled always at how the first splash erases all the comforting warm rays of the spectrum. Once these cheerful rays — red, orange, yellow—are winnowed out, all the rest belong to chill and night and death, helping us to understand why it is not red blood and scarlet flames that paint the real horror of war but the terrible grayness of gas, the ghastly blue of Very lights. At 1,000 feet the last hint of blue tapers into a nameless gray and this finally into black; the eye falters. The sun is defeated and color is banished forever, until man flashes an electric ray into what has been jet black for billions of years.

At 1,500 feet we were favored with the chance to observe a fish wholly new to science—at least two feet long, its color an unpleasant pale olive drab, the shade of water-soaked flesh. I called the corpse-hued stranger the "pallid sailfin." And a new anglerfish emerged from all the ocean

WHINING *like a bomb, the bathysphere blasts off its wing bolt as Beebe leaps aside to avoid decapitation (opposite). The furious pressure, built up by a leak during a test dive, would have crushed to pulp anyone inside.*

and hesitated long enough close to my window for me to make it out. Its three tall tentacles tipped with pale yellow light organs suggested a name: "three-starred anglerfish." No pioneer peering at a Martian landscape could ever have a greater thrill than I did, seeing this fish.

On our ascent, at 1,900 feet, aching limbs were forgotten at the sight of a gorgeous creature, about six inches long, with five unbelievably beautiful lines of light along its sides. Each line was composed of large yellow lights, each surrounded by a semicircle of intensely purple spots. My name for it is the "five-lined constellation fish." In my memory it will live as one of the loveliest things I have ever seen.

With telephoned notes and my scrawling attempts to help, artist Else Bostelmann and I went into an artistic huddle. Little by little the several new fishes I had seen materialized in her paintings.

Day after day weather held good and August 15, 1934, was no exception. At 9:45 A.M. Barton and I were dunked into the magic circle once more. To the three great moments of a bathysphere diver—the first flash of animal life, the level of eternal darkness, and the discovery of a strange new fish—a fourth was added on this last dive. At 1,680 feet I fathomed the "explosion" mystery. In the course of several dives I had seen creatures several inches long dart toward the window, turn, and—explode! Sometimes I dodged as if I had been struck. Now my eyes were focused. At the flash—so strong it illumined my face and the window's inner sill—I saw a large red shrimp and an outpouring of flame. The mystery was over. In the black depths the flame-throwing shrimp blinds his enemies with luminous fluid.

An enormous fish, dimly outlined, slid into view at 2,450 feet. I summoned Barton to the window immediately but the fish disappeared. Without warning it came again, shadowlike. The full length of it swam by my eyes and was gone forever. At least 20 feet long, thick-bodied.

What was it? I cannot say. Perhaps a small whale or blackfish or whale shark. For the majority of the size-conscious human race this marine monster would, I suppose, be the supreme sight of the expedition. But I soon forgot it.

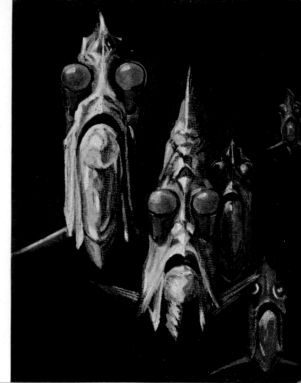

FROM WILLIAM BEEBE

CROUCHING *in the cramped chamber, Beebe scans a wonderland Alice never dreamed of. Off Bermuda he spied the first silver hatchetfish seen alive by man. Else Bostelmann's painting of the tiny popeyed monster closely resembles the photograph (opposite) taken years later by National Geographic staff naturalist Paul A. Zahl at the Strait of Messina in Italy.*

At 11:12 A.M. we came to rest gently at 3,000 feet, and I knew that this was our ultimate floor. Here it seemed as if all future nights in the upper world must be considered only relative degrees of twilight. I could never again use the word "black" with any conviction!

A cross swell arose and on deck the crew paid out a bit of cable to ease the strain. We were swinging at 3,028 feet. There were only about a dozen turns of cable left on the reel, and a full half of the drum showed its naked, wooden core. Would we come up? We would.

Before we began to ascend I had to stop making notes, so numb were my fingers from the cold steel of the windowsill. Changing from my cushion to the floor was like shifting to a cake of ice.

I thought of a gondola 60,000 feet up in the stratosphere, with a pressure of one pound to the square inch. Then through the telephone we learned that at this moment we were under pressure of 1,360 pounds to the square inch. Each window held back more than 19 tons of water, while a total of 7,016 tons was piled up in all directions on the bathysphere itself.

The only other place comparable to these nether regions must surely be naked space itself, far beyond the atmosphere, between the stars, where sunlight has no grip upon the dust and rubbish of planetary air. In the blackness of space, the shining planets, comets, suns, and stars must be closely akin to the world of life as it appears to the eyes of an awed human being in the open ocean half a mile down.

Ever since the beginnings of history, when man first dared to sail the open sea, thousands upon thousands of human beings had reached these depths. But all these men were dead, drowned victims of war, or tempest and other acts of God.

We were the first living souls to roam so far in Davy Jones's locker and return.

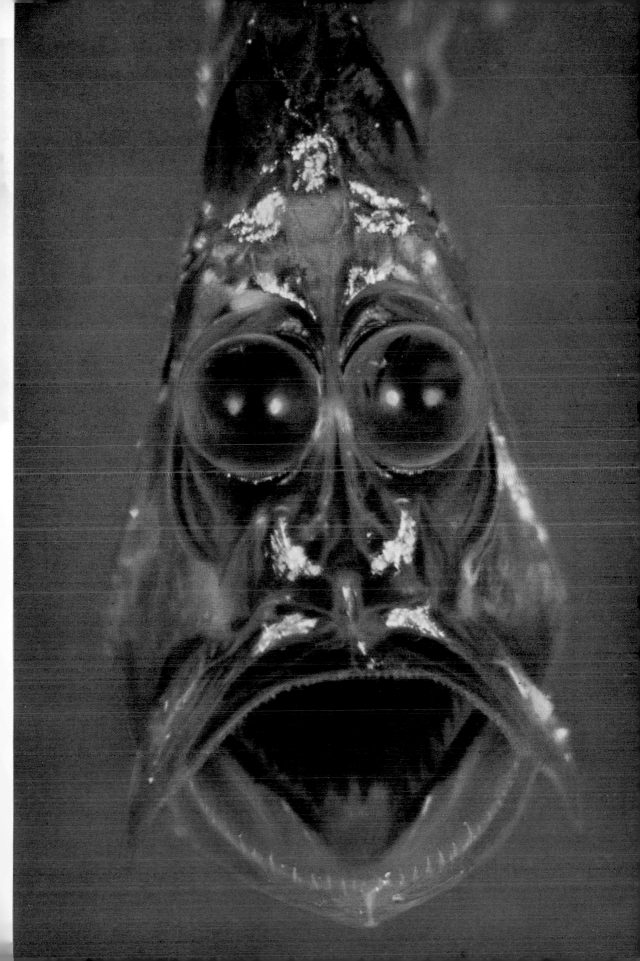

Mountains Under the Sea

*Led by Maurice Ewing,
sea scientists fathom
the Mid-Atlantic Ridge,
world's longest range*

ATLANTIS CREWMEN STRAIN TO UNTANGLE A FOULED
DEEP-SEA TRAWL IN A RISING ATLANTIC STORM;
ROBERT F. SISSON, NATIONAL GEOGRAPHIC PHOTOGRAPHER

"STAND BY to lower away!" All hands crowded to the rail of our steel-hulled ketch *Atlantis*, hove to on the gray swells. Our horn sounded a nerve-shattering *bla-a-a* through the thick fog.

Now came the tense moment we had eagerly been aiming for in weeks of preparation. Swung out over the starboard side was our 40-foot steel coring tube, 2½ inches in diameter, with a sharp cutting edge and 1,000 pounds of lead weights on top to drive it deep into the ocean mud.

"Cast off and stand clear!" ordered Capt. Adrian K. Lane. A grinding roar like a squadron of bombers flying over low came from the big winch down in the hold, the heavy steel wire rattling and slapping as it unreeled. It took an hour to pay out nearly three miles of wire. Then tension slackened. Bottom. At once the winch was reversed to begin the long haul up.

It was the summer of 1948. With the backing of Columbia University, Woods Hole Oceanographic Institution, and the National Geographic Society, we were exploring the gloom-shrouded peaks and valleys of the longest mountain range on earth—the Mid Atlantic Ridge.

This mighty submarine chain, 300 to 600 miles wide, runs nearly 10,000 miles from Iceland almost to the Antarctic Circle, and crests to an average height of 10,000 feet. Its highest peaks break the surface to form the islands of the Azores, St. Peter and St. Paul Rocks, Ascension, Tristan da Cunha, Gough, and Bouvet.

Since its discovery by the British survey ship H.M.S. *Challenger* in 1873, the ridge has inevitably been connected by romantics with the legend of the lost Atlantis, the mythical Atlantic continent which Plato said sank beneath the waves "in a single day and one fatal night." Though our research vessel was named *Atlantis*, we had no illusions about solving this fanciful mystery story.

At last the coring tube broke surface and we swung it aboard. A smear on the outside showed it had penetrated 26 feet into the Atlantic's hidden bottom—deeper than we had ever driven a tube before. The 26 feet of mud jammed inside the corer represented at least 250,000 years of earth history: a chronology of everything that has happened in and around the

THE AUTHOR, DIRECTOR OF COLUMBIA UNIVERSITY'S LAMONT GEOLOGICAL OBSERVATORY, EXAMINES A 60-MILLION-YEAR-OLD ROCK DREDGED FROM THE FLANKS OF THE MID-ATLANTIC RIDGE; DON FAY

Atlantic Basin far back into Ice Age times—evolution of life, changes of climate, risings and sinkings of the ocean bed.

During our first Mid-Atlantic Ridge Expedition, in 1947, the corer had brought up from a seamount near Bermuda a fine-grained chalk from the Eocene Age—a deposit 60 million years old! So far as I know, this was the first time that sediments older than a few thousand years had been recovered from considerable depths in any ocean basin.

But the chief discovery of the first voyage was made by our echo sounder. Pinging the depths along the ridge one day in August, it traced a steep trench, then a sharply rising peak, 9,700 feet from foot to crown—higher than the Matterhorn towers above Zermatt, Switzerland.

Crowded in with our coring tubes and dredges for the 1948 voyage were 2,000 brightly colored toy balloons. Once every hour, around the clock, we inflated two of

*Mid-Atlantic Ridge, discovered in 1873
by survey ship H.M.S. Challenger,
snakes 10,000 miles from Iceland almost
to Antarctica. It has frequent earthquakes.*

1948, FIRST CRUISE

R I D G E

NORTH
AMERICA

*Pico Island, highest peak
of Mid-Atlantic Ridge, rises
27,000 feet above ocean floor
and 7,615 above sea level.*

GRAND BANKS

*From mile-deep Muir Seamount
Atlantis brought up a core, or
cross section, of ocean bottom
spanning 60 million years.*

Woods
Hole

PICO

AZORES

MADEIRA
ISLANDS

—1947 CRUISE

A T L A N T I C

MUIR
SEAMOUNT

CANARY
ISLANDS

BERMUDA

Sargasso Sea

*Midway between the Canary Islands and
Bermuda, Atlantis discovered a
spectacular undersea range
50 miles long, 10 miles
wide, 9,700 feet high.*

*Sargasso Sea has less
plankton, greater
transparency, than
any other part of
North Atlantic.
Secchi disk
was visible
at 217 feet.*

1948, SECOND CRUISE

AFRICA

M I D - A T L A N T I C

A T L A N T I C   O C E A N

— ANTIGUA

*Heading home east of Antigua,
Atlantis plumbed greatest depth
of the cruise—21,000 feet.*

CAPE VERDE
ISLANDS

Dakar

BARBADOS

SOUTH

AMERICA

AS ATLANTIS ZIGZAGGED *between
continents, her scientists charted
depths by echo sounding, and with
dredges and bottom corers read
the Atlantic's ancient history
in pages of rock and sediment.
Diesel engine and 7,200 square
feet of sail gave the 146-foot,
steel-hulled ketch great cruising
range and a speed of 10 knots.
Two laboratories left little room
for 10 scientists and 18 crewmen.*

ROBERT F. SISSON, NATIONAL GEOGRAPHIC PHOTOGRAPHER
NATIONAL GEOGRAPHIC MAP BY VICTOR KELLEY

them to float a small TNT charge. When it exploded, our hydrophones picked up the reflected sound waves from the mud floor and the bedrock below. Timing the separate signals, we established the thickness of sediment. The bright balloons often attracted sea gulls and petrels which quickly flew off with loud squawks of injured dignity when the explosions showered them with water.

Sharks were more troublesome kibitzers. Suddenly the hydrophones would fail and we would find the tips of sharks' teeth in the towing cable. One bit off a good dose of castor oil used in the sound pickup apparatus. It served him right!

With the Blake trawl, a long conical net, we hauled up specimens of deep-sea life, among them a brilliant red starfish of a new species, and a vicious-looking fish whose lower jaw slid in and out instead of opening in the usual way.

Behind the ship we towed our own "fish"—a magnetometer that recorded changes in magnetism of the rocks on the bottom, the first time this had been done in the ocean basins. When the magnetometer recorded an increase or distortion of magnetism, it was a strong indication that we were passing over old lava beds or volcanic areas. At the same point our depth sounder often would show a mountain or small rise on the bottom, confirming that there are many peaks of volcanic origin in the Atlantic Basin.

Off the Azores we made a photograph of the ocean floor at 1,800 fathoms. It showed mud penetrated with small holes, queer little trails apparently left by some creature moving along the bottom, and mounds two or three inches wide. What made them is a mystery.

Our first deep-sea color photographs were made around a seamount in 900 to 2,400 feet of water. One picture showed ripples in the bottom sand which must have been formed by undersea currents, though no one had believed that currents reach a depth as great as this.

"Big gun" in our exploration equipment was the deep-sea dredge. Dragging it along the basin floor or against the steep wall of a mountain, we retrieved valuable samples of ocean rocks. But groping with a metal bag at the end of two or three miles of wire stands out as one of the hardest tasks of the submarine geologist.

Once the dredge, bumping along a sloping bottom, swung the ship around several times. Now it stuck fast on a mountainside and started a run of bad luck. All efforts to free the cable failed. There was nothing left to do but break it.

All hands were ordered below, for the terrific backlash of a snapped cable could clip a man's head off. Then full speed ahead. The wire parted far below; there was no backlash, but we lost the dredge.

A HURRICANE crossed our track a day behind us as we sailed into Woods Hole, Massachusetts, for restocking. A month later *Atlantis* was back at sea. Since I couldn't make this cruise, Bruce Heezen, one of my graduate assistants at Columbia, headed the scientific staff. Again, *Atlantis* ran out of luck.

A resistor on the big winch burned out. Then wind ripped the mainsail so badly it could not be used. A valuable undersea camera was lost because the winch operator didn't hear the lookout shout "Hold it!" The rig broke water at high speed and pulled up hard against the pulley, breaking the wire and plunging the camera into the sea. The backlash cut a deep gash in the winch operator's shoulder.

South of the Cape Verde Islands, with the coring tube at 2,900 fathoms, the wire snapped and whipped back wickedly, barely missing several crewmen. Down to Davy Jones's locker went 2½ miles of irreplaceable wire!

As the ship sailed for home the mainsail tore away again. Not long after, seaman Fred Kent developed an abdominal pain so severe he couldn't eat or sleep. With no doctor on board, *Atlantis* made for Barbados, engine at full speed.

Next evening a loud thud sounded. The propeller had come loose at the very moment it was needed most! There was no choice except to make the best possible speed by sail, but with only mizzen and headsails *Atlantis* limped at four knots.

Kent became delirious. Morphine eased his pain. Next morning the propeller fell off and sank. That night the mizzen sail ripped! The ketch crawled along at two or three knots.

HOW DEEP *is the ocean's mud? TNT bounces sound waves off the bottom and the bedrock below. Time between echoes tells the thickness of sediment. Yellow Secchi disk, lowered into the sea, measures transparency. Plankton cut visibility.*

After feverish work the mainsail was repaired; *Atlantis* picked up speed and reached Barbados. Kent was transferred to a hospital until he was able to fly home.

Off on the homeward tack at last, *Atlantis* found the deepest trough of the cruise—3,500 fathoms—east of the Caribbean island of Antigua. Soon after, a squall caught the ship with all sails set. First Mate Arvid Karlson threw the helm hard over to "spill wind" and relieve the weakened mainsail. But the next day an-

other blow ripped it beyond hope of repair.

Without her mainsail and propeller, the crippled ketch made exasperatingly slow progress. Still the sea would not let up. Two days from home, the worst storm of the entire cruise blew a hatch cover off. The crew hove to and rode out the blow. Then, to top it off, the storm passed and they were becalmed, with no wind at all.

Finally, the sea showed mercy. A fair breeze sprang up and *Atlantis* sailed into port at last, three days before Christmas.

TWO-MILE PLUNGE *to a hard sea bed bent the corer (left), which samples bottom. A trawl netted starfish and mollusks.*

For months our team had labored long and slept little. But we had no regrets. We had dredged up ancient volcanic rocks and unknown fish, and proved the value of undersea color photography. We had discovered abyssal plains and introduced a major exploration technique — underwater magnetic and seismic reflection measurements. Our record of ocean topography now covered every "pimple," every peak and dip, along a track of 60,000 miles — a priceless library of the sea bottom.

297

Exploring a New World Undersea

Take a deep breath and follow Capt. Jacques-Yves Cousteau below the sea into twilight regions silent as a tomb yet filled with wondrous life

A PAIR OF SEA GOGGLES opened my eyes upon a largely neglected kingdom in 1936, and from that moment I never looked back. I began free diving the year round in warm and icy waters. Yet always I rebelled against the limitations imposed by a single lungful of air. I wanted to go deeper and stay longer.

Why? To study marine life in its own environment. The best way to observe fish is to become a fish—or a reasonable facsimile thereof. I needed an underwater breathing device. And out of this need came the Aqua-Lung, which I developed with Emile Gagnan, the brilliant Parisian engineer. We tested the device successfully in 1943. Now man was free to glide, unhurried, fathoms deep in the sea.

In the winter of 1951-2, I took a group of scientists eager to exploit the capacities of the Aqua-Lung to the Red Sea. We planned to study the area's coral kingdoms and photograph them in true color. We sailed on *Calypso*, a war-surplus minesweeper remodeled into a floating laboratory and diving platform. This was the

first of numerous National Geographic-*Calypso* oceanographic expeditions.

We started diving near the island of Abu Latt, in the Farasan Bank. We had to be wary of descending too deep, which exposes the diver to a phenomenon known as "rapture of the depths"—a narcosis caused by excess nitrogen. The chief symptom is the sensation of becoming, to put it bluntly, as drunk as a hoot owl. Mild elation grows into ecstasy; danger reactions fade. The diver may pass out, lose his mouthpiece, and drown.

The bends, or caisson disease, was another danger. This ailment has an odd history. Sand hogs building the Brooklyn Bridge in the 1870's worked in underwater caissons under considerable pressure. Emerging at the end of their shift, they would double up with terrible pains in their joints. Fashionable women of the period affected a drooping posture known as the "Grecian Bend." Wryly, the sand hogs called their condition "the bends."

One other menace gave us food for thought, and a bit of inferiority complex.

299

On our first deep dive off Abu Latt, photographer Jacques Ertaud, chief diver Frédéric Dumas, and I found ourselves on a merry-go-round of sharks. From a depth of 160 feet we looked up and saw sinister dark profiles against the shining surface. Around us glided gray shadows, one of them ten feet long. Others lurked over a sand shoal below. And here we were, almost naked, far from the safety of the upper world. I could only conclude that we were mad.

A big shark, 13 feet long, swam slowly up behind Dumas and began sniffing at his ankles. The sight unnerved me and I hooted through my mouthpiece as loudly as I could. Dumas gave no sign of hearing. Finally the shark turned, majestic as an ocean liner, and slid away. To him we must have looked like strange bubble-blowing fish with two tails, worth investigating but not safe to attack.

WE TURNED our attention to other sights. Huge sea snails crawled on the ocean floor. Giant clams held their shells half open and spread gaily colored mantles. A great jellyfish was attacked and eaten right in front of us by a school of large, velvet-brown fish.

Between 10 and 30 feet we found innumerable worms, slugs, and hairy crabs —a whole crowd of vermin-on-holiday looking as if they had "dressed ship" for the occasion. We swam into crowds of small fish so densely packed we could not see through them, much less avoid them, and against our skin we felt the tap-tap of thousands of little snouts.

Into one such shoal Dumas dropped a

MORAY EEL, *like the crocodile in Alice's wonderland, "welcomes little fishes in with gently smiling jaws." Many divers fear the moray and its needle-sharp teeth more than the shark.*

Beware the bristling spines of the lionfish (opposite); they contain deadly poison with no known antidote. The undersea camera (upper) "breathes" with a baby Aqua-Lung to prevent its collapse under pressure.

AQUA-LUNG PHOTOGRAPHER IN THE RED SEA; LOUIS MALLE AND JACQUES ERTAUD

RED SEA LIONFISH AND (OPPOSITE) INDIAN OCEAN MORAY EEL; LUIS MARDEN, NATIONAL GEOGRAPHIC STAFF

CALYPSO, *floating laboratory and magic carpet to marine wonderlands, called at Príncipe Island on the 1956 expedition that brought back man's first photographs of the floor of 25,000-foot-deep Romanche Trench.*

Puerto Rico

Diving saucer, tested off Puerto Rico, Guadeloupe, and the Cape Verde Islands in 1959, gave science new eyes beneath the sea.

CAPE VERDE
ISLANDS

Guadeloupe

CARIBBEAN SEA

ATLANTIC OCEAN

Equator

Romanche
Trench

SHIPBOARD NATURALIST
hunts marine specimens in Gulf of Guinea corals. Bushlike gorgonians were also dredged up during 1961-2 biological survey of South American coastal waters from Recife to below Montevideo.

• Recife

BRAZIL

• Rio de Janeiro

0   1000
NAUTICAL MILES
NATIONAL GEOGRAPHIC MAP BY S. STEFANOFF

• Montevideo

CALYPSO DIVER *explores for oil with a gravimeter on floor of Persian Gulf. This marine field, prospected in 1954, produced 40,000 barrels a day in 1962.*

FRANCE

Marseille
Toulon
•MONACO

Corsica

M E D I T E R R A N E A N   S E A

Cape
Taínaron—

In the Mediterranean, Cousteau made bathyscaph descents, photosurveyed bottom and "deep scattering layer" with Edgerton flash cameras, prospected for natural gas. In 1962 two Aqua-Lungers stayed under one week, sortieing five hours a day from a steel chamber 33 feet down. In 1963 Cousteau experimented with manned stations under the Red Sea off Port Sudan.

PERSIAN
GULF

S A U D I
A R A B I A

Trucial
Coast

GULF OF
OMAN

RED
SEA

Port Sudan •

Abu Latt

Farasan Bank

HAND REACHES *back 2,100 years for a wine jar from a Greek ship found off Marseille in 1952. In five years Cousteau's men salvaged 7,000 amphorae.*

JACQUES-YVES COUSTEAU

GULF OF GUINEA
Príncipe

In 1954-5 Cousteau explored haunts of the coelacanth, a "living fossil" fish, around the Comoro Islands and filmed life of the coral shelves in the Aldabra Islands.

ALDABRA
ISLANDS

INDIAN
OCEAN

COMORO
ISLANDS

MADAGASCAR

CAPTAIN COUSTEAU, *Neptune of the Nuclear Age, has explored his underwater realm from Caribbean to Indian Ocean on National Geographic Society-Calypso expeditions. Co-inventor of the Aqua-Lung, Director of Monaco's Oceanographic Museum, the retired French Navy officer here launches his diving saucer.*

STREAMLINED AS TORPEDOES, *pelagic snappers streak past the camera 30 feet below the*

100-gram cartridge of TNT and brought up 200 pounds of coral fishes. Spilled on *Calypso*'s deck, they formed a vibrant rainbow until their colors faded. Our marine biologists, Cherbonnier and Mercier, lost little time filling their jars of formaldehyde. "I love animals," Cherbonnier said. "What an irony that I must kill them to study them."

One day we were adopted by a striking pair of greenish-blue and orange parrotfish, each a yard long and weighing about 65 pounds. Fin to fin we swam beside them, an eerie but exhilarating experience. We noticed a curious thing. Like cows browsing in a stone pasture, the parrotfish grazed on coral. They bit off chunks of it with their beaks and crunched it to get at the living matter inside. Every now and then they ejected behind them a cloud of white grains — sand, the same as that covering the lagoon! We had found one of

nature's reef-building machines at work.

We were down here to photograph as well as to observe. To take color pictures in the depths we used the most powerful flash bulbs we could obtain—400,000 candlepower. We operated in a weird studio. Utter silence lay upon us like a benediction. Only the backdrop of the sea wall was stable; I floated, my camera floated, the men holding the reflectors floated.

I pressed the flash button. Darkness flowered into blinding light, then all was gray and shadowy once more. Not until the film was developed would we be certain that the miracle was indeed fact, that at depths where neither fish nor man could detect them, colors existed as brilliant as any at the surface.

Our Aqua-Lungs enabled us to find treasures of another sort later in 1952. Diving to the mud bottom of the Mediterranean off Marseille, France, we discovered the

surface of the Indian Ocean. Photoflash reveals living colors of the submarine world.

wreck of a Greek merchant ship that had sunk 2,100 years ago. The treasure? A cargo of Greek and Roman wine jars – amphorae – almost every one with an octopus making his home inside; also thousands of black Campanian dishes mass-produced from wooden forms.

THE FOLLOWING YEAR, six miles from Toulon Harbor, I learn what it is like to go down to the dark floor of the sea in that dirigible of the depths, the bathyscaph. Our objective is to prove the usefulness of this two-man submarine as an undersea laboratory. For our dive we choose a deep gorge in the sea floor.

In our gondola below the submarine's hull, which is filled with light gasoline for buoyancy, Lt. Comdr. Georges Houot of the French Navy swings shut a heavy door and tightens the 16 bolts. I think of condemned men locking themselves in their own cell. The interior is a tight fit – 6½ feet in diameter. I settle into a painful crouch before the conical plexiglass window. Houot turns the oxygen valve, then pushes controls which flood the air lock.

As we start down, I stare through the porthole. Dumas swims by, filming our descent. I see no fish or plankton.

I switch on a droplight. At 525 feet we hit the "soup" – the mysterious deep scattering layer, or DSL, of creatures whose bodies reflect echo-sound beams. "It's a purée of tiny organisms, one or two millimeters in diameter," I tell Houot excitedly. "There seem to be billions of them! Yet the water between them is clear."

At 1,200 feet I turn off the light and accustom my eyes to the obscurity. There is still a faint tinge of blue in the water. The first fish appear: dreadful little things about two inches long with transparent tails and bulbous eyes. We sink through

305

levels reached by William Beebe and Otis Barton in 1934 (page 285). At 3,300 feet the density of life increases. From a passing blur a beautiful squid materializes. Before it vanishes it leaves a blob of ink — not the familiar dark brown, but *white* ink!

I switch off the searchlight a moment. The squid ink glows in the dark.

My excited description does not impress the pilot. "Let me have a look," he says skeptically. The next squid makes a believer of him. It lays a white cloud that practically blots out the window.

We are approaching the bottom. "Four thousand feet," says Houot. For the first time, our bathyscaph is about to *land*.

"A shark!" I shout.

Houot laughs and says something about nitrogen narcosis. I pull him down to look over my shoulder. He sees a charming little shark, about three feet long, with a broad, flat head and protruding eyes. Suddenly I see something so startling that I burst out laughing. Spread on the sea bottom lies a newspaper.

Houot and I agree that bathyscaph dives upset some traditional ideas about the sea. So far as we can tell, there is biologically speaking no deep scattering layer, but rather a great bowl of living soup extending on down and *growing thicker the deeper into the "tureen" we go.* "People," I observe, "have told me that nothing lives in the depths of the sea."

TAKING THE PLUNGE, *the bathyscaph blows bubbles from its air lock, flooded for diving. Aqua-Lungers double-check removal of locks on ballast magnets. Inability to drop ballast could trap craft and men at the bottom of the sea.*

radiotelephone we heard a voice from the tender: "*Allo,* bathyscaph. The topmen are off in the rubber boat. . . ."

We sank into the green depths.

At 4,600 feet I asked Houot to slow the descent. He discharged iron pellets, reducing our fall to ten inches a second. "According to the echo-sound graph," he said, "the bottom is about 200 feet below."

I saw a vague, cloudy shape beyond the droplights. "We're down already," I said.

"Absurd. Depth gauge, sonic detector, and vertical speed indicator all say we're still going down."

He was right. But the cloud?

Our dangling guide chain touched gently. The depth gauge read 4,920 feet. We were standing on an undulating shelf of mud. The cloud we had seen was a cliff rising sheer above us. "Shall we start the motors and drive off?" I asked.

Houot pressed the shot release button, then ran both motors ahead. The bathyscaph started sluggishly, pulled free — and things began to happen.

I saw a great block of hard mud tumble off the ledge, dislodging more big lumps. Clouds bloomed below, boiled up, spread.

"Houot! We've started an avalanche!"

We laughed nervously and agreed to rest on the ledge until the sediment settled. When it didn't subside after 20 minutes we set off across the canyon by compass.

It was a mad crossing. We had the impression of flying over a sea of cumulus clouds, then of being immersed in yellow fog. The porthole looked as if it had been blanked out with cardboard.

Suddenly we became aware of a chilling fact: Our motors were still running, but particles no longer rushed at our window. *We were not moving!*

Had we struck the other side? Were we now buried deep in soft mud?

Houot cut the motors and we sat in a blind steel ball 5,250 feet down, ponder-

One of the most exciting dives I ever made was in the bathyscaph off Toulon in 1954. I had taken a month off from my duties aboard *Calypso* to concentrate on deep photography. Now, as I squeezed through the hatch with my cameras, I noted that Houot's briefcase with sandwiches and bottles of vintage wine was safely aboard.

While Houot ticked off the safety precautions on his check list, I crouched in the rocking ball wondering if there wasn't a simpler way of visiting the ocean floor. Through the porthole I could see two Aqua-Lungers cleaning the lenses of the electronic flash camera provided by the National Geographic Society. Then on the

ing whether canyons with huge shelves also have overhangs capable of trapping a little submarine that always wants to go up.

An hour passed, and the water still had not cleared. An iron bracket only a foot beyond our window remained invisible.

We decided to surface. Houot jettisoned a lot of shot. An inch outside the port, mud particles remained motionless. Our theory of an overhang gained considerable substance. Only a little movement of the needle on the vertical speed indicator—that was all we wanted, from the bottom of our hearts.

And then it came to us: In the hour we had waited the gasoline must have cooled. Unquestionably, we had grown really heavy.

Houot squirted out more shot. We heard it hailing down on our sphere. A moment passed. Suddenly the speed indicator stirred. Specks slid down the window. We were climbing!

I decided this was a good dive. Every dive is a good dive, if you return.

Back on *Calypso*, we cruised off the Trucial Coast in the Persian Gulf. The British Petroleum Company had commissioned us to make a survey of underwater oil-bearing structures. When this job was completed, we left in holiday mood for 2,500 miles of blue water and atolls in the Indian Ocean. *Calypso* had a new distinction—she was now an official oceanographic ship of France.

UNDERSEA AVALANCHE *smothered bathyscaph in clouds of mud during Cousteau's dive into Toulon Canyon. Shrimp dance above.*

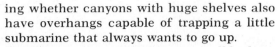
DIMENSIONS IN DIAGRAM BELOW ARE EXAGGERATED FOR CLARITY. ROLF KLEP

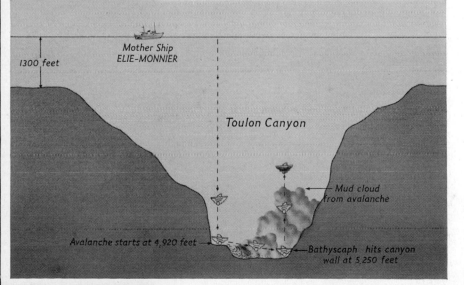

1300 feet

Mother Ship
ELIE-MONNIER

Toulon Canyon

Mud cloud from avalanche

Avalanche starts at 4,920 feet

Bathyscaph hits canyon wall at 5,250 feet

We ran out of a Gulf of Oman monsoon and sailed into crystal days. Near the equator, 600 miles east of Africa, the lookouts called "Whales!" I saw the spouts of three big sperms and turned to pursue. We wanted a whale for close study.

We threw a harpoon at one, but it glanced off and the whale turned across our bows. The collision nearly knocked me off my feet. Loose gear clattered. The glass fell out of the chartroom door.

Shoulder to shoulder the whales turned away, the wounded one helped along by its comrades. I listened with the echosounder to tiny mouselike squeaks—the beast seemed to be shrieking repeatedly.

Suddenly, from all quarters of the sea, whales arose in pairs and converged on the ship. I believe they answered the shrieks of distress. In 15 minutes there were 27 whales around us. Two babies swam crazily alongside big cows.

All at once we felt a thud aft, and *Calypso* faltered. A moment later we sighted a bright red patch in the sea—a 15-foot baby whale with four incisions scored across its back. The other whales gathered around it, but the infant was sorely hurt. Our propeller blades are very sharp.

Then we saw a marvelous thing. Close off the port bow a tremendous black bull whale climbed out of the water to perhaps three quarters of his length and rolled his eyes toward us to view his enemy. It was a superb act of defiance. The pack vanished, and the baby was left alone, staining the sea with blood.

Then the sharks glided in. They made no move to attack the whale while it was alive. We winched it alongside, and engineer André Laban and I, in diving gear, went down in a steel cage to observe what was happening underwater.

On the platform above, men with boathooks flailed away at the sharks, bashing them on the head as they sniffed close.

A diver gave the injured whale the coup de grace with a rifle bullet. This was the signal for the sharks to attack in a frenzy. They set their teeth into the whale at the waterline, flat noses above water, and shook like terriers to loosen the flesh—oblivious of the hammering boathooks.

The crew baited hooks and threw them over. Soon the deck was littered with sharks. Barefooted men hopped away from gaping jaws and thrashing tails.

Night ended the strange battle. Inky cumulus lay on the horizon against a rose-orange sky, and the sea was violet. We threw the sharks overboard and sailed on.

O N A BRIGHT Mediterranean day in the summer of 1955, some Greek fishermen got the surprise of their lives. For more than three years the National Geographic Society had been helping Dr. Harold E. Edgerton, the noted Massachusetts Institute of Technology

SECRETS OF LIFE 24,600 *feet deep in the sea stand revealed in Dr. Edgerton's remarkable picture of the seemingly eroded floor of Romanche Trench. Never before had living organisms (circled) been photographed at such a depth.*

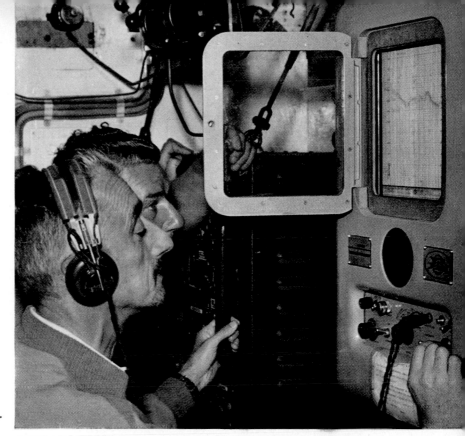

DEEPEST ANCHORAGE *is achieved when* Calypso *drops her hook in 4½-mile-deep Romanche Trench in mid-Atlantic, July, 1956. Cousteau (right) uses headset and depth recorder to chart the sea floor. Dr. Harold E. Edgerton (below) checks nylon cable which moored the ship for two days at this fantastic depth. Varied colors show how much cable is down.*

To photograph the ocean floor, Edgerton lowers his automatic camera, designed to take pressures up to 8½ tons per square inch.

engineer, in his efforts to carry photography to the depths. Now he reported aboard *Calypso* with a camera that had withstood tests of 17,000 pounds to the square inch, a three-mile length of nylon line no thicker than your little finger, and a grin that said, "This time I think I've really got it."

Skeptically we examine the line. We know that Dr. Edgerton has been working on a revolutionary cable, weightless in water because it would have the same specific gravity as the sea. We know that lowering and raising miles of heavy wire cable require powerful winches, and that wire tends to break of its own weight. But this puny looking cord?

"It will work," he says. "It has a breaking point of 1,500 pounds and an elasticity of about 20 percent. Let's try it out."

Off Cape Taínaron, Greece, we tie a chunk of pig iron to the nylon cable and lower it from a launch into 14,000 feet of water. The pig hits bottom and the launch dances at anchor. Dr. Edgerton's grin grows wider.

All right, we think, so far so good. We'll use it as a fixed radar target while we make a few underwater pictures.

Calypso is working about two miles away when a Greek trawler spots the empty launch and makes for it, obviously thinking it a derelict. We cannot move because we have a camera down. Through glasses we see the trawler crew attempt to heave the launch aboard—and discover the astonishing fact that it is anchored at this depth. We fire colored Very lights and the trawler hastily departs without the prize.

I have a strong wish to eavesdrop at the fishermen's tavern that night as they try to make their pals believe they found an empty boat anchored in 14,000 feet of water!

To our amazement and delight, the nylon withstands every test. Once its elasticity actually pulls the 360-ton *Calypso* backward. In 10,000 feet on two miles of thread we ride securely at anchor. And on this cruise Dr. Edgerton's abyssal camera makes the deepest photographs ever taken in the Mediterranean.

BUG-EYED SEA MONSTER *hovers over the Caribbean's coral-studded floor off Guadeloupe. Diving saucer was developed by the Cousteau team, with Society help, to explore the continental shelves.*

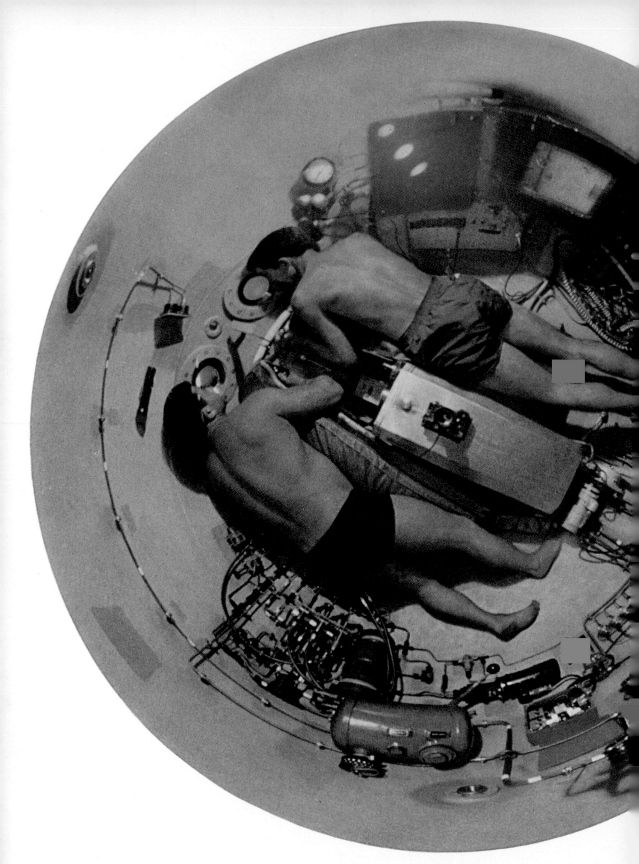

LYING PRONE, *crewmen face plexiglass ports, select speeds with switch, rotate hydrojets with levers. Instruments girdle saucer's steel cabin: depth gauges, barometer, compass, ammeters, hydraulic pump, tape recorder, sonar unit. Air-cleansing system emits oxygen.*

At 14,000 feet it reveals few living things, mainly shrimp and one small fish. At 13,320 feet it takes a nice clear picture. What of? An old tin can!

A year later, in mid-Atlantic, we use the nylon cable and hook into the cold floor of the Romanche Trench at 24,600 feet—deepest anchorage ever achieved. The crew, jubilant, celebrates with songs, toasts, and mock-heroic speeches.

Dr. Edgerton, known to us as "Papa Flash," has brought a camera that will withstand the horrendous pressures of the trench—5½ tons to the square inch. Into the brine it goes, and two and a half hours later reaches the sea floor.

For three hours we patiently bounce the camera up and down, hoping that some of the 800 exposures it takes automatically—four a minute—will occur at the right height and moment. All we know is that somewhere in the void below electronic flashes of light are exploding every quarter-minute in depths dark since time began.

It turns out that we have indeed been lucky. Our bag is two clear pictures of the rocky bottom. They lack much in artistic composition but are of great interest to scientists.

W E OF CALYPSO lived the pioneering days of free diving. By the late 1950's we knew the time was ripe for a craft that would take us to the continental shelf—at depths of roughly 600 feet—the richest zone of sea life. A submarine or bathyscaph would be too clumsy for intimate reef exploration. We needed a radically new craft.

Water trials of various models led us to a flattened sphere —two dished halves of three-quarter-inch steel. Propellers were rejected in favor of hydrojets—a system that takes in water and forces it out through nozzles on each side of the hull. It took courage to invest in such an unorthodox idea, but the National Geographic Society provided financial backing, and so did Air Liquide Cie. in France and the EDO Foundation in the United States.

We tested our 3½-ton diving saucer off Point Aguila, Puerto Rico, in a series of shallow dives we called "the auto school." My turn would come later; still, I was jealous of the men inside. When the saucer surfaced after the first test, pilot Albert Falco popped out and yelled: *"Ça c'est de la bagnole!"* Loosely, "What a hot rod!"

Off Guadeloupe, where the land drops sharply into the deep, the dives grew longer. Papa Flash, who went down on the sixth dive, logged this description: "Slowly sinking, we could see *Calypso* above us. Falco turned on the jets and we began to move. It was like being in an automobile, except that we had more room and lolled on our foam mattresses like Romans at a banquet. Falco spotted a squadron of squid in perfect formation. As he cut the jets we settled into an undersea garden with a crunch of coral. A host of fishes circled us. One beauty, a queen angelfish, passed near the camera, insisting on a close-up, unafraid of the saucer."

Finally, in the Mediterranean off Corsica, Falco and I undertake a dive to design depth—1,000 feet.

I open the oxygen inlet and put on the fan. Falco opens two

NATIONAL GEOGRAPHIC STAFF MAN THOMAS J. ABERCROMBIE SUSPENDED A 12-INCH POLISHED GLASS BALL IN THE SAUCER'S CABIN TO REFLECT THE INTERIOR AND ENABLE THE CAMERA (CENTER) TO CATCH THIS PANORAMA. CREW USUALLY WEARS COVERALLS IN THE COOL DEPTHS.

racks of carbon dioxide absorbents and turns on the hydraulic plant. We slip into the water, and the soft glow of blue filters through the portholes. We move to the edge of a steep incline at 400 feet.

Then Falco pumps mercury forward and we tilt downward...600 feet...800...950. At 1,001 feet there is a gentle bump—bottom. At last our saucer is at the depth we want her. We glide by huge rocks and cliff faces, their colors shining under our lamps, and surface after four hours.

This is revolutionary. The way lies open for research in a marine twilight zone no man could explore freely before.

IN SEPTEMBER, 1961, we sailed for South America to explore the continental shelf. From the shoreline of Brazil to a depth of 5,000 feet, we made a census of sea life. Our efforts were rewarded with a clearer view of the movement and development of fauna in the ocean, and the discovery of a hundred new species of marine animals.

But we were not finished with innovations for studying fish and men beneath the waves. The next year our research and development laboratory, l'Office Française de Recherches Sous-Marines in Marseille, established Continental Shelf Station Number One. "Conshelf One" consisted of a steel cylinder 17 feet long and 8 feet in diameter. Chains anchored it to the floor of a rocky cove near Marseille, 33 feet down. In this combination dwelling and workshop, divers Albert Falco and Claude Wesly lived and worked in continuous submersion for a full week. Falco called it *Diogenes*, after the Greek philosopher who lived in a tub.

In the cylinder, where they slept, ate, and relaxed, Falco and Wesly breathed compressed air pumped from the surface. To go outside, they donned Aqua-Lungs and dived through the liquid door formed by an open hatch in the deck. Internal air pressure kept the water from entering.

Every day the divers went through this blue pool to work in the sea for five hours, building artificial fish houses and corrals, exploring an ancient shipwreck 85 feet down. Workday ended, they returned to the cylinder and a hot meal, prepared on the surface and brought to them by divers.

Then they watched TV, read, listened to the radio or the phonograph, or puttered about in the workshop.

They suffered little from loneliness. We on the surface were linked to them by telephone and closed-circuit television. Twice a day doctors visited them to check on their physical and emotional well-being. When Wesly complained of a toothache, we sent him a diving dentist. When they needed haircuts, a barber swam down!

Of great interest to us was their mental reaction during the prolonged stay where men have never lived before. At first exhilarated, they fell into deep depression after a few days. But halfway through the experiment they rebounded to normal, and at the end wished they could have remained longer. "To stay on the sea bed," said Falco, "that's tempting."

To bring the Conshelf men back to atmosphere without days of imprisonment in decompression chambers, we worked out a special procedure. For two hours they breathed a mixture of 80 percent oxygen and 20 percent nitrogen—almost exactly the reverse proportion of the air we breathe. Swimming to the surface, they experienced no aftereffects except a momentary dizziness as they emerged into bright sunlight after a week below.

We believe that continental shelf stations will soon be established for crews of offshore oil rigs and research labs. Men will live deeper and stay longer than in Conshelf One. The real study of the littoral sea will begin when scientists actually live there, swimming in the depths.

People sometimes ask us of *Calypso* why we are always striving to go deeper and deeper. The answer is simple. We have explored, we have charted, we have probed with our electronic eyes, we have let a little light into the depths. But the watery floor of our silent world is still covered with question marks.

SNUG AS A BUG, *the diving saucer rides in* Calypso's *hold on a transatlantic crossing. Underway, cables coiled on the main deck are sometimes unreeled to drag camera- and flash-bearing sleds to snap pictures on the ocean bottom.*

THOMAS J. ABERCROMBIE, NATIONAL GEOGRAPHIC STAFF

Man in the Sea – the Link Cylinder

For the first time, a diver dwells more than 24 hours 200 feet down. Lord Kilbracken reports the feat.

O N THE MORNING of September 6, 1962, Belgian diver Robert Stenuit blew a kiss to his wife on the deck of the research vessel *Sea Diver* and knifed into the waters of Villefranche Bay on the French Riviera. Alongside the chunky white motor yacht, and about nine-tenths submerged, floated an 11-foot cylinder, pre-filled with a helium-oxygen mixture and equipped with emergency rations for three days. Stenuit, wearing a frogman's rubber suit, swim fins, and face mask,

ARTIST PIERRE MION PORTRAYS THE REVOLUTIONARY LINK DIVING CYLINDER ANCHORED BELOW ITS TENDER. OPPOSITE: DIVER ENTERS HIS "SEA BUNGALOW"; BATES LITTLEHALES, NATIONAL GEOGRAPHIC PHOTOGRAPHER

dived to the bottom of the cylinder and disappeared under it at 9:50 A.M.

The cylinder dipped under the waves. Internal pressure was raised to the equivalent of that at 200 feet under water. Stenuit began winching himself down. By noon he had reached a depth of 200 feet. The big dive was on.

I had boarded the *Sea Diver* in Monaco at the invitation of her owner and skipper, Edwin A. Link, who had conducted the underwater "excavation" of Port Royal (page 204). Link was now engaged in a revolutionary "Man-in-Sea" project. His new invention, a diving cylinder, will enable divers to do useful work at far greater depths and for longer periods than ever before. The project had strong backers, among them the National Geographic Society and the Smithsonian Institution.

With his shy smile, Link told me of the vital implications behind his work. "Man can go to great depths in a bathyscaph," he said, "but he remains a prisoner inside." Thus a bathyscaph is of limited use for such undersea operations as salvaging, prospecting and drilling for oil, bridge building, and pile driving.

A helmet diver, Link went on, is seriously handicapped by his cumbersome equipment. He can spend perhaps three or four hours at 200 feet. But then he must return to the surface very slowly to avoid the bends. He is constantly exposed to the cold of the depths. And he cannot eat or drink during his immersion.

To get the best of two worlds—the submariner's and the self-contained diver's—Link had designed and built his cylinder, a submersible compression chamber. A man could leave it "in his skin" at depths

319

down to 400 feet. He could work for hours at a time, returning to the chamber for rest and refreshment. And though he would still have to go back to surface pressure gradually, he could do so in the relative warmth and comfort of the cylinder—under water, aboard ship, or ashore.

The cylinder has three airtight and watertight round hatches. Two are back-to-back at the entrance, one opening outward to withstand water pressure, the other swinging inward against the pressure of air inside. The third divides the cylinder into compartments, each with an internal diameter of almost a yard—first a small air lock, then the instrument-packed main chamber, nearly six feet long, where the diver lives when he is not finning about in the wet world outside.

The diver can look through three tilted portholes. To leave the cylinder he makes sure that the internal atmosphere has a pressure equal to that of the water outside. All hatches may then be opened. The cylinder retains air as does an inverted wine glass in a basin of water. The diver, using self-contained breathing apparatus, can come and go as he pleases.

"My little 'sea bungalow' has all the modern conveniences," Link pointed out. "Electric light, heat, air conditioning, telephone. These two hoses from the ship supply the breathing mixture and return the exhaust. No face mask is needed inside. At shallow depths we can use compressed air, but for all long-duration deep dives I intend to use a helium-oxygen mixture to prevent nitrogen narcosis. No

Inventor Edwin A. Link explains his project

Project MAN-IN-SEA seeks ways of enabling divers to live and work on the ocean floor at depths of 1,000 feet for weeks, even months. If it is successful we will possess the key to the scientific secrets and animal, mineral, and vegetable wealth of 10,000,000 square miles of sea bed.

Most important, by staying down for long periods a diver would multiply many times the amount of work he could do. No matter how deep the dive, he would face the time-consuming decompression period only once.

Our long-range program envisions three major pieces of equipment: an underwater pressure chamber serving as living quarters; a smaller one-man chamber to act as elevator between bottom and surface; a decompression chamber on the surface large enough for treating several men at one time. The elevator chamber served all three functions in the test reported here by John Godley, third Baron Kilbracken.

In future experiments we plan to send animals, then men, to various depths for various periods of time. We will continue Project Man-in-Sea in this unspectacular scientific manner, checking each step with care before proceeding to the next.

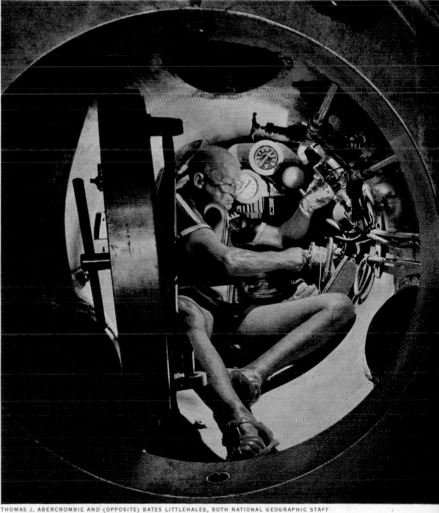

THOMAS J. ABERCROMBIE AND (OPPOSITE) BATES LITTLEHALES, BOTH NATIONAL GEOGRAPHIC STAFF

LIKE UMBILICAL CORDS, *hoses and cables tie the cylinder to its mother ship. Ed Link (above) tests his invention.*

321

one knows what its effect will be under these conditions. An important part of the trials will be to find out."

Now the test was under way. If all went well, Robert Stenuit would remain at 200 feet for a day or more—a feat never before accomplished, a major advance.

DURING THE FIRST 20 hours everything went on schedule. There was only one minor difficulty. We could not understand what Stenuit was saying over the telephone. He was breathing almost neat helium (97 percent). The gas, much lighter than nitrogen, made his vocal cords vibrate so fast that his voice was a grotesque combination of Donald Duck's and Popeye's. We could not even tell "yes" from "no," so we told him to use the two-syllable "O.K." and send longer messages in Morse code.

Several times Stenuit left the cylinder to explore. He reported that the water was cold, but otherwise he was comfortable enough. He ate two meals. He even slept that night, though it wasn't easy in a cramped, semivertical position.

The next morning he reported "All well" in Morse. He felt quite prepared to spend at least 48 hours at that depth. Then we found out that during the night there had been an unexpectedly high wastage of helium. Slight leaks in the breathing system, designed to recapture, purify, and reuse the expensive gas, had been exaggerated by high internal pressure.

Fifteen bottles of helium remained on board the ship. Each would last about 90 minutes. Link had calculated that Stenuit would have to remain on helium for the first 17 hours of the decompression period. So we had enough to keep him down at 200 feet until noon. For him to stay longer would require more.

Link had adequate reserves ashore. He sent his 19-foot launch *Reef Diver* to collect what was needed.

But shortly after the launch departed a mistral began to blow. The bay had been millpond calm at dawn. At noon, when *Reef Diver* returned with 15 bottles of helium, there was a heavy chop.

As the men shifted weight, *Reef Diver* pitched violently. Suddenly the stern was

DOWN GOES REEF DIVER with a precious cargo of helium! Returning to Sea Diver *from the French Riviera, the launch wallowed in waves kicked up by a mistral. As it shipped water, the crew fought to shift the heavy cylinders (left). But while* Sea Diver's *men watched helplessly, the boat sank in 240 feet. Thus Stenuit's sojourn in the depths was cut from the proposed 48 hours to 24. The mishap put Link's chamber to practical use for the first time. With it divers raised the launch and some of the helium.*

BATES LITTLEHALES, NATIONAL GEOGRAPHIC PHOTOGRAPHER

almost awash. Her bow rose as the three crewmen tried their utmost to push the load forward. They hadn't time. *Reef Diver* reared up, throwing them into the sea. Then she plunged beneath the waves with her precious cargo.

Now Stenuit's situation became dangerous. If we started immediately to haul the cylinder up we might still have just enough helium to decompress him—as long as the leaks grew no worse, and if nothing else happened to prolong the decompression schedule.

We did not tell Stenuit why we were cutting short his test dive, and he objected strongly when we started raising him. He was prepared to stay at 200 feet for another couple of days.

In normal weather Link could have brought him aboard at once and left him in the cylinder for the long decompression period. But the sea was now so rough that it was safer to leave him in the water. We brought him up to 100 feet and started decompression. He had been at 200-foot pressure for 25 hours, 20 minutes.

With early evening there came a slight lull in the wind. The crew quickly brought the cylinder, swinging crazily, on deck. We were gradually decreasing pressure inside the cylinder, according to schedule, so the helium leak was diminishing. *That* danger seemed to be over.

Another replaced it. Since standard decompression tables gave no information for a dive of this duration, a conservative schedule had been adopted. But at 4:50 the next morning, when the pressure in the cylinder had been reduced to the equivalent of 53 feet under water, Stenuit reported that he was getting the bends in his right wrist.

This wrecked our decompression schedule. Pressure had to be increased immediately to the equivalent of 70 feet down and held there for 12 hours. It was fortunate indeed that the leak had diminished and little helium was being lost.

Under the revised schedule, Stenuit's total decompression took no less than 65 hours. He had to spend almost 2½ days in the cylinder after it had been brought aboard. We could see him through the portholes and he could see us, but he had

BATES LITTLEHALES AND (ABOVE) THOMAS J. ABERCROMBIE, BOTH NATIONAL GEOGRAPHIC STAFF

HERMETICALLY SEALED *in the Link cylinder back on* Sea Diver's *deck, Robert Stenuit gulps coffee from a thermos (opposite) as he sweats out his 65-hour decompression. Lt. Comdr. Robert Bornmann, a U. S. Navy doctor (above), checks the oxygen percentage of the breathing mixture. Annie Stenuit keeps tabs on her husband through a porthole.*

to remain sealed inside. It was, of course, an easy matter to get supplies to him by means of the air-lock chamber.

At 6:20 A.M. on September 20 he left the cylindrical "sea bungalow" after 3 days, 20 hours, and 30 minutes. Doctors found him in perfect physical condition.

Stenuit now concedes that his "bends" may have been only a cramp. The decompression schedule seemed to have been within acceptable limits as far as they could be calculated by inference. This was confirmed by later experiments. But no unnecessary risks could be taken, and the diver's symptoms were at once relieved when the pressure was increased.

THERE CAN BE NO DOUBT whatever that Robert Stenuit's dive proved an outstanding achievement – and a success. It showed that the human frame can withstand the pressure of seven atmospheres for an indefinite period and that no damage or discomfort is caused by breathing helium under great pressure for an unprecedented 25 hours.

But though an immense step forward, the trial was only a beginning. Ed Link is confident that soon he will be able to keep a man down at 400 feet for a week. This would make it possible for a diver to do useful work almost anywhere on the vast, virtually unexplored continental shelves. Link already has in mind a far larger "sea house" from which teams of divers could work at depths down to 1,000 feet and stay submerged indefinitely.

Down goes the bathyscaph into cold, black regions unknown
to man. Suddenly—a shock, a cracking sound, the cabin trembles....
Jacques Piccard takes you nearly seven miles into the sea on

Man's Deepest Dive

IT IS HARDLY DAYLIGHT. The sky is heavy. The sea has grown rougher and rougher. A few dozen yards away on the water flares mark the spot for our attempt.

"Do you think we shall be able to make the dive?" asks Giuseppe Buono, our engineer. He has prepared the bathyscaph *Trieste* for diving 64 times.

Now he wonders—is it sheer madness to descend under existing conditions, to go down nearly seven miles! I wonder, too.

It is January 23, 1960, and we are 220 miles from our base at Guam. *Trieste*, towed here through the choppy Pacific by a U. S. Navy tug, looks like a battle victim rather than an undersea laboratory about to explore Mariana Trench—deepest place yet found in all the oceans.

The vertical current meter, partly broken, hangs miserably on its support. The surface telephone for pre-dive communication has been torn away; the tachometer, indicating speed of descent and ascent, has been demolished during the towing. Waves ceaselessly sweep the deck.

Yet, should we risk months of delay because a few instruments—important but not vital—are lacking?

TRIESTE SURFACES AFTER RECORD-BREAKING DIVE OF 35,800 FEET; THOMAS J. ABERCROMBIE, NATIONAL GEOGRAPHIC STAFF

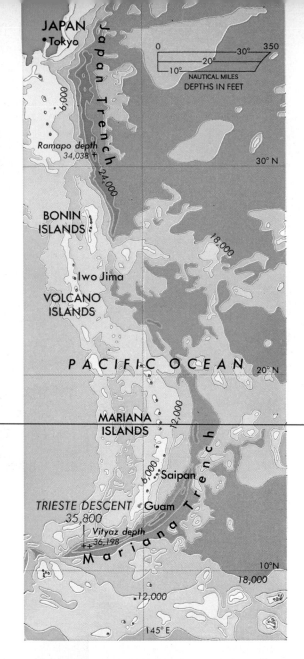

JAPAN
•Tokyo

Japan Trench

0   30°   350
    20°
10°
NAUTICAL MILES
DEPTHS IN FEET

Ramapo depth
34,038 +

24,000

9,000

30° N

BONIN
ISLANDS

18,000

•Iwo Jima

VOLCANO
ISLANDS

P A C I F I C   O C E A N   20° N

MARIANA
ISLANDS

12,000

•Saipan

TRIESTE DESCENT •Guam
35,800
| Vityaz depth
+ 36,198

6,000

Mariana Trench

10°N

18,000

12,000

145° E

"I am going to check the main electric circuits," I tell Buono. "If everything is in order we dive immediately."

It is broad daylight now. The sea is not calming. A few hundred yards away the tug is rolling and pitching. Having released *Trieste*, she seems at loose ends.

With me in the bathyscaph's six-foot-four-inch spherical cabin is Lt. Don Walsh, U. S. Navy officer in charge of *Trieste*. If this trip goes as planned, he will take over as pilot, and I, having shown *Trieste*'s capabilities, will return to Switzerland to construct a new machine.

Our cabin hangs like a bomber's belly turret from the underside of the 58-foot, cigar-shaped float (page 281). As Walsh and I look through the rear porthole we see water rising in the entrance tube that leads through the float to a conning tower on its deck. Moments later, all apparent motion of the cabin ceases. The dive is beginning. It is 8:23 A.M.

Ten minutes later, at a depth of 300 feet, the relative weight of the craft suddenly diminishes in a colder layer of water, and the bathyscaph stops. A dilemma: We can wait until the lighter-than-water gasoline of the float cools enough to resume the descent, but we would lose precious time, and it is absolutely necessary to surface before nightfall. The alternative, to release gasoline, would mean sacrificing some of the precious liquid needed to lift us back to the surface.

Previous calculations showed that we can safely release several hundred cubic feet of gasoline. The remainder will be

🛳 Guam

M a r i a n a   Trench

Trieste touches bottom
at a record 35,800 feet ◄

January 23, 1960: As the U. S. Navy tug *Wandank* stands by 220 miles off Guam, the bathyscaph *Trieste* dives nearly seven miles into Mariana Trench. The vertical dimension is exaggerated for clarity.

VICTOR J. KELLEY, NATIONAL GEOGRAPHIC CARTOGRAPHER

THOMAS J. ABERCROMBIE, NATIONAL GEOGRAPHIC STAFF

CLINGING *to the wallowing* Trieste, Piccard *(at right) helps replace a snapped towline. With gasoline for lift and iron pellets for ballast, the U. S. Navy bathyscaph probed Mariana Trench (opposite), a mile deeper than Everest is high.*

more than sufficient to ascend. I open the gasoline valve for a moment or two and the descent resumes.

Another layer of cold water stops *Trieste* 35 feet farther down. I release more gasoline. Five minutes later, at a depth of 425 feet, *Trieste* halts again—and again at 530 feet. Walsh watches a new electric thermometer that gives the water's temperature. This is the first time in 65 dives in *Trieste* that I have observed this phenomenon of repeated stratification.

The craft finally decides to descend seriously, and at about three feet per second —the speed of an elderly elevator—we sink through a column of water which seems extraordinarily empty of life. Perhaps the passage of the bathyscaph causes creatures to flee. I have never been able to perceive fish during a rapid descent.

At 1,500 feet darkness is total and the cabin begins to feel cold. We have taken

warm clothes along and it feels good to struggle into them. We both were soaked when we came aboard.

At 5,000 feet comes a call on the undersea telephone. Buono says everything has gone normally in spite of the rough sea. At 10,000 feet another telephone conversation, another at more than 13,000.

Through the porthole we see passing torrents of plankton-bearing water. Still dropping at three feet per second, we pass 18,600 feet, 24,000 feet.

"We are where no one has been," murmurs Walsh. Silently I acquiesce.

At 26,000 feet I reduce speed. We have already dumped ballast, six tons of iron pellets, to hold our descent in check. Outside the water is magnificently limpid— no trace of life, no plankton.

Suddenly, at 32,500 feet, we are startled by a rather heavy shock which makes the cabin tremble. "Bottom?" Walsh asks.

329

The depth finder has shown nothing. What shall we do? Have we encountered an undersea monster? For a few minutes we stop everything on board that makes noise: oxygen passing through the injector, humming electronic instruments, everything. We hear only tiny cracking sounds, like ants in an anthill, little sounds coming from everywhere. Shrimps? The cabin's paint cracking? We do not know yet. Everything seems normal. The descent is regular.

"We aren't losing gasoline," I say. "Let's go on and we'll see later."

The telephone has gone silent. Our eyes pass from porthole to depth finder, from depth finder to porthole. We should reach the bottom at any moment. . . .

At 12:56 P.M. I say to Walsh, "Don, look, on the depth finder."

"Finally."

Yes, finally—the bottom, quite distinct on the finder, 300 feet below us. In ten minutes, at 1:06, *Trieste* makes a perfect landing on a carpet of uniform ivory color that the sea has laid down during the course of thousands of years.

Like a free balloon on a windless day, indifferent to the almost 200,000 tons of water pressing on the cabin from all sides, *Trieste* balances on her guide cable. And in a beam of light we receive the reply to a question oceanographers have been asking for decades. Slowly, very slowly, a fish, a true fish—about a foot long and half as wide, apparently of the sole family—moves away, swimming half in the ooze, and disappears into the eternal night.

Slowly also (Is everything slow at the bottom of the sea?), Walsh holds out his hand to me. Then as a matter of duty he skeptically calls the surface: "*Trieste* on bottom. . . . Six three zero zero fathoms. Over." Suddenly he gives a start.

"I hear you weakly but clearly. Please repeat the depth."

Don does, carefully. "Everything O.K."

We have established the first voice communication between the surface and the great depths of the ocean!

"Can you switch on the rear searchlight?" Don asks and looks through the porthole. "That noise, that jolt," he says quietly. "It was the big plexiglass panel of the entry tube that cracked."

It must have contracted more than its exterior steel frame allowed. Several cracks are clearly visible. No danger, but if these cracks do not close during the ascent the tube may be difficult to empty. For that prospect, especially in the heavy seas on the surface, we need daylight. Of the 30 minutes we intended to spend on the bottom 20 have elapsed. There is not a minute to lose. Regretfully we cast a final look upon this horizonless world.

WITH MY HAND on the switch, I see through the porthole a stream of pellets pouring from one of the ballast silos and then sinking into sediment as soft as powdered talc. The impact produces an immense shining cloud, first in front of us, then above, and finally stretching out like a great cumulus.

As we ascend, we traverse the cloud, rising above it as it disappears into the night that we restore to the abyss. It will be hours, perhaps days, before all the sediment returns to the bottom where it has lain, doubtless for centuries.

Trieste behaves perfectly during the ascent: no vibration, no rolling, not a movement inside nor a jolt that might betray our increasingly rapid rise. At last a gleam of daylight appears at the porthole. Sea dawn—late afternoon daylight—begins to illuminate the cabin with blue and pallid light.

The last few hundred yards are quickly traversed, and at 4:56, almost exactly our estimated time of arrival, *Trieste* pierces the surface. Soon we are out on the bathyscaph's deck in the afternoon air.

The sea is violent, the wind blowing harder than in the morning, the waves heavier and higher. But the weather is unimportant. For in the name of science and humanity, *Trieste* has taken possession of the abyss, last extreme on our earth.

SPRAY-DRENCHED AND BONE-TIRED, *the author and Lt. Don Walsh pull away from* Trieste *after their dive to a corrected depth of 35,800 feet. Piccard's father, Auguste, designed the bathyscaph to plumb the ocean depths as his balloons once sailed the stratosphere.*

THOMAS J. ABERCROMBIE, NATIONAL GEOGRAPHIC STAFF

MALLORY *perished in 1924 on his third attempt to conquer Everest. He once voiced the spirit of all who climb a peak: "Have we vanquished an enemy? None but ourselves."*

DONALD McLEISH. LEFT: ROYAL GEOGRAPHICAL SOCIETY

"THAT AWFUL MOUNTAIN," *the Swiss called their 14,690-foot Matterhorn, labeling it unclimbable until Whymper's assaults.*

Challenging the Mighty Mountains

BEFORE MAN BEGAN to climb mountains he worshiped them. He named them Himalaya, "the Abode of Snow"; Denali, "the Great One"; Kilimanjaro, "Mountain of the Demon of Cold." Zeus reigned atop Olympus. Atlas stood on African peaks and balanced the sky on his shoulders. Prometheus, who stole fire from heaven, was chained to Mount Caucasus.

Late in the 18th century Europeans overcame their awe and conquered Mont Blanc. Then other great peaks in the Alps were tamed. "Impossible" climbs in time became "an easy day for a lady." In 1865 Edward Whymper, after seven failures, scaled that mountain of "beauty and magic and terror," the Matterhorn. It was his "most glorious hour." But tragedy stained the triumph. On the descent the rope snapped and four of his companions plunged to their deaths, hurtling from precipice to precipice—nearly 4,000 feet.

Why climb a mountain? "Because it is there," said George Leigh-Mallory, who perished on Mount Everest in 1924. Other men might give other reasons: adventure, science, to test themselves, to explore unknown ranges as Joseph Rock did in China, to map a mighty mountain as Bradford Washburn did in Alaska. But Mallory's explanation is best: Men climb in answer to a challenge.

OLD CLOTHES BUT NEW ROPE
mark today's rock climber.
These American Alpine Club
members accept the challenge of
British Columbia's Bugaboos.

FASHIONABLE CLIMBERS *of 1864*
gather at "The Club-Room of
Zermatt," drawn by Whymper,
who conquered the Matterhorn
the next year. He was the
greatest of the early alpinists.

BARRY C. BISHOP, NATIONAL GEOGRAPHIC STAFF

Many have met that challenge: Hudson and Mummery in the Alps, the Duke of the Abruzzi in Africa and Alaska, Moore and Burdsall in China, Herzog and Hillary in the Himalayas. Many told in *National Geographic* how it felt to stand on a summit. Walter Woodburn Hyde described in 1913 his sensations atop Mont Blanc: "Do you open your eyes wide in astonishment at the wonderful sight? By no means! You shut them as tight as you can and throw yourself down on the snow in utter weariness of mind and body, resenting the impertinence of your guides, who urge you to look about."

In 1921 F. L. Bird wrote about his ascent of Mount Demavend, "the Persian Olympus" and guidepost to Alexander the Great, Genghis Khan, and Tamerlane. "A feeling of utter insignificance comes over one with the realization that he is at last on the summit of the great landmark which has borne the scrutiny of heroes of many ages."

H. F. Lambart, member of the expedition which first climbed Mount Logan, recalled that triumph in the June, 1926, *National Geographic*. "With a strange feeling of unconcern, almost of unreality, we came to the culmination of planning and weeks of labor and stepped out on to the small, triangular summit, the

STAFF MAN BARRY BISHOP *surmounts earth's highest peak, May 22, 1963. The National Geographic Society's American Mount Everest Expedition this day achieved its historic twin assault from the South Col and the West Ridge. Night caught the climbers at 28,000 feet without oxygen, tents, or sleeping bags. Bishop and two others suffered frostbite. Worth it? Said Bishop: "I would have crawled on my hands and knees to get there."*

highest point in the Dominion of Canada, and the second highest on the continent.... On reaching the summit we encountered that strange apparition known as 'the specter of the Brocken,' the weird phenomenon seen on the tops of very high mountains, under certain conditions of light and atmosphere, whereby the figure of each observer is seen silhouetted against the fog banks in the center of a complete circular rainbow of miniature size."

On the crest of Mount Roraima in South America, G. H. H. Tate found an appalling silence. "One feels oppressed, dwarfed," he noted in 1930, "almost as if one were a trespasser." Three years later British planes skimmed over Mount Everest. L. V. S. Blacker told *Geographic* readers he "looked down through the open floor and saw what no man since time began had ever seen before. No words can tell the awfulness of that vision.... Over the topmost peak, we passed through the famous plume of the mountain, that awesome, miles-long white streamer which men see and marvel at 200 miles away."

Mountains were not destined to be solely a man's world. In 1911 Dora Keen recounted her climbs in the Alps—"for pleasure, for the wonderful views and the vigorous exertion." In 1934 Miriam O'Brien Underhill related how she be-

JOHN E. FLETCHER, NATIONAL GEOGRAPHIC PHOTOGRAPHER. ABOVE: LONDON TIMES

MAN FIRST LOOKED *on Everest's inviolate crown in 1933 when two supercharged British biplanes struggled over the 29,028-foot peak.*

BRITISH TEAM *which conquered Everest in 1953 receives the Society's Hubbard Medal from President Eisenhower. Sir Edmund Hillary, shaking hands, and Sir John Hunt, the expedition leader, reported the epic climb before a National Geographic audience—an occasion compared by Gilbert Grosvenor (at left) to the day "when Robert Peary came to recount the discovery of the North Pole."*

came the first woman to scale the Grépon and Matterhorn *sans hommes*. "Non-climbers often ask me how a woman can be strong enough for exertion that would tax an 'athletic young man,'" she wrote. Her answer: "technique, knowing how to use strength to the best advantage."

Technique, stamina, desire—these are the tools of climbing. Without them all the special gear ever contrived won't get you to the top. Hillary and Tenzing, conquering Everest in 1953, depended as much on these as on oxygen.

So did the Society-sponsored American Mount Everest Expedition of 1963, whose mountaineer-scientists (their leader, Norman Dyhrenfurth, called them "climbing eggheads") tackled the mountain to study glaciers, radiation, and the deterioration of bodies and minds in the brutal world of high altitude. They conquered the summit from the previously unclimbed West Ridge as well as from the South Col route. Five Americans and one Sherpa made it, four on the same day! One was National Geographic staff man Barry C. Bishop, who carried the Society's flag to earth's highest point. He is of the same breed as Israel C. Russell, who 73 years before led the first National Geographic expedition, an assault on Alaska's Mount St. Elias. To such men a challenge must be met.

Mount St. Elias: the Society's First Expedition

In 1890 Israel C. Russell dared avalanches and grizzly bears to explore a glacial wonderland

W E PITCHED TENTS on a strip of shingle skirting the shore of Yakutat Bay. The two boats from the U.S.S. *Pinta* spread their white wings and sailed away. Thus, on June 28, our last connection with civilization was broken. We were alone in the unexplored borderlands between southern Alaska and Canada.

My companions included topographer Mark B. Kerr, seven camp hands hired in Seattle, and Bud and Tweed, the camp foreman's dogs. The expedition, organized by the National Geographic Society and the U. S. Geological Survey, was to study and map the vicinity of Mount St. Elias and, if practicable, ascend the peak itself.

On the morning of July 2, with Bud and Tweed, I started out to choose a line of march toward St. Elias. All about me were wild cliffs stretching up toward snow-

covered peaks. Now and then avalanches awakened echoes, filling the air with a Babel of tongues. Up a mountainside thick with alder and currant I climbed, often on hands and knees. Then I tramped on across snowfields to a great ridge.

From here I saw, for the first time, the huge pyramid of St. Elias. Although 36 miles distant, it dominated all other peaks, standing out boldly against the northwestern sky. I drank in the magnificent landscape, endeavoring to impress every detail upon my memory. Then, for the sun was already declining, I started back.

The quickest way down was to slide on the snow. Using my alpenstock as a brake, I tobogganed several hundred feet, the dogs bounding along beside me. On looking up, I was startled to see two huge grizzly bears not more than 150 yards away.

337

GEOLOGIST RUSSELL (ABOVE) PHOTOGRAPHED MOUNT ST. ELIAS FROM HIS CAMP ON LIBBEY GLACIER

The bears were not at all disturbed by my presence and, in spite of my shouts, one came leisurely toward me. Accelerating my slide, I soon reached the thicket clothing the slope of the mountain, and my unwelcome companions were lost to sight.

I struggled through tangled vegetation until the sun went down. Then, after starting a fire and sharing my few pieces of bread with the dogs, I stretched myself on a bank of lichens to sleep. But the mosquitoes were too energetic. I concluded to press on through the gathering darkness. An hour of hard work, and I came out of the forest. Two miles more, and I rejoiced to see our campfire.

On July 3, I continued my exploration by canoeing to a glaciated island. Climbing its topmost dome, I found a wonderful panorama of icebergs, glaciers, and snow-covered mountains, each hoary peak a monarch robed in ermine.

From a valley to the north flows a great glacier that ends in magnificent ice cliffs. Huge masses, undermined by the sea, topple over into the water with tremendous crashes — like a cannonade rolling across the waters and echoing from cliff to cliff.

Sometimes the thunder of the glacier continues all day. Roar succeeds roar, and these salutes are answered gun for gun by nearby Hubbard Glacier, a magnificent ice stream which, like the mountain that supplies its drainage, was named in honor of Gardiner Greene Hubbard, President of the National Geographic Society.

338

The Fourth of July we spent cutting a trail up the mountain I visited during my first tramp. The next day we established an advance camp above timberline, where Mr. Kerr and myself, with swarms of mosquitoes, passed the night.

DAY AFTER DAY we explored the vast ice fields. We camped on a rocky island overgrown with vegetation. This oasis in a sea of ice we named Blossom Island, for the foreground of every view is a bank of flowers nodding in the wind. Only the creative breath has touched this garden which we, the first of wanderers, have invaded. No battles have here been fought, no kings have ruled, no poets have sung of its ruggedness.

North of the island extends a great ice stream that we named Marvine Glacier. Above it cathedral-like forms and spires of purest white project against the sky, recalling the ecclesiastic architecture of the Old World. To the west lies an exceedingly rugged range that includes Mount Cook. Above this mass of mountains towers St. Elias (map, page 259).

On August 2, we started for the snow peak at the head of Marvine Glacier, hoping to find a pass leading to St. Elias. With tent, blankets, rations, oilstove, and coal oil, we felt equal to any emergency. The morning of our departure was foggy with occasional showers. As we advanced, the weather grew worse and soon all the mountains were shut from view. Early in

the afternoon we reached the upper part of the glacier where it makes a rugged descent and is greatly broken by the fall.

We endeavored to find a passage up the center of the crevassed ice, but we soon came to an impassable gulf. The storm increased, and we concluded to find a camping ground as soon as possible.

Near the mouth of a gorge we scraped aside a mass of shale fallen from the cliff above and built a rock wall along the lower margin. Here we pitched the tent, spread blankets, and prepared supper.

Darkness settled and rain fell in torrents, beating through our little tent. We rolled ourselves in our blankets, determined to rest in spite of the storm. Avalanches, already numerous, became more frequent. A crash told of tons of ice and rock sliding down on the glacier. Another roar was followed by another, another, and still another. It seemed as if pandemonium reigned on the mountains.

Looking out, I saw rocks as large as one's head bounding within a few feet of our tent. One struck the alpenstock to which the ridgerope was fastened. Our tent "went by the board," and the rain poured in. Before we could gather our soaked blankets, mud and stones flowed in upon them. We retreated to the edge of the glacier and pitched our tent again. Wet and cold, we sought to wear the night away. Sleep was impossible.

Toward morning a cold wind swept down the glacier and the rain ceased. An hour after sunrise a rift in the mist revealed the wonderful blue of the heavens. Never was the sun more welcome.

Two days later Mr. Kerr and I tramped up the glacier to the great amphitheater in which it has its source. Far down the opposite side of the divide we saw a large glacier flowing south. We named it Seward Glacier in honor of William H. Seward, the Secretary of State who negotiated the purchase of Alaska.

The following day we advanced our camp across a pass in the mountains and down the western slope. Once Kerr lost his support and slid down the slope. A descent into a yawning chasm seemed inevitable until he hit a rough surface and was able to control his slide.

We marched to a little island of debris on the ice and pitched our tent. When our camp hands visited the site after we had left it, they found that an avalanche had plowed to within 15 or 20 feet of where we had slept. They remarked that if we had been in camp the roar probably would have scared us to death.

On August 8, several hours of climbing brought Kerr and me to the crest of a ridge. The clouds, parting toward the northeast, revealed several giant peaks with one stranger rising far above the rest. We dubbed it Mount Logan in honor of Sir William E. Logan, the founder of the Geological Survey of Canada.

The clouds grew denser, shutting off all hope of extending our work, so we

339

Alaskan expeditions of 1909, '10, and '11

ATTACKING *a stupendous project on foot and in a whaleboat, Ralph S. Tarr and Lawrence Martin led three Society-sponsored expeditions that studied and mapped Alaska's glaciers.*

The photographer washed his films in seawater cluttered with icebergs. But the survey's findings melted some of the mystery that shrouded the Ice Age in North America.

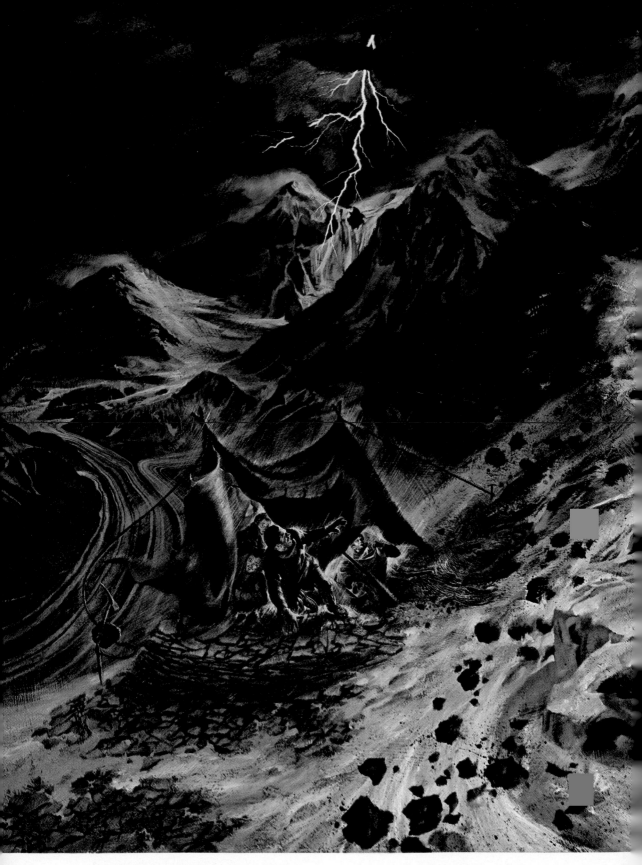

THUNDERING AVALANCHE, *loosed by rain, clips Russell's tent on Marvine Glacier. "One might fancy," he said, "that the* *evil spirits of the hills had prepared for us a reception." His team pushed on toward St. Elias, across ice fields and*

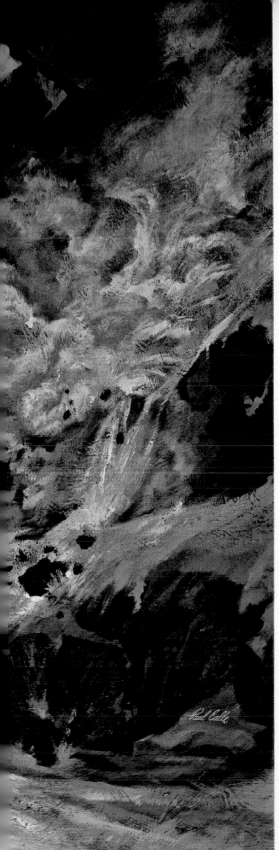

treacherous passes. They mapped 600 square miles and discovered 19,850-foot Mount Logan, loftiest peak in Canada.

returned to camp. A delicious cup of coffee, some bacon and griddle cakes, followed by a restful pipe, ended the day. As we were turning in, a huge ice pinnacle on the glacier fell with a great crash. Rain began to fall and the night was cold and disagreeable. How it passed I do not know. Scarcely anything less serious than the blowing away of our tent could have awakened me.

Detained by the weather, we made an excursion to another glacier. One day the glare of the snow made me snow-blind. I made my way with great difficulty to the top of a mountain spur. There I rested with my eyes bound up with tea leaves, and when evening came found the pain in my head much relieved.

When the weather cleared we pushed on. On August 21, we came upon a vast crevassed plain. Threading the labyrinth of gulfs, we found a place to camp. The sky was clear, the stars brilliant. Everything seemed favorable for an attempt to reach the top of St. Elias.

We set out at three o'clock in the morning, taking only our waterproof coats, some food, and surveying instruments. We found the snow hard and made rapid headway. The light was so evenly diffused that there were no shadows. The winds were still, but strange forebodings of change filled the air.

Early in the day a cloud bank enshrouded the summit. Then it began to snow. To go on would be rash. With our goal almost reached, we were obliged to turn back.

ON AUGUST 25, Kerr and I, with blankets, tents, oilstoves, and what rations remained, returned to the trail to try again. About noon we reached the place where we had bivouacked in the storm, and discovered that we had scarcely enough oil to cook a meal. Kerr volunteered to descend to the lower camp, procure some oil, and return the following day. That left me with a double load to carry through deep snow to the high camp we had previously used.

Trudging wearily on, I reached the camp at sunset and pitched my tent. After cooking some supper, I rolled myself in a blanket and slept the sleep of exhaustion. Snow drifting into my tent awoke me in the morning. I looked out into a blinding snowstorm.

The storm raged all day and night and most of another day. My coal oil finished, I filled a can with bacon grease and made a wick of a cotton rag. Over this "witch lamp" I did my

MOUNT ST. ELIAS *yielded in 1946 to Harvard mountaineers, here toiling up its slopes. The*

cooking. The snow buried my tent. With a basin for a shovel, I cleared the roof to keep it from caving in. I also began a tunnel in case the tent became uninhabitable.

The next morning the tent collapsed. I had no alternative but to build a snowhouse and move in. At right angles to my tunnel I dug a chamber six feet long by four feet wide and three feet high. Here I placed blankets and supplies. At the entrance I hung my rubber coat on an alpenstock. Thus sheltered from the tempest, I passed the day and the night following.

The darkness and silence in my narrow, tomblike cell were oppressive. I slept soundly, however, and in the morning was awakened by the croaking of a raven.

What a glorious sight awaited me! The heavens were without a cloud. St. Elias was one vast pyramid of alabaster. There was no wind; no sound broke the solitude; not an object moved. Even the raven had gone. I was alone with the mountains.

The surface of the snow did not melt sufficiently during the day to freeze and form a crust during the night. The season

Duke of the Abruzzi conquered the 18,008-foot peak seven years after Russell's 1890 try.

was too far advanced to allow the snow to harden enough for a final climb.

After six days alone, I abandoned the tent and oilstove and started down. Midway to the next camping place I saw my companions coming up to search. The sight of humans in that vast solitude was so strange that I watched them for some time before shouting. Each man wore colored glasses and carried a long alpenstock, and several had packs strapped on their backs. Weeks of hard tramping had left many rents in their clothes, which had been mended with cloth of any color available. To a stranger they would have appeared to be a band of brigands.

On September 6, we reached Blossom Island. Before we returned to the coast I made one final excursion out upon the glaciers. The day was bright and beautiful, and the mountains revealed their full magnificence. St. Elias rose clear and sharp without a cloud to obscure its dizzy height. It appeared to be one sheer precipice. I doubt if a more impressive mountain face exists anywhere in the world.

343

Mapping the Roof of North America

For 28 years Bradford Washburn lived his dream—creating a classic portrait of Mt. McKinley

"**B**ELT FASTENED?" Terry Moore shouted above the idling engine. I nodded. "Okay, here we go!" Our tiny two-seater plane bumped down the gravel runway at Chelatna Lake, Alaska, and left the ground. Ahead, wrapped in a blanket of fog, towered the white cone of 20,320-foot Mount McKinley, loftiest peak in North America. We planned to climb it by an "impossible" new route, up the rugged West Buttress. And a third of the way would be by plane! More important, this 1951 assault was crucial to the making of the first large-scale map of McKinley.

Below our wings yawned Kahiltna Glacier, its snout buried under masses of

THE AUTHOR PHOTOGRAPHED MOUNT McKINLEY (RIGHT) ON FLIGHTS IN 1936 AND 1937 SPONSORED BY THE NATIONAL GEOGRAPHIC SOCIETY. IN 1935, ONLY 25 (ABOVE), HE LED THE SOCIETY'S YUKON EXPEDITION.

broken ice and boulders as big as bunga-
lows. Even a helicopter couldn't land
there. Above loomed solid fog. It was like
flying through a gigantic tunnel.

Dr. Terris Moore is not only a famed
mountaineer—conqueror of Minya Konka
(page 364)—but a noted educator. Right
now I was less interested in the fact that
he was President of the University of Alaska than in his qualifications as a bush
pilot, which I knew to be excellent. He
faced the unenviable task of landing on a
little-known glacier under a cloud bank
that threatened to meet the valley floor
and even block our avenue of retreat.

Without warning, a tiny patch of blue
sky appeared; then a shaft of sunlight
moved like a spotlight across the glacier,
guiding us to the spot where we wanted to
land. It swept across a surface of smooth
snow. We touched down perfectly.

Dumping supplies, Terry waved, "So
long, partner," and took off in a swirl of
snow. I was alone at 7,700 feet, close under McKinley's flanks. It was so quiet I
could hear my heart beat. Lightly it began
to snow, and the world turned white.

MY MAP PROJECT had begun 19 years
before. While a student at Harvard
I came upon Dr. Eduard Imhof's
map of the Jungfrau in the Swiss Alps,
the finest I had ever seen. From that moment I hoped that it would someday be
possible for me to map a part of our North
American mountains with that same superb system of cliff drawing and shadow
representation.

Then, in 1936, on an expedition sponsored by the National Geographic Society,
I saw for the first time the mighty tower
of McKinley, which the Indians have long
called Denali, the Great One.

I recall flying around and over the peak
in a Lockheed Electra, sitting on a gasoline can by the open door and snapping
pictures with a bulky camera—while a
rope around my waist let me lean out far
enough, and no farther. That expedition
resulted in the first complete photographic
record of North America's ice-encrusted
rooftop. And it showed me the need for a
detailed map of this Alaskan wilderness.

Only 250 miles from the Arctic Circle
(map, page 259), McKinley is a natural

BRADFORD WASHBURN

SNUG IN A 7-FOOT TENT *at 18,000 feet, the author radios for an airdrop of supplies. On this 1947 survey he spent 89 days on McKinley. He first used air support and lightweight radio in the 1933-4 conquest of Alaska's Mount Crillon. Dynamite and seismograph revealed 1,100-foot depth of South Crillon Glacier (opposite).*

laboratory for scientific research: cosmic ray and weather observations, high frequency radio studies, tests of the effects of oxygen deficiency on the human body. Yet no maps had ever been made of the mountain's east, west, or south side. One was necessary for scientists and others who needed to know how to get around McKinley's peaks and icy passes.

I first set foot on the mountain in 1942. I remember, on that and subsequent expeditions, how the wind would bump the theodolite against my face, forcing me to start my sightings all over again, after making sure the instrument hadn't been thrown out of position. One time on the North Peak I stood on a point of snow so narrow that I had to chop out a tiny level spot for the tripod; one careless step would have sent me sailing 14,000 feet down to the valley. I learned early that map making on McKinley is no joke.

HUNGER ENDED my lonely reverie on Kahiltna Glacier. I had a bite to eat and some hot tea in my tent and listened to the tick of snowflakes on the thin fabric walls. The sun had disappeared behind clouds, but the long twilight of Alaska's summer lingered.

As the weather cleared I heard Terry Moore's voice on my radio: "N-1088-A to

LANDING AT 10,000 FEET, *at the head of Kahiltna Glacier, Terris Moore taxis up to the 1951 expedition's base camp with supplies and mail. No plane had landed higher on McKinley's flanks.*

Ski-equipped planes also played a vital role in Washburn's first exploration for the National Geographic Society in 1935. Flying over glaciers where lethal crevasses were hidden by snow, his team surveyed

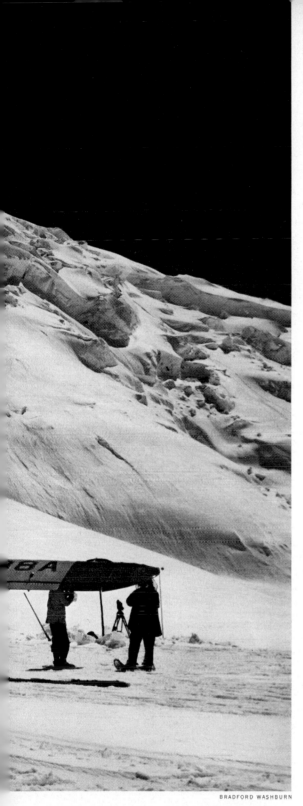

BRADFORD WASHBURN

5,000 square miles of Canada's Yukon, discovering 19 mountain peaks more than 10,000 feet high in wilderness regions no human eye had ever seen. Even sled dogs flew in this rugged land.

KW034. Can you see or hear me? I'm flying through drizzling snow about five miles below your camp." He was returning with his next passenger, Henry Buchtel. I crawled out and looked down the glacier. There he was. Two minutes later he landed, and Henry unloaded his gear.

For the next two days Kahiltna Valley was buried beneath a sea of fog and snow. Then the skies cleared, and in two swift relays the plane brought Jim Gale and Bill Hackett to our little camp.

We worked until midnight breaking trail up the vast, smooth slopes to Kahiltna Pass, 10,300 feet high, and finally set foot on this lofty saddle—the first persons in history to do so. The northern sky turned deep red as twilight merged into dawn.

Next day supplies came hurtling from the sky, dropped by a U. S. Air Force plane. But they caused us a sudden fright because one bag nearly hit a tent. "Watch where you're throwing that stuff!" we yelled into the radio.

"Mighty sorry, fellows," came the reply as the C-47 circled. This time the pilot was right on target—a marker we'd left for him to aim at. We buried 500 pounds of food, including 48 loaves of bread, in a natural deepfreeze outside our door. To thaw a loaf we'd take it to bed with us.

Then we scaled nearby Kahiltna Dome, previously unclimbed. With our theodolite we took sights on the surrounding peaks — which yielded significant new data for the map. When our fingers grew too cold to work we had a cup of tea in the igloo we'd built. An igloo is a wonderful shelter — cool and shady on a sunny day, warm and quiet in the wildest storm.

Our surveys near the base camp were just about finished when four other members of the team joined us. They had circled the mountain by pack train from the north and climbed the other side of Kahiltna Pass to make the rendezvous.

Now for the assault on McKinley.

We had planned our route to avoid huge crevasses and avalanches, major dangers of the old route up the other side of the mountain. At first we followed a broad hollow packed with hundreds of feet of snow. When a crevasse blocked our way, we climbed to the crest of a parallel ridge. A patch of blue-green ice like an inclined

skating rink made us shed snowshoes and don crampons. The ice slopes ended 3,000 feet above the base camp in a massive granite shoulder that rose with dramatic suddenness to the 16,000-foot crest of the West Buttress. In the shadow of the cliff we set up our first advanced camp, "Windy Corner." We spent a cozy night in our igloo and woke up in the middle of a roaring blizzard. Its force increased through the day; by suppertime, gusts hit 80 miles an hour, and snow fell so thickly we couldn't see.

When it cleared next day we pushed on, knotted rope tied around our snowshoes to keep from slipping backward on the steepening slope. After a while we began to slip several inches every step. I took off my snowshoes and promptly broke through the crust to my waist. I put them back on and we started to shovel steps. After an hour's work, I looked back. We had covered only 100 feet.

Utterly exhausted, we set up "Crow's Nest" camp at 15,400 feet. The last slope to the crest of the West Buttress rose sharply 600 feet above our shelf. Roped together, wearing crampons, Gale and I chopped steps in the most wretched snow imaginable: a thin crust, a layer of granular snow like buckshot, finally a solid mass of hard blue ice. Neither of us spoke. We just chopped and chopped.

With the ridge only a stone's throw away, rising wind drove us back to Crow's Nest camp. Next day Jim, Bill Hackett, and I made it to the crest.

We kept on, climbing through dense fog

FROM THE HIGHEST *observation station in North America, McKinley's summit, Dr. Washburn takes a sighting that adds 20 feet to the mountain's previously accepted altitude. To steady theodolite in such gusty stations, he pours water around its legs, freezing them fast.*

One goal still beckoned—the summit. We had all stood there before, yet we had a compelling desire to climb that crest once more. A plumelike cloud enveloped the cone, but it melted away and the great peak rose directly ahead, magnificent in a fresh coat of silver frost. Four hours later we topped the last drift. The amazing panorama burst upon us. It stretched 400 miles from horizon to horizon, 100,000 square miles in a single sweeping glance!

The lowlands shone deep emerald, and river after river sparkled in the afternoon sun. As Hudson Stuck said after his first ascent of McKinley, it was "like looking out the very windows of heaven."

OUR EXPEDITION was over, but the work of making a first-class map had scarcely begun. There was much desk work still to be done: examining photographs, computing the results of observations, correlating our data with that supplied by the Coast and Geodetic Survey and with hundreds of photographs taken by the U. S. Air Force. By the time it was completed the entire project represented the efforts of topographers, geologists, climbers, packers, pilots, dog drivers, photographers, cartographers, and printers—nearly 200 people, who had labored in the finest possible teamwork.

Except for the thrill of surveying from the top of McKinley, the most exciting experience in all the years of my endeavor came in July, 1960, when I watched the first map roll off the press. In the contour lines that delineated summits, cliffs, and valleys, in the fine lines that gave delicate shadings and shadow to the rugged surfaces of snow, ice, and rock, was a reconnaissance sheet that would be as intelligible to the layman as to the expert. Accurate, and yet beautiful, here was the map I had envisioned for 28 years.

to a plateau where sharp rock protruded from icy snow. It was the foot of McKinley's final cone and the site of our last camp. Altitude: 17,000 feet.

July 10 dawned clear. It was relatively easy going to Denali Pass. As the grade lessened, a bundle appeared ahead. I gave a shout of joy. It was a cache of cosmic ray equipment left by our 1947 expedition, which had climbed the other side of McKinley. We shook hands heartily. We had conquered McKinley's West Buttress.

Suddenly Jim leaned over and picked up a tiny bird, a redpoll, which lay frozen in a crack between rocks. In 1947 we had found a redpoll and a Lapland longspur. Every year many migrating birds must be swept to their death far up on McKinley by warm spring gales.

DETAIL FROM "MAP OF MOUNT McKINLEY, ALASKA," SURVEYED AND EDITED BY BRADFORD WASHBURN, PRODUCED BY SWISS FEDERAL

A DREAM FULFILLED, *the author's map of Mount McKinley has been acclaimed a masterpiece. Now Director of Boston's* *Museum of Science, he surveyed the mountain on seven expeditions over a period of 15 years. Ground sightings*

Browne Tower
14,600

17,425

12,060

Thayer Basin
12,355

15,000
15,790

11,980

12,000

14,550

E a s t   B u t t r e s s
14,730   11,920   11,390

14,630

10,000   10,980

9370

N o r t h w e s t   F o r k,   R u t h   G l a c i e r

Southeast Spur
13,100

11,280

12,090

11,170

INSTITUTE OF TOPOGRAPHY, SPONSORED BY SWISS FOUNDATION FOR ALPINE RESEARCH, PHOTOGRAMMETRY BY WILD HEERBRUGG, LTD. © MUSEUM OF SCIENCE, BOSTON

formed the framework; aerial photos—
obliques by Washburn and verticals by
the U. S. Air Force—developed the details.

Skilled Swiss map makers printed it.
The result: McKinley as it might look
to an airman thousands of feet above.

In Quest of China's Holy Mountains

Pistol-packing botanist Joseph F. Rock penetrated an Oriental "Wild West" to sights no Westerner had seen

I WAS QUARTERED in a miserable old temple full of coffins in the village of Ichehsun in the Chinese-Tibetan borderlands. We had fought off bandits all the way from Kunming, and now hundreds of them were besieging me and my party of 12 trusty Nashis and 71 soldiers assigned to protect us by the Chinese authorities.

Outside the village, the heads of brigands captured the previous week hung from poles. Our soldiers said the place could no longer be held. Already one of our men had been killed, and three taken. Capture seemed inevitable.

I distributed $600 in silver to my men, checked my two .45 caliber revolvers, and waited. It was a long night. Every minute we expected the firing to start. At 4 A.M. we heard the bandits outside, but at dawn there was not one to be seen! The villagers said that the brigands had gone ahead to intercept us. I decided to move on anyway.

It was April, 1925. We were headed for the snow-capped Amne Machin Mountains in western China, named for the god who Tibetans believe resides within. During a previous National Geographic expedition I had heard rumors that this range might be higher than Mount Everest. Despite warnings that they were the forbidden stronghold of a warlike tribe of Tibetans, I was determined to visit these holy mountains. Now, back in China on an expedition for the Arnold Arboretum of Harvard University, I was within reach of the goal—if I could make it alive.

After 15 weary weeks of playing "I spy" with bandits, we reached the town of Choni, a march of some 700 miles from Ichehsun and less than 300 miles from the mountains. Go by way of the grasslands on the east bank of the Yellow River, the Choni people told us. But many a prayer wheel was to rattle and whirl before we started, for a war broke out between Moslem and Tibetan tribes.

It was a slaughter reminiscent of the days of Genghis Khan. On horseback, the nomad Tibetans charged the Moslems, impaling them on 30-foot lances as men spear frogs. Under a skilled leader they would have won. But there was no coordination among the wild Tibetans; during the battle one group sneaked back to rob the tents of their allies. The better-trained Moslems countercharged, routing the nomads. Women and children were slaughtered. Many a Tibetan

THE EXPEDITION, *refreshed and resupplied, loads at Kangting during the exploration of Minya Konka. Yaks and mules lug plant presses for botanical specimens.*

was hung by his thumbs and disemboweled, and had his abdomen filled with hot stones. Moslems galloped about, each with 10 or 15 human heads tied to his saddle, and more than 150 heads were strung from posts like garlands of flowers.

We had to winter in Choni amid this carnage, but with spring we pushed on. Reaching a huge monastery 8,000 feet above sea level, I called on the abbot. His beautifully paneled room had fine carpets and silver chests filled with gold images. He asked if I had ever seen people with the heads of dogs, sheep, and cattle.

I said such people did not exist.

He smiled politely. "Oh, yes they do," he said. "Our books tell us so."

The childlike credulity of this man, leader of 5,000 lamas, was astounding. He also believed that the earth was flat.

It was early in May when we left, yet a blizzard raged. For days we trudged over snow-covered or water-soaked land.

After pitching camp, our nomad escorts would sit about and smoke, lighting their pipes with smoldering yak dung. Great was their astonishment when I played my phonograph and the voices of Caruso and Melba filled the air. They roared with laughter at the pathetic songs from "La Bohème" and "Pagliacci."

While at one camp I called on an 81-year-old Buddha, then went to take tea with his steward. This sounds charming, but a Tibetan tea party is a gastronomic nightmare. In the big tent a mud stove roared. An old woman brought bowls from a pile of sheep manure, which served for fuel as well as a sideboard. She scoured the bowls with ground sheep dung, polished them with a filthy rag. She poured tea into these bowls, passed them around, and set before me a wooden box of yak butter covered with old dung dust.

I shrank from tea or food, but whistled up courage to raise the bowl to my lips

BANDIT ESCORT *flanks Dr. Rock at Mount Jambeyang, a sacred peak in the land of Konka Ling. Here he encountered dread Drashetsongpen, lama turned highwayman.*

and take one sip. Just then the old Buddha sent word that he was ready to have his picture taken. I gladly left the party.

Three days' travel brought us to the monastery at Dzangar. Now we were in mountain regions, and our escort left us.

We hired fresh yaks and guides for the final leg. Spies informed the Ngoloks, a wild tribe of the mountains, of our plans. One came boldly to our camp. "You had better not go, for the Ngoloks are waiting to rob and murder you," he warned.

This threat notwithstanding, we loaded up and set off. A glorious day. We rode through forested valleys, up grassy hills, over sunlit mountain passes. From tree branches hung mutton shoulder blades, inscribed with the sacred formula, *Om mani padme hum* (O the jewel in the Lotus). They were suspended low so that passersby would touch them, set them in motion, and thus say the prayers.

We pitched camp 12,500 feet high, at the foot of a mountain. Next morning I climbed to its summit. Not a cloud was in the sky. And there before me, a massive cone of snow and ice sparkling like crystal, towered Amne Machin. I lingered alone, lost in reverie. I could understand now why Tibetans worship these soaring peaks as emblems of purity.

Exploring for the National Geographic Society, I set out in 1928 for another mountain range in southwest China unknown to the Western world. It was in the land of Konka Ling, near the lama kingdom of Muli. I had met the King of Muli before; now I turned to him for help in exploring this region of amazing scenery and pious robbers who turn from pillage to prayer—and back to pillage.

At the king's gate lamas ushered us into the royal presence. The king, dressed in yellow satin, cordially led me to a chair. The mountain we sought, he said, is called

357

Konka Risumgongba, after the god of the outlaws, who dwells there.

It is the wish of every Tibetan to walk around these peaks and thus gain merit. But for 20 years the gratification of this wish has been reserved to the outlaws led by Drashetsongpen, a former lama. His bands of 600 or 700 men go up and down the land robbing caravans. When there are no caravans, he robs his neighbors. Fortunately for us he is on friendly terms with the Muli king. He rides the king's roads and the king shares in the loot.

I lunched with the king—he at his small table, I at mine. We ate fried eggs, bits of mutton, beef, noodles, rice, and a bowl of sour yak cream and melted yak butter. His lama interpreter stood for hours with folded hands and bowed head until I said, "Poor Mr. Tung must certainly be hungry."

The king laughed and placed odds and ends from his plate before the lama, as though feeding his favorite dog, then motioned him to sit on the floor and regale himself on the royal leavings.

The king agreed to write strong letters to all the big thieves of Konka Ling. He assured me that we would have little to fear, but begged me not to stay too long.

I started out with 36 mules and horses, 21 of my Nashis, and a lama guide. After a weary march we came to the village of Garu. The natives, proud kinsmen of the outlaws, walked about with an insolent air. Tall and well-built, they resembled Apache Indians, with plaited hair hanging from well-modeled heads. From this tribe the king recruited his best soldiers. But the warriors, every one of whom had killed his man, were loath to escort us around the peaks for fear of the outlaws. I asked, as though in contempt of their cowardice, "Am I to be accompanied by Garu men — or women?" and threatened to send word to the king. They quickly agreed to protect me with their lives.

We set out one cold, rainy morning, each mounted warrior armed with rifle and *gawu*, a portable shrine to protect against bullets. Through forests we ascended the Konka Ling Plateau and crossed a 10,000-foot pass. The men yelled *Lhu ryellah!* (The gods are victorious!), accustomed shout of every Tibetan on a pass.

EXPLORING THE LAND THAT TIME FORGOT, *Dr. Rock led two National Geographic expeditions (1923-24 and 1927-30) into the unmapped Tibetan borderlands of China. Bedeviled by bandits, lashed by blizzards, he pushed through desolate defiles, crossed razor-backed ranges to gather thousands of plants, including 493 kinds of rhododendron; he also assembled a Noah's Ark of bird and mammal specimens. Through the pages of* National Geographic *he gave the world its first close look at the holy mountains of Amne Machin, Konka Ling, and Minya Konka.*

At the raging Yalung River (right), Rock's men slide a mule across on a cable. Mule skinner inches up hand over hand.

STATUTE MILES
NATIONAL GEOGRAPHIC MAP BY IRVIN ALLEMAN

South China Sea

OPPOSITE: JOSEPH F. ROCK

We camped on a gentle slope facing one of the sacred mountains, Chanadordje—"Holder of the Thunderbolt." I took in its mass, a truncated pyramid flanked by broad buttresses like the wings of some stupendous bat.

In a torrential rain we ran headlong into Drashetsongpen. His entourage was composed of outlaw scum, their sullen faces hinting at loot and murder. But he uncovered his head, bowed, and asked where we intended to camp. I hesitated. He put his hand on his chest and said, "You have nothing to fear. I have given orders you shall remain unmolested."

Later we learned that a hailstorm had destroyed the bandits' barley crop shortly after we left. Drashetsongpen blamed us and vowed that if we came his way again he would kill us for certain.

Climbing the sacred mountain Chanadordje, I had gasped at the sight of a white pyramid piercing the sky far to the north. My guides said this was Minya Konka, vast, unexplored. I decided to spend the following year investigating it.

IN THE SPRING of 1929 we were on our way to Minya Konka, laboring over steep trails to the foot of a high pass beyond Chanadordje. A blizzard swirled down, and we were unable to see even a few feet ahead. We struggled over fallen logs, up and up, until I spied through the whirling snow a cairn of sticks and stones denoting the top of the pass. Never did I exclaim more heartily with my Tibetans, "Lha rgellah!"

The descent was a nightmare. Men, beasts, and loads catapulted into deep snow up to our necks; only part of our caravan reached camp that night. To go on was impossible, for my men were snow-blind and suffering terribly. Fortunately I had a supply of cocaine; with it I made a solution which I dropped into their eyes

FREDERICK R. WULSIN. OPPOSITE: JOSEPH F. ROCK

SIX-FOOT TRUMPETS *sound weird blasts as puff-cheeked young lamas invite all the countryside to a Buddhist rite. Between expeditions Dr. Rock brought two faithful Nashi aides to Washington. Robed warrior with matchlock gun (right) studied photography; his companion learned taxidermy. Both used their new skills in subsequent National Geographic explorations.*

MAGIC OF THE ORIENT comes alive in the author's unique album. Dr. Rock pioneered in color photography while in western China, but his task was trying. Natives often ran from the camera; at 18,000 feet he had to dry negatives over yak dung fires to keep them from freezing.

The King of Muli (left) wears the robe of a Living Buddha; among outlaws his word was law. Family of a Hlihin chieftain pose proudly (lower), and a Nashi youth models his leopard skins.

Demons of the netherworld (right) whirl in a fiendish dance, part of a Tibetan mystery play. The delicate figure of Donker (lower), a goddess of mercy, is sculptured in many-colored butter for the Choni Butter Festival.

DR. ROCK MADE THESE AUTOCHROMES, FIRST NATURAL COLOR PHOTOGRAPHS EVER TAKEN IN THE TIBETAN BORDERLANDS, DURING THE NATIONAL GEOGRAPHIC EXPEDITION OF 1927-30

1925 PHOTOGRAPHS BY DR. ROCK, HAND-TINTED BY HASHIME MURAYAMA

Americans first to scale Minya Konka

NUMBING WINDS *howl across rock and snow as if to tear the tent from the bosom of Minya Konka. Inside the chattering walls of canvas huddle three veteran mountaineers, Terris Moore, Richard L. Burdsall, and Arthur B. Emmons 3d. Inspired by Joseph Rock's report of the 24,900-foot peak in the highlands of western China, they seek its untrod summit.*

It is October, 1932. Porters have been left behind at the 17,000-foot snowline, and for weeks the three men have backpacked supplies from one camp to the next, clawing up the northwest flank, imperiled by snowslides and hidden crevasses. The thin air tortures their lungs and saps strength.

Now at 22,000 feet they draw on their last reserves for the final assault. Emmons suffers an injury and must stay. But at 5 A.M. on October 28, Moore probes the darkness with a flashlight. Burdsall, at the end of a 50-foot rope, gropes his way after Moore.

By dawn they are climbing 300 feet an hour, cautiously belaying each other over the tumbled ice blocks. Then there is a ridge—an oval platform. They have done it. "The view was vast and superb," they wrote in National Geographic. *For several frigid minutes Moore flew Old Glory (above) on Minya Konka's conquered crown. This was, at that time, the highest point on earth where the flag had waved.*

to relieve the pain. I followed this treatment with cold compresses.

Now we climbed and climbed up a rocky spur. Snow lay deep but frozen hard, and we crept to 16,500 feet.

Suddenly, as we turned a bend, long-hidden Minya Konka rose before us in sublime majesty, like a white promontory of clouds in a turquoise-blue sky. I could not help exclaiming for joy. I marveled at the sight which I, the first Westerner ever to stand here, was privileged to see.

An immense range extended north and south, peerless Minya Konka rising high above its sister peaks. Flanking it was a great glacier. Clouds rested on the summits of some of the mountains, and two appeared to be united by a graceful spur.

I explored to my heart's content. A friendly Tibetan guided me to a tiny monastery at the very foot of Minya Konka's mighty glacier. The lamas led me to a narrow room with a dimly lit chapel on one side. Here stood a golden shrine studded with jewels and containing the body of an incarnation of the Living Buddha.

All was hushed. But outside, the glacier stream roared and thunder rolled. Here, alone, in the presence of a sacred mummy, I listened to a tempest break over the icy peak of Minya Konka. Was this the year 1929, or had time been set back a thousand years? Was it all a dream?

Four lamas quietly entered, lighted a tiny butter lamp, placed it before the mummy, and in deep basso voices began to mumble prayers. One lama wafted juniper incense as an offering. A shower of barley grains descended. Every afternoon for more than half a century the Buddha had received this homage.

The following morning I climbed to the rocky backbone of a ridge at 17,000 feet. I sat on a boulder and drank in the beauty and grandeur of Minya Konka. At last I left, regretfully but happily. Tradition says that anyone gazing upon the peak will have all his past sins wiped off the slate, so that he may begin life anew.

MIGHTY MINYA KONKA, *photographed for the first time, was caught like a bride unawares. Glaciers brocade her low-cut gown of snow; winds toss back her veil of cloud.*

Triumph on Everest

Numbed by altitude, climbers huddle below earth's mightiest peak
to launch a final assault. Sir Edmund Hillary relates his story
to Beverley M. Bowie of the National Geographic staff.

NIGHT on the South Col. The wind screeches across the ridge and sets the canvas cracking like a rifle range. I'm braced between Tenzing Norkey and the tent wall. Whenever my head falls back against the roof it's as if I'd run my brain into a pneumatic drill.

On the other side of Tenzing are Alf Gregory and George Lowe, hunched up in their sleeping bags, twisting, heaving around, trying to find some position less cold and miserable. We're using the oxygen sleeping sets, one liter per minute. Makes it easier to doze. But up here you dribble a good bit in your sleep, and when your bottle gives out you wake suddenly, as if somebody had turned on the light. Your face mask is clammy and frigid.

I keep looking at my watch, wondering if it's stopped. The hour hand finally creeps around to 4, and I strike a match. The thermometer reads 13° below zero F. It is still pitch dark.

I nudge Tenzing, mutter something about breakfast, and retreat callously to my bag. Pretty soon the primus has warmed the tent a few degrees—just enough to make it seem safe to sit up and eat. Scruffy, cramped, somewhat depressed, we gulp down cups of sugary hot

FLANKED ON THE RIGHT BY LHOTSE AND NUPTSE, EVEREST (CENTER) SOARS FIVE AND A HALF MILES INTO THE HIMALAYAN SKIES; NORMAN G. DYHRENFURTH

SIR EDMUND HILLARY,
conqueror of Everest

SIRDAR TENZING NORKEY,
on his 6th Everest climb,
reached top with Hillary

BRIGADIER SIR JOHN HUNT,
leader of the British
Everest Expedition

BRITISH EVEREST EXPEDITION *of 1953*
builds up for its great campaign at
Thyangboche monastery, 175 miles
from Katmandu, 15 from Everest.
An army of 450 porters shoulders in
15 tons of supplies, and John Hunt
organizes logistics for each phase
of the grim trail ahead.
Then laden Sherpas and climbers set up
advance camps higher, ever higher,
on the mountain's southwest flank.
It takes months of planning and testing,
weeks of brutal physical effort,
to place two men atop the icy summit.

SIR EDMUND HILLARY, ROYAL GEOGRAPHICAL SOCIETY AND ALPINE CLUB

water flavored with lemon crystals, munch some biscuits, and argue about which of us spent the worst night. Greg claims the honor, contending that sleeping between Lowe and Tenzing is like being caught in the jaws of a vise. But Lowe scores heavily when he points to a small heap of snow on his sleeping bag, blown through a pinhole in his side of the tent.

We sprawl about for five hours, waiting for the wind to die down. It doesn't.

At nine I bundle up and stumble over to the tent which John Hunt, leader of the expedition, shares with the first assault team, Tom Bourdillon and Charles Evans.

Both are exhausted from their attempt which got them to the South Peak. Hunt agrees that Tenzing and I must postpone our bid for the summit. He decides to go down with everyone but Greg, Lowe, Tenzing, Ang Nyima, Pemba, and me. No point in depleting the slim reserves of food we've hauled up here to Camp VIII.

An hour or so later they are packed and ready. Hunt, gray and drawn but with his blue eyes frostier than ever, grips my arm. Above the howling wind he says, "Most important thing—is for you chaps—to come back safely. Remember that. But get up if you can."

369

Everest, 29,028

South Peak, 28,700

George Leigh-Mallory
and Andrew Irvine vanished
at 27,950 feet in 1924

Lhotse, 27,923

Camp IX, 27,900

Southeast Ridge

Camp VIII, 25,800

South Col

Camp VII, 24,000

Camp VI, 23,000

Western Cwm

Camp V, 22,000

Camp IV, 21,200

Camp III, 20,200

Khumbu Glacier

Camp II, 19,400

Base Camp, 17,900 feet

Nuptse, 25,726

We watch them slog across the col and down the slopes toward the traverse, tired figures dwindling against the monstrous icy face of Lhotse. Then we turn back to our own chores.

I spend the afternoon sorting oxygen bottles, strapping them to their frames, and preparing our sleeping sets. All day we have used no masks. We can breathe well enough, but we work very slowly.

Night comes on, with the wind still intent on blowing us off the col. We catnap through the long hours, not as uncomfortably as before, since there's now more room. Tenzing and I have appropriated the Meade tent; Greg and Lowe share the pyramid.

By 8 A.M. the wind has eased off, but when I go to fetch Pemba I find him at the door of his tent, retching his heart out. Obviously, he won't be going anywhere today. Which leaves us only Ang Nyima to help on the carry. Blast old Pemba, I think, and with no remorse; the South Col is too high for pity.

We repack our loads and shove off. Lowe, Gregory, and Ang Nyima leave first, at 8:30, with about

HUNT'S PLAN *calls for a "Jacob's Ladder in action, with...climbers toiling endlessly up and down." They pack three tons up Khumbu Glacier to Camp III (below), already as high as McKinley, then move the supplies up the Western Cwm for Camps IV to VIII. Camp IX is only a bivouac. Cotton-nylon tents can weather 100-mile gales.*

INDIAN AIR FORCE. INSET: GEORGE LOWE, ROYAL GEOGRAPHICAL SOCIETY AND ALPINE CLUB

45 pounds apiece; they will cut steps for us so that we can save energy and oxygen. We follow at ten, carrying our sleeping bags, air mattresses, food, and extra clothing on top of our breathing sets.

At the foot of the big couloir we climb the staircase Lowe has chipped, only to duck as a barrage of ice chunks splatters down at us from 300 feet above. We pull aside until the fellows up top have moved out along the Southeast Ridge. Then we scramble after them and catch up about noon at the site of the wind-ripped tent left there by Lambert, the Swiss climber, and Tenzing the year before.

A nice view from here. We photograph everything in sight and move up to the dump John Hunt had placed at 27,350 feet two days ago. Adding all that to our loads is impossible. But the stuff has to go up. Greg packs the oxygen, Lowe ties on food and fuel, and we all look at the tent. Finally I say to Lowe: "Look, I'll take the tent if you'll make the route."

He grins and moves off in the lead. He's going extremely well. In fact, this is George Lowe's big day on Everest. He was good on the Lhotse Face, but up here he's really showing what he can do.

With 50 to 63 pounds on our backs we plug on up the steepening ridge. By 2 P.M., at 27,900 feet, we start casting around for a tent site, but the whole slope pitches away like a barn roof. For half an hour we search, climbing and traversing, until finally we come on a ledge about six feet by four, angled down at about 30 degrees.

"Now, there's a lovely spot for a camp," says George enthusiastically, and dumps his load on it at once. The others are pretty keen to get on down the mountain, too, and we can't blame them. But Ang Nyima, though he's dead beat, asks politely if he can stay up here to help us down the next day. We send him along. One more night this high on Everest would weaken him so much he'd be of no use to anyone.

A LONELY MOMENT, as we watched old George and Greg and Ang Nyima turn back. Now Tenzing and I are really alone. The tent is our first job. For two hours we scrape at the rocks and the snow and the frozen gravel, trying to make a platform for it. We settle for two terraces about a yard wide, six feet long, and about a foot different in height. Then we spend another two hours getting the tent itself up and securing it to some flimsy rock belays and to oxygen bottles which I bury in the snow.

About 6:30 we crawl into our sleeping bags, light the primus, and get supper: tinned apricots, dates, sardines, biscuits, jam, honey. The wind comes in gusts. When I hear it whistle up on the ridge, I brace myself against the canvas and try to hold the tent down as it gets ready to take off. In between squalls I doze, slumping on the upper shelf with my legs dangling over Tenzing's bench.

We use only four hours of oxygen, in two-hour shifts. In between, Tenzing heats up a few drinks. We don't talk much. I wonder how George and the boys fared going down, and what John Hunt must be thinking. And over and over again I do my mental arithmetic on the amount of climbing oxygen we have left, the amount we're likely to use, the amount that may still be left in the bottles Tom Bourdillon and

NEW WEAPONS *crack Everest's defenses. Sherpas grin when taught to use "English air" (opposite), but bottled oxygen keeps them going at heights where they'd soon be unconscious without it; a sleeping set gives them rest at night.*

A physiologist (above) checks the carbon dioxide content in John Hunt's breath at 21,200 feet. The less CO_2, the better his adjustment to altitude. Acclimatized, the mountaineer breathes faster to offset thin air; his heart works harder.

Boots, designed for Everest, keep feet warm and dry on snowy upper reaches. Aluminum ladder (left) moves supplies over breaks in the jumbled ice fields.

Charles Evans cached on their way down from the South Peak.

Four A.M. We poke our heads out of the tent door. The wind is mercifully still. Far off, the valleys of Nepal still sleep in darkness, but the summits of Makalu and Ama Dablam have caught the sun; and Tenzing, pointing past me, picks out the monastery at Thyangboche, 14,400 feet below, where even now the lamas are offering special prayers for our safe return.

My feet had been a bit damp the night before and, to let them dry out and warm up with less risk of frostbite, I had pulled my boots off and used them to prop the toe of my sleeping bag off the cold ground. Now the boots are frozen as stiff as medieval armor.

I cook them over the primus. It takes a good hour to thaw them, and the smell of leather and rubberized fabric is gruesome; but finally the boots are soft enough to wiggle into, and we can set out.

Climbing strongly, we make for the hollow where Evans and Bourdillon left their oxygen bottles. The cylinders are easy to spot. Pawing the ice from the gauges, I read pleasant news: about 1,000 pounds pressure—enough to take us down to the South Col if we're lucky. In short, we can plow all the oxygen on our backs into our attack on the peak itself and our return to this niche.

We push on. About 400 feet from the South Peak we are brought to a stop: Which route? Bourdillon and Evans took the ridge to the left, then on their way back came down the face. The ridge is a most unsavory mixture of steep

SNOWPRINTS *mark the path of conquerors up the final ridge from the South Peak. To right, a 10,000-foot drop to Kangshung Glacier. To left, a 7,500-foot plunge to the Western Cwm.*

loose rock and snow. I regard it with grave suspicion. We decide on the face.

We start up and I realize at once we're on dangerous ground. By the sixth step Tenzing sinks through the thin frozen crust and is up to his hips in the snow. Then the whole crust for ten feet around breaks up and we slide down three steps. We stop, but the crust, gathering speed, slithers on out of sight. We plow on.

Halfway, I turn to Tenzing and say, "What do you think of it?"

"Very bad, very dangerous!"

"Shall we go on?"

He shrugs. "Just as you wish."

I make a quick decision. In ordinary mountaineering terms, the risk isn't justifiable. But this is Everest, and you take long odds, because the goal is worth it. Or so I try to convince myself.

We go on, and we get a break. A few yards higher we run into some snow that's packed hard. Chipping steps, we make our way quite rapidly. At 9 a.m. we are standing on the South Peak.

We have these advantages over Evans and Bourdillon: Thanks to a higher camp, we're here four hours earlier, and we have more oxygen and more strength left to finish the job. But just how big a job is it? That's something no one can tell us.

To size it up, we scoop out a seat for ourselves just below the South Peak, remove our masks, and study the summit above. The true crown is out of sight, somewhere up above the ridge that turns its blade right in our faces now. It looks like a fair cow, as we'd say in New Zealand. On the right, cornices overhanging a drop of 10,000 feet to the Kangshung Glacier on Everest's eastern flank; on the left, steep snow sloping to the lip of the big rock wall that looms over the Western Cwm.

We don't need to talk much. It's obvious that our only route lies between the cornices and the cliffs on the left. If the snow is firm, we have a chance. I check the oxygen once more. One full bottle left for each of us. That's 800 liters and at three liters per minute, about 4½ hours of climbing. Enough? Well, it will have to be.

We put our sets on again, lighter for the discarded bottles. I feel very fit, and keen to get at the problem. We crampon down to the start of the ridge, and I sink my ax blade into the snow of the upward slope. It is everything we could have asked— crystalline and solid and well packed. Two or three whacks chip a step big enough even for our elephantine high-altitude boots, and a good shove buries the ax shaft half its length, making a very decent belay.

I LEAD OFF, cutting a 40-foot line of steps, resting, and taking a few turns of the rope around my ax as Tenzing comes up to join me. Then he belays me as I carve another flight. We move along steadily, giving the rickety cornices a fairly wide berth and taking an occasional glance over the rock face on our left. About 7,500 feet below I can just make out the tents of Camp IV, and I flap my arms and shout, with no particular hope that anyone will see or hear me.

Tenzing has begun to drag a little on the rope, and his breathing seems more rapid. As we halt on one tiny ledge, I ask, "How does it go, Tenzing?"

"All right."

I know, however, that like most Sherpas Tenzing has only a vague notion of the way his oxygen set works. He may be getting groggy and not even realize it. So I check his exhaust tube and find the valves almost completely blocked with ice; he's probably been getting no great benefit from his oxygen for some minutes.

I cut another line of steps for perhaps half an hour. Then we find ourselves staring at an obstacle we've dreaded ever since we spotted it on the aerial photos and through our binoculars from Thyangboche: a great rock about 40 feet high, planted right across the ridge. No route on it. And no way around it except—

Except where the snow cornice on the right, pulling away a little from the rock, has left a thin gap, a kind of chimney. We look at it with rather mixed emotions. I'm not one of those blokes who says to himself, "I'll get up, come hell or high water." Mountains mean a lot to me, but not that much. I just say to Tenzing, "Well, we'll give it a good go."

I jam my way into the crack. With my back to the cornice, I face the rock and grope for handholds, kicking my crampons into the snow behind me and jacking myself upwards. I use everything I have—

knees, elbows, shoulders, even the oxygen set on my back – trying to get a purchase and exert some critical leverage.

Constantly at the back of my mind is the fear that the cornice might break off. Of course, Tenzing has me belayed on a bit of rock, which provides a certain moral support. But if the snow gives way and I find myself dangling over the Kangshung Glacier, it isn't going to matter enormously whether Tenzing can hold me for five minutes or fifty.

Foot by foot I hump and wriggle and pull myself up the chimney. The crack is only a rope's length long, but it's a good half hour before I can reach over the ledge at the top and drag myself onto it. I lie there, panting furiously, surprised somehow that I've scraped together enough energy to make it. Then I give Tenzing a taut rope and signal him to come along.

For the first time the conviction seeps through me that we are really going to go all the way.

I go on chipping a line of steps, then another, and another. We follow the ridge as it curves around to the right, wondering where the top can possibly be, or if it exists at all. I cut around the back of one crag, only to have a higher one stare me in the face. It seems endless.

Suddenly I realize that the ridge ahead doesn't slope up, but down. I look quickly to my right. There, about 40 feet above my head, is a softly rounded, snowy dome.

The summit.

One last question concerns me: Is the top itself just a large, delicately poised cornice? The thought has haunted me all the way along the ridge.

I cut my way cautiously up the next few feet, probing ahead with my ax. The snow is solid, firmly packed. A few more whacks of the ax, a few very weary steps. We are there. We are on the summit of Everest.

I feel no great elation at first, just relief and a sense of wonder. Then I turn to Tenzing and shake his hand. Even through the snow glasses, the ice-encrusted mask, I can see that happy, flashing smile. He throws his arms around my shoulders, and we thump each other, and there is very little we can say or need to say.

My watch shows 11:30. Two hours and a half it has taken us from the South Peak; five hours from our tent.

376

MAKALU'S JAGGED PYRAMID LOOMS TO SOUTHEAST; FIVE-PEAKED KANCHENJUNGA, WORLD'S THIRD HIGHEST MOUNTAIN, DOMINATES THE HORIZON

FROM EARTH'S SUMMIT, *a barren sea of peaks stretching to the horizon in ice-crested waves greets Hillary and Tenzing.*

They began their assault at wind-lashed Camp VIII on the South Col, toiling up steps (right) hacked by the three-man support party. On a sloping ledge at 27,900 feet they pitch their tent—Camp IX.

Early next morning they make their play, first clawing up to the South Peak, high point for Evans and Bourdillon, the first assault team. Hillary and Tenzing push on, up the perilous final ridge, a knife's edge between ghastly precipices. Suddenly there is nothing above, the world below!

I fish out the camera I have kept warm inside my shirt; it will be necessary to take shots down every ridge if we're to prove that we've been up here. I also take pictures of Tenzing holding up his ice ax with its flags standing out stiffly in the wind—the flags of the United Nations, Great Britain, Nepal, India.

We look about for any signs that Mallory and Irvine may have been here before us; there are none. I take care, however, to photograph the route which they and the other great climbers followed up from the North Col and along the rugged Northeast Ridge. Then I point the camera hopefully at unclimbed Makalu, at the fantastic hulk of Kanchenjunga on the far horizon, at Cho Oyu to the Northwest, at the ranges of Nepal receding into the distance, wave on glittering wave.

Scooping a small hole in the snow, Tenzing buries a few offerings to the gods that many Buddhists believe inhabit these heights: a small blue pencil given him by his daughter, a bar of chocolate, some biscuits, a cluster of lollypops. I place near these gifts a little crucifix that John Hunt has received from a friend and passed over to me on the South Col.

IT'S TIME to go down now. I replace my oxygen mask and suck in the air gratefully, though without it I found my breathing was not too uncomfortable. We move off without a backward glance. Reaction has set in. We are both tired.

We crampon along the steps I have cut, moving fast. We know the route, we know what's ahead. Even the rock chimney looks reassuringly familiar. We plunge into it and kick our way down as if there's no more danger that the cornice will politely take leave of the ridge.

Back on the South Peak once more, we halt for a swig of lemonade before tackling the section we both dread—the great snow slope on the reverse face. It skids down the summit aimed right at a glacier 10,000 feet below. An ice-ax belay won't hold in the soft snow. If one of us begins to slide, it could start a disastrous avalanche. I am determined to pack the treacherous snow into safe and stable steps.

We begin our descent. Facing out and down, we get the uncomfortable sensation of being too heavy, ready to sway forward and fall. We place our boots into each step as if we're walking a high wire.

Forty steps more. Twenty. Five... we are down and can slant over to the relative safety of the Southeast Ridge.

Now it's only a long, rough tramp down to the South Col. Before we get there, a lone figure stumps up to meet us – George Lowe, carrying hot soup and emergency oxygen. I grin weakly at George. "Well, we knocked the blighter off!"

As we clamber down the ice steps to Camp VII, which we have assumed is deserted, we're startled by a loud, cheerful shout. It's Charles Wylie and his Sherpas, hurrying out of the tents to greet us and press hot drinks into our numbed hands. The Sherpas crowd around and shake our hands, saluting Tenzing—one of their own—with new and even more affectionate respect. I hear the phrase, *"Everest khatm ho gya,* Sahib! Everest has had it!"

Camp VII, however, is no hotel, and we are eager to get off the mountain. Pressing down past Camps VI and V, we break out into the upper cwm itself and push along toward Camp IV. As we get within sight of it, we see little figures making their way up the track toward us.

We make no signal until we are about 50 yards away. Then George jerks his thumb up and waves his ax in the direction of the summit. With a whoop, they break into a run and fling themselves upon us. John Hunt, too tired to do much more than smile, puts his arm around me and lets his head fall on my chest.

It is a strange and moving moment. I am so weary myself that it is as if I were watching all this happen to another person. All I know is a great gladness that we can bring back to John the victory he did so much to achieve.

VICTORY! *Like a triumphant gladiator Tenzing puts his foot on Everest's vanquished head and raises his ice ax with its wind-whipped flags. The time: 11:30 A.M., May 29, 1953. Hillary made this picture. There are none of him because "Tenzing is no photographer, and Everest is no place to begin teaching him."*

SIR EDMUND HILLARY, ROYAL GEOGRAPHICAL SOCIETY AND ALPINE CLUB

SMILES SPREAD *as Margaret Gilliard plays back voices of "sing-sing" dancers in New Britain, where her ornithologist husband sought rare birds.*

E. THOMAS GILLIARD. RIGHT: JOHN SCOFIELD, NATIONAL GEOGRAPHIC STAFF

Exploring Lands of Exotic Life

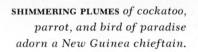

SHIMMERING PLUMES *of cockatoo, parrot, and bird of paradise adorn a New Guinea chieftain.*

"ELEPHANTS BREED IN THAT PART of Africa which lies beyond the deserts and wilderness of the Syrtes...they are also found among the Ethiopians and Troglodites...but India brings forth the biggest: as also the dragons." Romans of the first century felt a thrill of wonder as they read Pliny's *Historia Naturalis.* Man's pulse has always quickened to tales of strange people and weird beasts in far-off, exotic lands.

For centuries fact and fable were woven together. Ancient Greeks read of fierce Amazons, giant one-eyed Cyclopes, and the monster Scylla, which had "six long necks, each ending in a grisly head." Medieval map makers showed clearly the lands of "dog-faced" people. Then came men like Cook, Darwin, Humboldt—thirsting for knowledge, traversing oceans and jungles to see and report firsthand the true marvels of nature and man.

Continuing this great quest, National Geographic expeditions explore exotic life in the remote corners of the world. Probing the wilderness of Brazil—"that one great wild, untidy, luxuriant hothouse," Darwin called it—Paul Zahl tracks monsters of the insect world. Pushing up Venezuela's Orinoco River, Ernest G. Holt hears in the night-darkened jungle the same sounds Humboldt had

CARL AKELEY, *famous Africa explorer,
collected elephants for museums
and relaxed by joining Nandi warriors
in their sport — lion-spearing.*
AMERICAN MUSEUM OF NATURAL HISTORY

VOLKMAR WENTZEL, NATIONAL GEOGRAPHIC STAFF (ALSO BELOW)

LURCHING ALONG *at 12 miles a day, S. Dillon Ripley
pursues rare birds in Nepal — "a naturalist's paradise."*

PLATTER-LIPPED
*woman of the
Sara tribe
smiles at her
look-alike in
the Geographic.
Walter Weber,
staff artist
and naturalist,
pauses on an
expedition in
central Africa.*

heard: "the whining, flute-like notes of the small sapajous, the grunting murmur of the striped nocturnal ape... the fitful roar of the great tiger." Penetrating the arid heart of Australia, Charles P. Mountford goes among aborigines whom Cook had described as "wholy naked, their skins the Color of wood soot."

Strange and wonderful are the ways of the family of man. "The Siwai woman's life is as narrow as the little path she walks to and from her garden," Eleanor Schirmer Oliver writes of the Solomon Islanders. "If a man is asked if he has a good wife, he will say she 'makes a good garden.'"

Pygmy boys and girls spin tops made from forest nuts or soar aloft on liana swings, reports Anne Eisner Putnam from the Congo. "Some dashed about with a noisy beetle tied to a string; as they ran they excitedly yelled the French word for airplane: *avion! avion!*"

Avion! Civilization overruns ancient ways of life with jet-plane speed. In Brazil Harald Schultz races to the Xingu River to record the culture of the Suyá Indians before they swap their nakedness and wooden lip disks for modern garb. In the remote, unpacified highlands of New Guinea Karl Heider hurries to complete a pictorial study of the Stone Age Dani people before a government

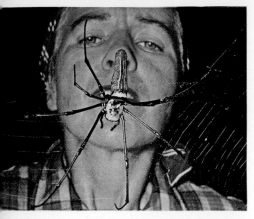

COCK-OF-THE-ROCK, a bright flame in the green jungles of British Guiana, revealed its courtship dance to E. Thomas Gilliard.

DANGLING SPIDER *in Thailand is headed for Wilda Ross's specimen bag. She and her entomologist husband, Edward, travel the world for insects.*

NATURALIST JANE GOODALL *feeds David Greybeard in Tanganyika. Aided by a grant from the Society, she observes chimpanzees at close quarters, even joins their hunts. Once an irate male struck her.*

program whisks them into the 20th century. On the southwest coast of that great, green island John Scofield enters the dark, skull-strewn hut of head-hunters now groping for a new way of life.

Like scholars turning the pages of some endless book, naturalists discover new wonders from nature's inexhaustible store. An exciting message reaches Society headquarters: "We have found the curlew's nest." Arthur A. Allen has solved a 163-year-old mystery. First collected by Cook's party at Tahiti, the bristle-thighed curlew had kept secret its nesting place until Dr. Allen traced it far north to a lonely field in Alaska.

S. Dillon Ripley leads an expedition into Nepal and makes a remarkable find: "Careful stalking, for the birds were very shy, brought me within reach and I fired and secured one bird.... There in my hand lay a spiny babbler, *Acanthoptila nipalensis,* a species lost to science for 106 years!... No ornithologist had ever before seen the species alive." In New Britain's "land of fire" E. Thomas Gilliard discovered five birds new to science; in New Guinea he photographs for the first time the weird mating dance of glorious birds of paradise.

On a 33,000-mile odyssey Edward S. Ross presses the trigger of his camera

ALEXANDER WETMORE *prepares the skin of a Panama parrot. For more than 40 years he has studied the birds of Latin America. His retirement as Secretary of the Smithsonian Institution now allows more time to explore the rain forests. The renowned ornithologist is Vice Chairman of the National Geographic Society's Committee for Research and Exploration.*

to capture on film the intimate life of Africa's "smallest game." Bigger quarry was in Carl Akeley's mind when he trekked through Africa half a century earlier. Fearing that the demand for ivory would wipe out the thundering herds of elephants, he risked his life to bring back the big tuskers that have been preserved for millions to see in New York's American Museum of Natural History.

In Tanganyika a young Englishwoman writes: "Slowly and quietly... I moved toward the great apes until I was only 30 feet away. They watched me as I sat down, staring rather hard...." Thus Jane Goodall describes the moment — after months of painstaking effort — she was accepted by a group of chimpanzees as merely "a strange hairless primate who had suddenly appeared amongst the other mountain fauna." To observe the chimps' daily life, she learned to "creep on my belly along pig trails" and to climb steep slopes as they do, by grasping "roots worn smooth by constant use." Her discovery that the primates use sticks as simple tools and eat raw flesh set zoological circles buzzing.

Why do men and women face hardships and dangers like these to study life in exotic lands? Alexander Pope wrote: "All Nature is but Art, unknown to thee." The challenge is simply and everlastingly to know the art of nature and man.

Australia's Stone Age Men

Lost in the backwaters of time, they live as their forefathers did 50,000 years ago. National Geographic expedition leader Charles P. Mountford takes us to earth's most primitive people.

IN THE LONELY BORDERLAND between South Australia and the Northern Territory dwell some 300 aborigines—one of the most primitive tribes on earth. Their homeland is so inhospitable that few white men have ventured into it—indeed, none can live there unless he carries his own supplies. Yet these blackfellows of the Outback, without a stitch of clothing and with only five implements to aid their bare hands, have wrested a livelihood from their desolate surroundings for untold generations.

With spears and spear throwers the men hunt. With digging sticks, wooden carrying dishes, and grinding stones the women forage for food and prepare it.

I came here in 1945 to learn their ways. I took the train from Adelaide to Oodnadatta—40 hours to travel 650 miles—then drove 350 miles on roads so bad it took 30 more hours. This brought me to a mission station where I made my main camp.

From here I planned to cross an extensive desert to Ayers Rock, then explore along the barren Mann Ranges, the country of the Pitjendeldjara people.

I would go by camel, the most reliable means of crossing this country. Our dromedaries were descendants of those brought to Australia in 1866 to help explore its vast center. They drink whatever water there is, however foul, and fatten on wirelike twigs of desert plants.

As Tjundaga, a half-caste camel driver, led my caravan through red sand and spinifex, more and more wandering aborigines attached themselves to us. When we camped, I would sometimes share their strange food. I found that white wood

grubs, loathsome to look at, taste like roast pork—if you can get up courage to eat the first one. Lizard is like chicken, and kangaroo like delicately flavored beef. Honey ants are as sweet as honey. I must admit that dingo (wild dog) and cat are erased from my menu. I have my limits.

Some scientists believe a special skin mechanism enables the aborigine to sur-

UNCLOTHED REMBRANDT *portrays a kangaroo-man ancestor, with headdress, inside a sacred cave at Ayers Rock. The art style is authentic Stone Age.*

vive frosty nights and 120° summer days. With the temperature below freezing, they sleep quite well between two small fires and behind a low windbreak of boughs. On a still night the heat forms a warm blanket of air around the sleepers. On windy nights they must be cold indeed. I used an abundance of blankets and, although I too slept between fires, I felt no need to discard any bedclothes.

When aborigines travel on a cold day they clutch burning fire sticks. By carrying fires they avoid having to start fresh ones by friction; and the heat warms their naked bodies. I was so cold one day that I learned how to carry a fire stick and keep it alight—no simple trick. The warm air from the stick kept me comfortable.

WE REACHED Mount Conner, a mesa rising 800 feet above the desert. With Tjundaga, I climbed the mesa and took a bearing on Ayers Rock, just visible on the western horizon. But instead of using the bearing, I decided to test the camel man's bushcraft by making him navigate "blind." After he descended Mount Conner he would not see his objective for several days.

By lighting clumps of spinifex as we traveled, and keeping the smokes aligned, Tjundaga held a straight course across the featureless desert. But how he knew the direction to Ayers Rock, where he had never before been, is more than I know.

We camped at this enormous boulder for a week. The sides of the rock, rising sheer and smooth to its 1,100-foot summit, can be climbed at only one place. And here I found the angle so steep that had a fragment of rock slipped under my foot nothing in the world would have saved me.

We continued northwest to Katatjuta, Many Heads, an apt name for a group of round-topped rock pillars in the form of a hollow square. I had heard of a water hole near here and asked Matinya, a local aborigine, how big it was.

"Him *kapi bulka*" (big water).

Now a 100-gallon water hole is a kapi bulka to an aborigine who needs it only for drinking, but five times that would be too small for us with our 12 camels. I pursued the questioning. "S'pose him water along Katatjuta bigger than Mut-

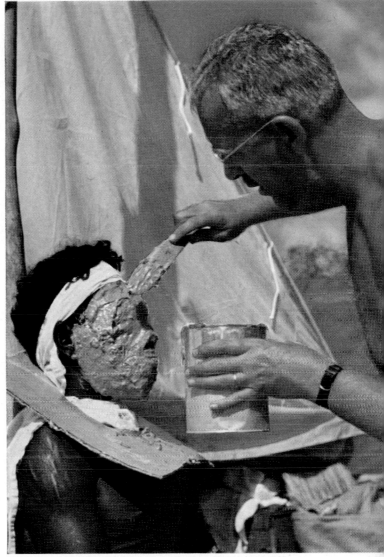

SMEARING MUD *on patient models, Frank Setzler of the Smithsonian Institution makes plaster masks of primitive faces for the National Museum in Washington, D. C.*

Ten Australians and five Americans studied the aborigines of little-known Arnhem Land, a Maine-sized reservation in northern Australia, on a 1948 expedition led by the author and sponsored by National Geographic Society, Smithsonian Institution, and the Australian Government.

rjilda" (one of the best water supplies in this region), "how big is he?"

"Him as big, as big—" I could almost hear his brain working as he strained for a simile—"him as big as the sea!"

He'd never been near the sea, but I decided to take the risk. After a day's camel journey—about 20 miles—we reached the gorge where lay Katatjuta water. I found a pool five feet long with a few inches of green water that wouldn't fill two camels, let alone 12. Smiling triumphantly, Matinya gestured at it with his fire stick. "Kapi bulka! Him big fella water all right."

Our camels were crying for water, so we headed for Erliwunyawunya, a large rock hole that fills after heavy rains. From here we could make a dash of 100 miles to the Mann Ranges.

In the dry months the water at Erliwunyawunya grows progressively fouler. The aborigines drink it without ill effects, but prefer to suck from a hole dug in the sand along its edge, thus filtering the water. Every drop that *we* drank was boiled.

Heading for the Mann Ranges, we learned that the water holes to the west were dry. Disastrous news. But an aborigine called me aside. "S'pose you want'em rain, we been make'em alonga you."

387

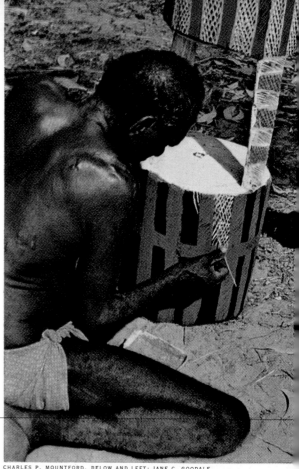

CHARLES P. MOUNTFORD. BELOW AND LEFT: JANE C. GOODALE

I accepted on the spot. The rituals centered around a fragment of pearl shell from the northwest coast, passed from tribe to tribe. Such shells, considered the fountainhead of all water, cross Australia on trade routes of more than 2,000 miles. The leader of the rituals sucks the shell to extract the essence of water, then spits into the sky to form the nuclei of clouds. When it was all over I asked the old leader, "How long before it rain?"

"Three days," he asserted confidently, "s'pose him rain been close up. Five days, s'pose him rain been far away."

"But s'pose it no more rain?"

"Him rain all right," he replied testily. "Me been mak'em rain; him always come."

I had not the slightest faith in the rite. Normally, the rainy season starts in November. This was August. But just as we reached Piltadi, four days later, it rained —enough to leave water in the rock holes for a month's journey.

Beside the Mann Ranges I sought some special boulders, believed to be the source of babies. It seems incredible, but aborigines do not know the facts of life. They affirm that the father has no part in pro creation, and that tiny spirit children, *yulanya*, emerge from these boulders and search for mothers.

Jabiaba, an old Pitjendeldjara, led me to three egg-shaped stones, one slightly broken. They were supposedly filled with yulanya, so small that only the medicine men could see them. If someone tampers with the cracked boulder, deformed babies will be born. But if you place twigs beside the other stones, the yulanyas will

come out. I asked how it was done. Jabiaba showed me, but with bad grace. "Too many babies all about," he grumbled. "No more get any sleep nighttime."

THIS IS BIRTH to the aborigines. But what of death? On a later National Geographic expedition to Melville Island, north of Darwin, I was allowed to join a burial rite of the Tiwi people. In a series of rituals, dancers enacted myths, even imitated scenes from the Wild West movies that some had seen in Darwin. Onlookers beat time on their buttocks and voiced the shrill mosquito call.

Then the chief mourner, son of the dead man, cut his head until the blood flowed. He collapsed in a paroxysm of grief that inspired mass hysteria. Women beat their bodies and groveled. Men wailed. Gradually the mourners drifted off until only the wizened widow remained.

The Tiwi have seen modern war. They may sing about aircraft and steamships and the machines of warfare. But they accept only what they want in their culture without damaging the old ways.

TIWI MOURNERS of Melville Island slide down through smoke and flame (far left) to singe hair from arms and legs, driving off evil spirits and purifying themselves for a funeral. Men carve and paint tall grave posts, no two alike, as painstakingly as tombstone cutters. Artists chew the ends of sticks to make paint brushes. Rains often wash away designs.

In 1954 the author led a National Geographic expedition to the land of the Tiwi. Accepted into the tribe, the scientists recorded these burial rites.

NEW GUINEA

NEW BRITAIN

Sepik

Asmat—
Casuarina Coast

• Telefomin
Mount Hagen •
KUBOR RANGE

Melville Island

Darwin •

ARNHEM
LAND

AUSTRALIA

Ayers Rock Mt. Conner
MANN RANGES— • ++
Piltadi   • Erliwunyawunya
          • Oodnadatta

0   500
STATUTE MILES

• Adelaide

FRENZIED DANCING *by grieving relatives in the* pukamani *ritual climaxes the months-long funeral ceremonies of the Tiwi. Mourners create their own steps and songs*

JANE C. GOODALE

as they placate the spirit before the harlequin columns that surround the grave.
Near the ritual's close, men slash their heads and women sob heartbrokenly.

Rare Birds and Wild Men

Surrounded by primitive tribesmen, E. Thomas Gilliard
finds unknown birds of radiant plumage
in the mountains of New Guinea and New Britain

NIGHT in the cloud forest of eastern New Guinea's highlands had been long and wet. But dawn had nearly come now, and the rain had stopped. We took off through the dripping vegetation, feeling our way up a steep, muddy trail cluttered with fallen trees. At 7,500 feet we reached our objective – a well-camouflaged 40-foot tower of poles and vines – and clambered up its shaky ladder.

To an onlooker our patrol might have appeared sinister. But to me it suddenly seemed comic. Here I was, half a world away from my home in Manhattan, clinging to a flimsy rung high above a forest no white man had ever visited. Why? To see some birds.

But what birds! Our quarry was no less than the birds of paradise – especially the most spectacular of them all, the King of Saxony. Only one had ever been taken alive to a zoo, and it died almost immediately. No pictures of the bird in its native habitat had been made. And though this was 1952, only one or two white men had ever witnessed its peculiar, long-fabled dance of courtship.

For this moment I had begun work nine months before, stocking up with food and equipment for 900 man-days in the jungle. At the National Geographic Society's headquarters in Washington I had worked day after day to master the mysteries of electronic lighting and special cameras. Now, reaching the top of my tower, I set up tripods, cameras, and sound recorder, and aimed a 16-inch telephoto lens at a little spirelike limb rising in the mist above the crown of a subtropical forest giant.

Presently, in the first rays of sunlight, I heard from afar soft hissing notes which sounded more reptilian than birdlike. My guide stiffened and pointed. A small bird, hardly larger than a robin, flew to the perch. Dipping and bowing, he began like a drunken devil to wave and toss his weird, exotic plumes.

We knew they were feathers, yet they strained credulity. Pointed, brilliant, they seemed to spring like horns from the bird's crown, trailing behind him in two fantastic parabolas. Here, indeed, was the King of Saxony, panoplied like a Teutonic monarch riding to battle with great plumes streaming from his casque of iron.

Through the binoculars I saw that his breast was egg-yellow, his plumes sky-blue. He grasped a slender vine and began to bounce up and down as though testing a diving board. As the tempo of his bouncing increased, he became uncontrollably excited, performing like a trapeze artist. From his beak the hissing continued, like steam escaping.

I scanned the perch for the female bird who must be there. I could not spot her rather drab body, but on the movie film we brought back it was possible to glimpse her demure entry into the nuptial chamber. As suddenly as it began the dance ended. The King, reaching a climax of ecstasy, flew off in a great flutter.

This strange scene symbolized the mystery that has surrounded these exotic birds ever since their plumes first reached Europe in 1522 with Magellan's seamen. Because the plumes of later specimens were attached to skins from which the feet had been removed, Europeans decided that the birds must have been blown

to earth from a celestial paradise. The legend faded, but the name remained.

To dispel some of the mystery which still clung to these birds, I had led an American Museum of Natural History expedition into the Mount Hagen area of New Guinea (map, page 389) in 1950. Armed with the going currency of soccer balls, red powder paint, glass beads, stick tobacco, and gold-lip oyster shells, we collected more than 3,500 bird, mammal, plant, and butterfly specimens. Of 171 species of birds, 23 were forms new to science.

We followed trails worn over the centuries by plodding bare feet. Our party sometimes numbered 100 men, added to by spectators and "young fella Marys"—girls enamored of some of our porters. We hunted with cameras and with shotguns specially bored to handle tiny shot, which does minimum damage to plumage.

In a little-known valley we made one of our most exciting discoveries—the dance ground of the *Archboldia* bowerbirds. In a four-foot clearing surrounded by tall ferns and padded with dried fronds, a male with a splendid golden crown spent hours each day decorating his bower and calling harshly, as he awaited visits from wandering females. I was so excited over the first bowerbird specimen brought in that I paid the finder a year's wages: a steel ax, two gold-lip shells, machete, table knife, mirror, matches, and other small items.

OUR 1952 EXPEDITION, cosponsored by Armand Denis, was to photograph birds of paradise in their native habitats rather than collect them. I explained the plan carefully through my pidgin interpreter to the native boys who had worked for me before. When I held up gold-lip shells, they got the idea. Grinning from ear to ear, they vanished into the jungle, 50 strong. The hunt was on.

A few mornings later Tai, my No. 1 boy,

THIRSTY PORTERS *snatch a drink while fording a river in New Britain. They balked at entering "land of fire" in the island's mountainous heart. Gilliard reached it, set up his gear (right), and discovered five new birds.*

E. THOMAS GILLIARD

E. THOMAS GILLIARD

GOSSAMER PLUMAGE *waves like a ballerina's skirt as the Greater Bird of Paradise (above) postures in a treetop to attract a mate. Close-up (left) shows his gold crown. The King of Saxony (upper left) signals his courtship by raising serrated flags. Vicious flightless cassowary (opposite) remained a village pet though he had disemboweled a man. After posing for this portrait, the 100-pound bird attacked a woman in the New Guinea settlement. Only penicillin saved her.*

397

LIKE A BLAZING TORCH, *bird of paradise plumes bedeck a blackened "strongfellow," or subchief, of the New Guinea highlands (left). He wears a fur cap from the opossum-like* kapul, *green scarab beetles as gems in his crown, and a necklace of pigtails. The chief above flaunts a flaming halo of plumage. Saxony feathers pierce his nose, along with sections of mother-of-pearl. A bailer shell sits on his brow.*

rushed into the cookhouse and exclaimed that he had found a Greater Bird of Paradise in a clump of casuarinas near an old graveyard, two hours' walk distant.

As we approached I heard high-pitched cawing interspersed with low growls. In the lacy top limbs a dozen birds flew about. Crawling cautiously through the grass, I reached the butt of a large tree and looked up. On a limb high above was the most gorgeous bird I have ever laid eyes on. Sunlight breaking through the leaves illuminated his perch, and against the dark green foliage his flame-colored plumes shimmered like fire. I watched entranced.

When we set up our camp in the Kubor Range, ten days' journey away, we entered true Stone Age territory. My wife Margaret was the first white woman the natives here had ever seen. They danced and howled about her in amazement, and one huge fellow, slick with pig grease, hoisted her aloft and carried her through the procession for some 30 yards.

In contrast to some people in Europe and America, these Kubor people regard naturalists with esteem — even as sane. This is because they themselves are amazingly well informed about birds, insects, and animals. To them, the white men who come to scratch for yellow metal in the stream beds are "long-long" — crazy.

PARADING THEIR WEALTH, *tribesmen at a Mount Hagen fair in eastern New Guinea carry*

gold-lip shells on plates of gum. They garner prestige by lending shells to one another.

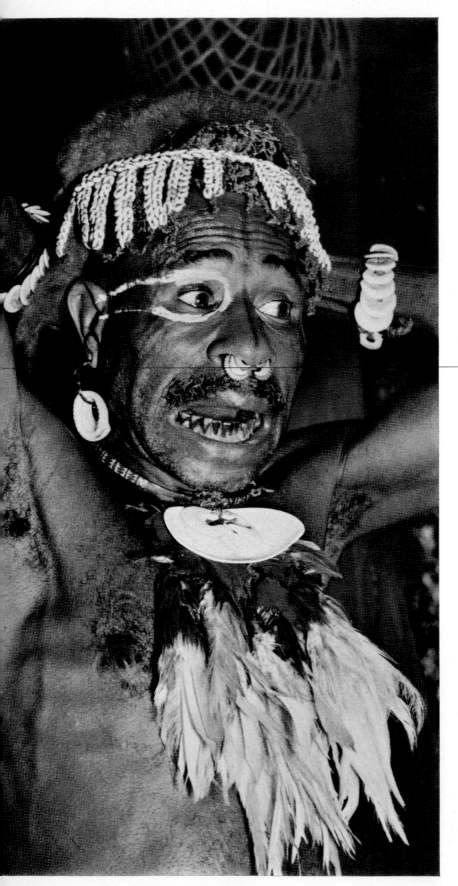

TRANCELIKE ECSTASY
*grips girl and man
mashing noses in a
"sing-sing" in the Kubor
Range of New Guinea.
Couples in this popular
social event sit facing
each other on a curved
platform surrounded by
chattering elders and
laughing children.
Swaying to rhythmic
chants, they brush noses,
then press harder as
the spell of the dance
grows. Heads roll in
opposite arcs, seemingly
hinged at the nose.
Final pressure sometimes
injures facial features,
eventually makes noses
soft and flabby.*

A RETIRED HEADHUNTER
*of New Guinea's Sepik
River preens for a dance.
Four parrot-plumed tassels
on his rattan collar
boast of four heads taken.
As he struggles to fix
a tiara of cowrie shells
on his cap of golden fur,
his grimace bares teeth
stained by betel nut.
Shells dangle from his
ears, pierce his nose,
clatter on his wrists.
The bailer shell beneath
his chin is so named
because coastal dwellers
use it to scoop water
from their canoes.
Fresh paint completes
the tribesman's toilet.
On with the ball!*

E. THOMAS GILLIARD

E. THOMAS GILLIARD, AMERICAN MUSEUM–ARMAND DENIS EXPEDITION

Ornithologists have frequently debated whether MacGregor's is a bird of paradise or a bowerbird. The natives say it does not build a courtship chamber on the ground as do most bowerbirds, and therefore is a bird of paradise. I accept their verdict.

A highlight of our stay with the Kubor people was a "sing-sing" in the village of Boma, a mountain chief. No blushing violet, Boma was so feathered he looked like a walking bird of paradise.

Margaret handed his No. 1 wife a mirror —which the chief snatched, giving his poor spouse a couple of black eyes.

From sunup to sundown, three days in a row, platoons of natives pounded the dance arena, led by a chieftain who intoned a restless chant which held all the relentless madness of delirium.

Then came the long-long man. Daubed with yellow mud and dead grass, he charged the assemblage like a cornered animal. Children screamed with delight.

In the evening, after hours of primping, the dancers came on again for the nose rubbing. Bodies glistening, swaying sin-uously, young girls and men sat facing each other under flickering torchlight in the smoky sing-sing house. A chant started, and as the music took hold, man and girl touched noses lightly. Each girl, eyes closed, swayed from the man on her left to the one on her right. Noses touched for longer and longer periods until at last girl and man rested against each other for as long as five minutes, faces frozen, nose mashed against nose.

WE RETURNED to New Guinea in 1953, planning to visit the Telefomin area in the interior. But word came of an uprising by the savage Mianmin, the "big pygmies" of that remote mountain region. Two patrol officers and two native policemen had been butchered. "If you can't shift your work to another area," the authorities told us flatly, "you might as well start back to America."

We shifted—deciding on a 200-mile trip up the Sepik River. Here, where hordes of mosquitoes can blacken a man with their bodies a minute after he leaves his tent, we photographed the Sepik headhunters.

In the not-so-distant past, when a boy reached 12 or so he was required to kill as an initiation into the men's cult. The victims, of any age and either sex, captives or idiots bought from another village, were bound and helpless. If the boy was unable to perform the ritual murder, a relative was allowed to guide the steel or bamboo knife. Actual headhunting was hardly more admirable. Ambush was the keynote. Women and children, more often than not, were the victims.

Sepik boys are not cowards, however. They still engage in one of the most dangerous of sports: treading for freshwater crocodiles. Walking into water up to their necks, they feel with their toes for a sleeping reptile, then duck under, grasp the creature under the jaw, and jam their thumbs into its eyes. They must hold on until their friends lift them and the crocodile clear of the water. If they let go....

When the Telefomin uprisings quieted down, we were able to move into the area and get back to our bird collecting. We took 220 species, including two new races of birds of paradise. We largely filled in the last great blank on the ornithological map of this dark, mysterious land. Our adventures in New Guinea were ended.

IN 1958 we had a new goal in view—the little-explored island of New Britain. Trekking inland in November, we made camp in a tiny village chopped from jungle. Here we had to wait while the mysterious "bush telegraph" told of our arrival. We could go no farther without the permission and assistance of Iangmili, chief of a tribe of extremely tall and remarkably uncordial wild men.

Soon the great man himself appeared. He towered well over six feet, carried a nine-foot-long spear, and wore an expression of skepticism on his sharp features. He listened to our proposal through an interpreter, answered "No," and vanished back into the jungle.

Only one thing to do now: go on anyhow.

Our objective was the Whiteman Range in an area the natives call, for reasons unknown, the "land of fire." A New Britain Barnum named Iason offered to lead us straight to the summit of the range. We hired him on the spot, and followed him over wretched trails through rain forests for miles before we realized that we'd been cruelly deluded. He kept our money and tobacco—and left, eyes shining with the gleam of the eternal knave, our choicest pidgin ringing in his ears.

Then a woodsman named Selselio came to our aid and guided us to the mountains. Here we started our serious work, and made a rare discovery: a long-billed honey eater. And in late December, pushing on to the summit forests, I received from my hunters a thicket warbler with a black mask, a new species. I named it *Cichlornis grosvenori* as a token of my gratitude to Gilbert Grosvenor and the National Geographic Society for their support of my field work in the South Pacific.

Margaret and I spent Christmas in relative comfort—except for an earthquake. The mountainside shook so hard water sloshed from our buckets. The tremors stopped. Then for nine straight days we continued hunting and working despite daily torrential rains.

In January, after 1,000 hours of high-mountain hunting, we started back, our specimen cases jammed. We had covered the last unexplored niche of birds and mammals on New Britain, completing a task begun more than half a century before. In spite of our triumphs, we had found no birds of paradise. They abound in New Guinea, yet none has ever been found in New Britain, only 55 miles away. Somehow, even the flightless cassowary has managed to cross the slim barrier of water between the two islands.

It is a riddle, but I wish there were a thousand more. It will be a sad day indeed when the last ornithological puzzle is solved, and the last shy, unclassified bird is tracked down, preserved, described, and interred forever in a scientific treatise.

GLOSSY WITH PAINT *and pig grease, New Guinea belles sit demurely on the sidelines awaiting their turn to dance. Furs, leaves, and woven armbands complement their shell jewelry. Single girls often wear a fortune in shells to attract prospective bridegrooms.*

JOHN SCOFIELD, NATIONAL GEOGRAPHIC STAFF

My Friends the Headhunters

In wild New Guinea, National Geographic's John Scofield finds a nightmare of fear where cannibals fight ghosts with burnished skulls

T HE OLD HEADHUNTER's boldly carved face radiated strength and bravery. He was the kind, I thought, who would as surely have been a leader had he been born in New Jersey instead of in Amman Namgai, a village on New Guinea's swampy southwest coast.

Singing his song of vengeance, he beat a savage rhythm on an hourglass-shaped drum. Its head of lizard skin had been glued with human blood. Behind him carvers cut stylized human figures along an enormous log. These were memorials to villagers slain by raiding headhunters from nearby Atsj.

Just that morning the Atsj people had welcomed me to this seldom-visited Asmat region (map, page 389). War canoes skimmed around the patrol boat that brought me. The warriors, wielding paddles ornamented with cockatoo feathers, beat a stirring rhythm on the sides of their craft.

I marveled that in 1961 such things could still exist. Wilderness airstrips had put places within reach that few white men had glimpsed. But the impact of the 20th century had not yet changed the people deeply.

"The last headhunting in the Asmat—real organized headhunting—took place about five years ago," anthropologist David Eyde told me in Amman Namgai. "But the ceremonials connected with it still go on."

In a Casuarina Coast village of houses on stilts, I climbed a notched log and ducked into a thatched room. Inside were three naked men. All wore bone ornaments in their noses. One, eyes heavy with sleep, rested his head on an object that glowed richly in the shaft of sunlight coming through the door—a rounded object, yellowed by handling until it gleamed like old ivory. I was looking at a human skull!

The man held it up and said something that sounded like *mani wi*. I knew that "wi" means head, and assumed that this was the skull of a man named Mani. But I had misunderstood. The word was *maneowé*—"our food." The skull

406

JOHN SCOFIELD, NATIONAL GEOGRAPHIC STAFF

FEAR AND VENGEANCE *loom large in the daily life of New Guinea's headhunters. Worried warrior (left) wears his mother's skull as protection against her ghost. A vertebra from her body dangles from his neck, and a dagger of bone juts from his woven armband. Pig-tusk armlets signify that he has taken two heads.*

Tribesmen (above), sitting on a wooden platform where the village dead are placed, display treasured skulls, ornamented with seeds, on a war shield.

Beating a lizard-skin drumhead glued with human blood, a frenzied villager (right) cries revenge for warriors killed in raids.

409

was that of a man he had killed and eaten.

In another house six skulls hung in the smoke-blackened rafters. Each had a hole in the temple through which the brains had been removed to be eaten. The old man who owned the house grinned impishly. I pantomimed the stroke of a bamboo knife. He nodded enthusiastically.

But, strangely, most of the grim relics I saw in these Casuarina Coast villages had nothing to do with headhunting. The cannibals of this jungled shore live in utter terror of their ancestors' spirits. To frighten away ghosts, they use the ghost's own mortal remains—the skull as pillow, vertebrae as necklaces, other bones as daggers and nose ornaments.

I learned much about these simple people from Father Cornelius H. van Kessel, the first outsider many of them had seen. I asked him the age of the skulls I had seen in almost every house.

"They're not old at all," he said. "These people were taking heads and eating their enemies until the Dutch stopped the practice about three years ago. This is really the last frontier, rough, unpredictable— and sometimes dangerous."

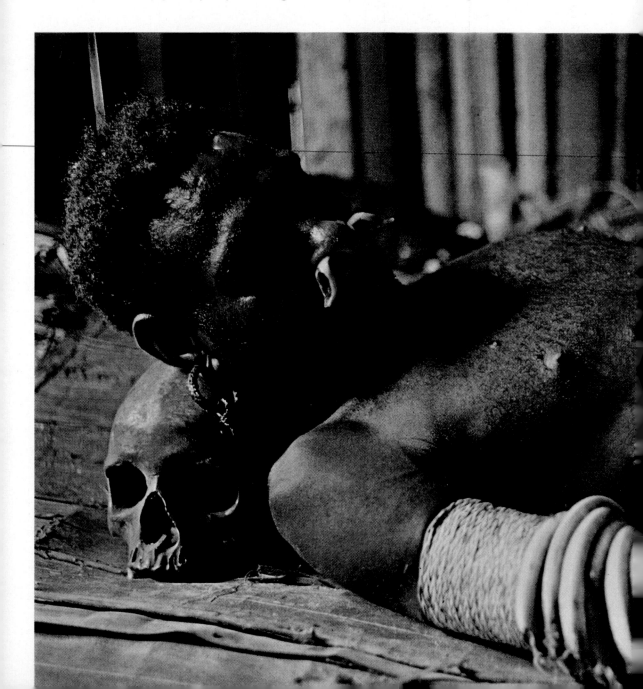

Only a few weeks after my visit, his words came back to me as newspapers reported the tragic disappearance of New York Governor Nelson Rockefeller's son Michael on this same desolate coast.

I never ceased to wonder at these gentle killers. Although agriculture, writing, and the wheel are unknown to them, they turn out some of the most beautiful wood carvings I have ever seen. Yet violence and murder have existed so recently among them that even teen-agers told me of headhunting raids they had taken part in.

To see more of this strange culture I journeyed up the Ewta River with a Dutch medical patrol. At the village of Otsjanep we set up camp that night in one end of the largest house—a thatched, tunnel-like affair on stilts where the men gathered in the evening to smoke, gossip, and boast of their headhunting.

In thoughtful mood the Dutch doctor pointed to a tall native clad in a pair of shorts, once red but now glossy and black with dirt. "I wonder," he said, "if we should have introduced clothing without giving him soap at the same time."

He pointed out that everything these people have—social organization, art, wood carving, personal adornment—depends for its motivation on headhunting.

"There's no answer," he concluded sadly. "We can't allow headhunting to go on. But when it disappears, must everything else go, too? Must these people become imitation white men, with no cultural institutions of their own?"

Then, as we drifted into sleep, I heard only the soft buzzing of cannibal conversation a few feet away and the indescribably beautiful music of a group of boys singing in the darkness outside.

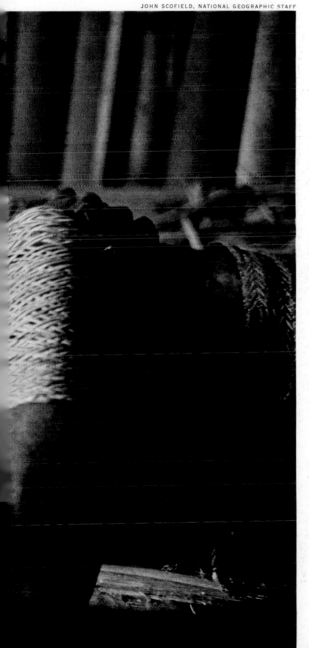

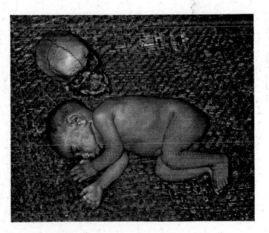

SKULL OF AN ENEMY *makes a pillow for this contented cannibal, whose armlets credit him with a dozen heads. A hole battered in the temple permitted the brains to be removed and eaten. Absence of lower jaw distinguishes this trophy from ancestral relic above. Baby, clad in a necklace, sleeps peacefully beside his forebear's skull.*

411

Hunting Africa's Largest Game

Naturalist Carl E. Akeley, stalking elephants for science,
meets the thunderous fury of a jungle giant head on,
and survives a fearful mauling to bring down the big one

O NE EVENING in Uganda, rather discouraged after not being able to locate elephants all day, we suddenly heard the squealing and trumpeting of a large herd drifting in our direction. Crashing down trees and quarreling among themselves for choice morsels of food, they made a tremendous din.

By eleven o'clock they were on three sides of us, some within 200 yards. Our men kept fires going all night for fear the elephants might raid the plantain grove in which we were camped.

At daylight I was off to hunt them, seeking specimens for the American Museum of Natural History of New York, which had sent me to Africa in 1909.

For a couple of miles I traveled through a scene of devastation: eight-foot grass trampled flat, trees knocked down and stripped of bark, branches, and leaves. Pausing at a wooded gulley, I discovered a cow elephant feeding barely 20 yards away. I retreated to a rocky hilltop. Here I received an impression of Africa that will remain with me to the last.

There was not a breath of wind. The forest, glistening in the morning sunlight, stretched away for miles to the east and west and up the slope to the north. Here and there in the high grass were elephants, singly and in groups, feeding and loafing along, to be swallowed in the dark shadows of the jungle. Their bodies shone with mud and water from the pool where they had drunk and bathed.

Troops of black and white Colobus monkeys raced about the trees swearing at the elephants. Chimpanzees shouted at one another, baboons barked, and great hornbills did their best to drown other noises with their discordant rasping chatter.

Suddenly the cow elephant uttered her peculiar shrill scream of warning. She had caught a whiff of air tainted by man. Not only elephants but all other forest folk instantly grew still. A minute before the noise had been appalling; now the silence was even more so. Then there came a gentle rustling as of leaves stirred by a breeze, increasing in volume. It sounded like a windstorm in the trees.

411

With my glasses I scoured the forest, but not a leaf seemed to be stirring. Then I realized that the sound was made by elephants on the move, hastening away from danger—their feet shuffling among the dry leaves, and their bodies scraping against the bushes.

With my gun bearers I went down into the forest. Elephant trails crisscrossed in all directions. Following one, I came upon another herd and spotted a pair of tusks worth collecting. I fired both barrels in quick succession at the beast's heart. He collapsed, and cows clustered around him. With their tusks and trunks they did their best to get him to his feet. Bulls patrolled in widening circles searching for the source of the trouble. I retired to a safe distance until they left.

On Mount Kenya (map, page 212) we found elephants that foraged up to the timberline—12,000 feet. In the sphagnum marshes at 14,500 feet I discovered the "maternity bed" of an elephant. Under the protection of a great mass of aerial roots and the foliage of a big tree at the edge of the forest, accessible from only one direction, was a deeply trodden bed of earth. Here a baby elephant had spent the first week or so of its life, while the mother watched over it and fed on the abundant vegetation nearby.

Most of our luck on Mount Kenya was bad. In fact, I was left much the worse for the experience. With a party of 15 natives, I had been following the spoor of three old bulls through a maze of jungle paths when I heard a cracking of bamboo about 200 yards away. I inspected the guns and cartridges and warmed my hands, numb from the morning mists, for I might soon need a supple trigger finger.

Suddenly I was conscious that an elephant was almost on top of me. I don't know how I knew. I wheeled around and tried to shove the gun's safety catch forward. It refused to budge.

My next memory is a tusk right at my chest. I grabbed it with my left hand, the other tusk with my right. Then I swung in between, going to the ground on my back. This was purely automatic; I had imagined myself doing it many times.

The bull drove his tusks in the ground on either side of me. As I looked into one wicked little eye I knew I could expect no mercy from the beast. I was being crushed.

A blow of the trunk knocked me out and scraped away most of my face. Evidently when the elephant surged down his tusks struck a stone or root that stopped them. This saved my life. But, using me for a prayer mat, the beast broke my nose and crushed several of my ribs into my lungs. Then he went away, probably thinking I was dead. I lay unconscious four or five hours. Later I was carried to a hotel in Nairobi where I recuperated until ready to venture forth again.

Though trailing the giant of the jungle had led me to the very brink of death, I always think of the elephant as a friend, an animal to be respected rather than to

DARKING IN *for the kill, a Masai warrior matches his puny spear against a lion. Akeley joined a similar hunt in Kenya during a lull in elephant collecting. Uganda's Napori hunters (left) charm their burnished blades before the chase.*

415

CARL E. AKELEY, LEFT: AMERICAN MUSEUM OF NATURAL HISTORY

THE ELEPHANT *reaches for foliage with gentle precision. Angry, it wields trunk and tusks as vicious weapons. One tusker pinned Akeley to the ground, crushed his ribs, flayed his face (above). But he had both barrels at the ready when he met the big bull at right.*

be feared. I like to think of the efforts elephants make to help along a wounded comrade, and of the way the husky elephants of a herd form a ring to protect the young and old when danger is scented.

I like to think of the splendid struggle for existence that the elephant has put up through the ages—his obstinate survival amid conditions that have killed off all his contemporaries of an earlier age; of the versatility with which he has adapted to his environment and defended himself against his enemies.

WHEN I RETURNED to the field some months later, in January, 1911, we worked between the Victoria Nile and Lake Albert in Uganda. This district was closed because of sleeping sickness and thus became an elephant reserve. We saw the results of this awful disease, whole villages in which not a living being was to be found. Those who had

escaped abandoned all their household utensils and food. Huts and gardens were left to the mercy of the elephants. They came in droves and destroyed the plantain groves and barkcloth trees.

I had to get one big bull to complete the group for the museum. One day I spotted a fine one through a small opening in the leaves. I fired at his head. The herd stampeded. Absolutely without warning, the elephant I had shot at burst across my path within 15 feet of me.

The old devil had grown tired of being hunted and had doubled back. Had this charge been straight at us we could hardly have escaped. Grabbing my gun, I stood ready to face his next charge. But it never came. Instead I heard the crashing of the bushes as he collapsed. That last effort had been too much for him.

After two years I had finally succeeded in getting the bull I needed. He stood 11 feet 3 inches at the shoulders, and had tusks of 100 and 102 pounds.

Farther and farther the wild beasts of Africa are being driven back into the strongholds of hills and forests. But wherever animal rights still triumph over human rights, the elephant, by virtue of his sagacity, his comradeship with his kind, and his venerability, remains in truth the jungle's overlord.

417

THE ELEPHANTS AKELEY HUNTED *parade again—*
through Akeley Memorial Hall in New York's
American Museum of Natural History. 419

Hunting Africa's Smallest Game

Armed with camera and tweezers,
Edward S. Ross stalks quarry
as tiny as a grain of sand

INSECTS live in a Lilliputian world; only by enlarging it can man see its details. Thus the camera is an excellent teacher of entomology. Stalking and photographing these tiny subjects in Africa under a National Geographic Society grant, I learn how they behave. My shutter and electronic flash freeze movements too fleeting for the human eye.

Africa's fame as a big game paradise eclipses its importance as the home of some of the world's strangest insects. My interest centers on the Embioptera, little-known insects which live in labyrinths of silk galleries spun with their front feet.

I travel by road and trail, camping most of the time in my truck, which looks like a covered wagon when the nylon tent is pitched over the back. Lions roar close by, but none venture into camp. On Mount Hoyo in the Congo a buffalo charged my assistant, who got away unharmed.

I peek into flowers, overturn stones, pry bark off trees. An entomologist on the hunt quickly learns to gauge the timidity of his prey. The warier insects must be approached stealthily. I creep close; my camera-shy target flutters away. Again I slip forward; again the insect escapes. After many false starts, I may get the picture at last.

The jungle teems with tiny creatures of the night. I hang out a sheet and bait it with a lamp. One night's catch can keep museum workers busy for months. On my 33,000-mile odyssey I captured 250,000. We mount and label them at the California Academy of Sciences and send most to specialists at home and abroad.

As I hunt insects, other wildlife may resent my intrusion. My ears pick up the rustle of snakes slithering out of my path; game crashes through the undergrowth.

I must compete with baboons, the original entomologists. Once I rashly allowed a pet baboon to accompany me on a collecting trip near Nairobi in Kenya. He insisted on looking for food under every stone I overturned. A ridiculous situation—man and ape vying for first grab. And once when I popped a new species of embiid into a vial of alcohol, my baboon snatched it and drained the contents, embiid and all!

TAILOR ANTS FORM LIVING CHAINS TO DRAW LEAVES TOGETHER FOR A NEST AS THE AUTHOR, CURATOR OF ENTOMOLOGY
AT THE CALIFORNIA ACADEMY OF SCIENCES, RECORDS THE CONSTRUCTION; EDWARD S. ROSS

FLATIDAE, 1½ TIMES LIFE-SIZE. OPPOSITE: DANAUS CHRYSIPPUS, 3 TIMES LIFE-SIZE. EDWARD S. ROSS

PTYELUS, 4 TIMES LIFE-SIZE

AFRICAN MONARCH BUTTERFLY, *bright wings scarred by a bird that mistook the tempting but evil-tasting insect as edible, alights as Dr. Ross's flash pops (opposite).*

"Camera in hand, I roam field and forest, never knowing what I'll shoot next," he says. A bevy of pink flatids (above) brighten a vine. Spittlebug nymph (left) peeks from its protective cloak of sap bubbles. A stalk-eyed fly (lower left) struts over a grass blade. And a giraffe weevil (below) displays its tubular head.

DIOPSIS, 8 TIMES LIFE-SIZE

TRACHELOPHORUS GIRAFFA, 6 TIMES LIFE-SIZE

Giant Insects of the Amazon

Ferocious ants and beetles big as bats confront National Geographic naturalist Paul A. Zahl in the steaming jungles of Brazil

T HE TIME was early October, the locale some miles east of Belém, Brazil. We were huddled against the crumbling walls of an abandoned chapel lost in jungle growth. Raindrops spattered from a million leaves. Something moved on the floor a yard or two away, and I felt a twinge of excitement.

A black creature with stiltlike legs and a pair of huge mandibles crept toward a small hole. It disappeared. Then came another . . . and another. The glistening black bodies were more than an inch long.

The size, the color, the form of these creatures told me they were the world's largest ants, *Dinoponera gigantea*, whose wickedly stinging females are at once the rulers, warriors, reproducers, and hunters of their jungle kingdom.

"On guard, *senhor,* one approaches,"

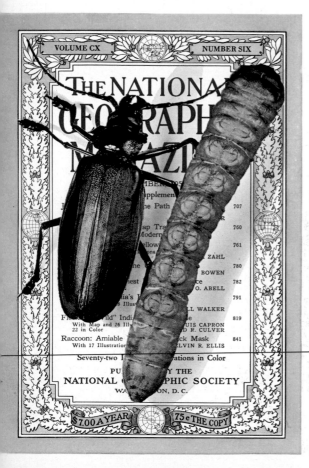

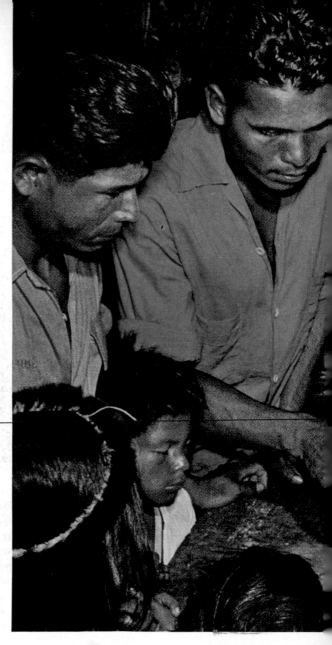

"MET ANY MONSTERS LATELY?" *the author asks members of the Paricura tribe. But these Indians of northern Brazil express only amazement at his specimens: Titanus at right, and Megasoma, one of the largest scarab beetles in the world.*

Dr. Zahl's 1957-8 expedition finally yielded 16 Titanus, four of them more than six inches long. One blankets National Geographic's cover together with a huge larva believed to be Titanus also.

Spider wasp (right) with blood-red wings and venomous sting wrestles with a dime. Even a gentle tree hopper (left) looks fierce when magnified four times.

PAUL A. ZAHL, NATIONAL GEOGRAPHIC STAFF

cried my assistant. I turned to see a heavily laden giantess bound for the hole. Gripped between her jaws was a beetle, its legs still thrashing. Then the chrome fingers of my 12-inch tweezers grasped the ant's hard thorax.

Immediately the lady dropped her load and attacked the metal with vicious mandibles. Her legs braced and strained, her abdomen contorted. I drew her close and watched droplets of venom swell from the stinger's sharp tip. The sting of one such ant causes fever, the natives say.

That afternoon I dropped many of these struggling furies into my specimen jar. And in following weeks I made the first photographic record of these astonishing creatures, found only in South America.

From Belém I flew to the heart of the Amazon Valley in pursuit of another six-legged savage, *Titanus giganteus*, one of the world's largest beetles.

"It will certainly be exciting if you bag some," John C. Pallister, distinguished coleopterist at the American Museum of Natural History, had told me. "But don't get your hopes up." Fewer than a score of Titanus had ever been recorded, he said.

In camp near the Rio Negro (map, page 108) the screeching of invisible macaws nearly split my eardrums, but there was little sign of other wildlife. It was strictly bug country, aswarm and acrawl with butterflies, ants, and beetles. Night and day I searched for Titanus. No luck. Instead I bagged a giant spider wasp, leaf-cutting ants, and scarab beetles. Good finds all, but I wanted that Titanus.

One night at an oil refinery on the river, I stood under a powerful light that cast its beckoning beam far into the jungle darkness. Around it a thousand insect satellites orbited.

Minutes passed into hours. Scores of victims dropped to earth at my feet. None even remotely resembled Titanus.

Suddenly there was a heavy thud. On the ground squirmed a tawny brown monster, a good four inches long. Its thick pincers could have slashed my fingers to the bone. I plunged my net violently down. Six taloned feet ripped the cheesecloth. Cautiously I maneuvered my prize into an empty paint can and slammed the lid.

Next morning in my hotel room I opened it to look at the creature in daylight. He was alive and struggling, a mammoth beetle—but not Titanus. This fellow was *Callipogon armillatus*, a near cousin.

I was still trying to down my disappointment when a knock came at the door. A boy handed me an envelope marked "Urgent! Deliver immediately!" I tore it open. "We have a six-legged beast out here.... The boys are afraid of it. Can you hurry before someone gets hurt?"

The note was signed by an American engineer at the refinery. Minutes later I entered an office where five Brazilians were rattling away in Portuguese, half in apprehension, half in amusement.

"He's under there," said the engineer, pointing to a large inverted wastebasket on which one of the men was sitting as if he were holding in check the fires of hell. I asked him to get up.

"Take care...Watch it...Look out for those teeth...." The warnings flew in Portuguese. I kicked over the basket and in an instant had the creature ensnared. He was nearly five inches long. Here, at last, was a true *Titanus giganteus*.

I added it to my strange assortment of baggage and went aboard a passenger ship bound back downstream for Belém. Next morning found me in my stateroom, the door and windows locked, and Titanus loose and stalking about. I studied him carefully. I watched how his jaw pincers could crack a matchstick. I tied a string around his thorax and led him around like a poodle. When we docked at Belém, I must confess I knew more of beetle behavior than I did of Amazonian scenery.

My search continued some weeks but I never found another Titanus. When I got back to New York, however, a package came to me from an American I'd met in Brazil. It contained 15 enormous shiny specimens of elusive old Titanus—to me the most beautiful gift in the world!

NUTCRACKER JAWS *of the world's largest ant,* Dinoponera gigantea, *clutch a golden beetle. The female of this species is far deadlier than the male and fights all the colony's battles.*

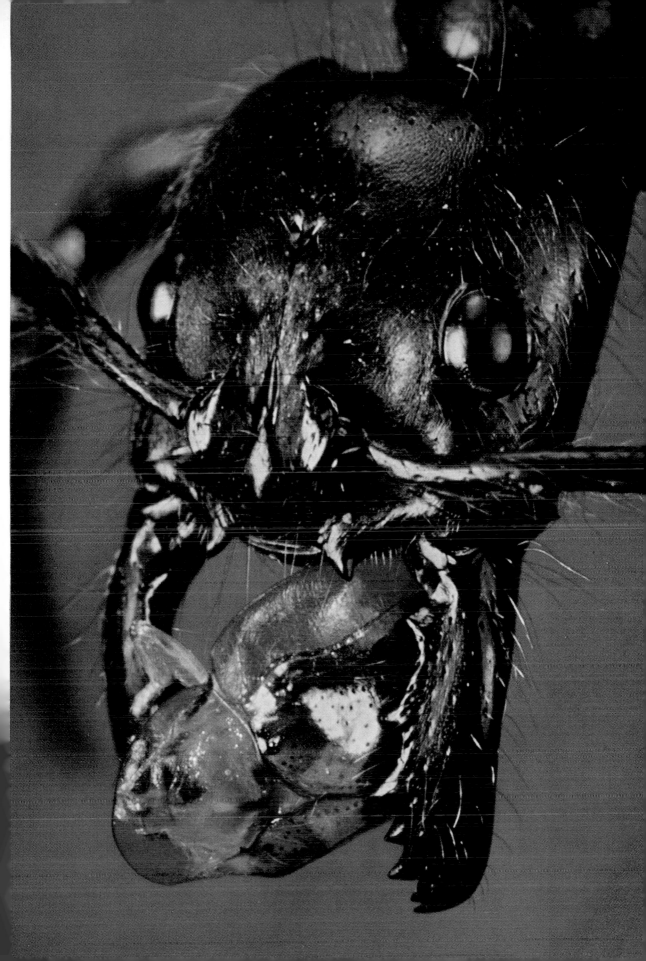

Brazil's Big-lipped Indians

*The once-ferocious Suyá paddle down a jungle river
and discover civilization. Anthropologist Harald Schultz
returns with them to share their vanishing way of life.*

IT IS SUMMER in the Southern Hemisphere. From the heart of Brazil comes word that a primitive tribe, the Suyá, has discovered the 20th century and made peace with civilization.

To me at the São Paulo State Museum this news is most exciting. The Suyá have long been feared as one of Brazil's fiercest tribes. Little is known about them except that their men distort the lower lip grotesquely with disks of light wood.

What a challenge, what an opportunity for the student of primitive man! I study a map and make inquiries. . . .

The little Piper plane puts my co-worker Udo Loew and me down at the straw-thatched settlement of Diauarum on the upper reaches of the Xingu River (map, page 108). It is true, say the villagers, the Suyá came down making signs of peace. Yes, they may come again.

And then one day a voice rings out: "There come the Suyá!" Far up the river five boats have appeared. Three are of bark; the others are hollowed-out logs. In them ride some of the strangest humans I have ever seen. The men wear in the lower lip a large wooden disk, dyed red, which gives them a ducklike appearance. For this occasion they are clad in trousers or at least a short shirt. The women wear a red loincloth. Their natural tact has told them to cover their nakedness when visiting the *karaí*, the civilized. Their children are completely naked.

Landing, one of the men drags a heavy basket from his canoe. It is filled with roasted water pig—capybara. Taking a chance with a related language I ask for some, saying, "*Kutum vakukrẽ?*"

"Come," says the man, beaming, "you shall eat roasted water pig." He hands me the whole leg!

The Suyá have come to get medical treatment for dysentery. When they are well again they invite Loew and me to go home with them. Towing two of their canoes with our outboard motor, we chug upstream to a narrow inlet. From the bank there is no sign of an Indian village. But paths lead into the forest, and in the dim cathedral light that filters through the treetops we see a newly cleared area about 65 feet wide. Long poles have been bound horizontally to tree trunks and covered with leaves. Under these roofs hang rows of hammocks.

Fat fish are roasting on grills made of poles. Clay pots, wooden mortars and pestles lie nearby. Bows and bundles of arrows lean against "house pillars" formed by live tree trunks.

Here live the only Suyá in the world, no more than 65 people!

They are the most gracious hosts I have ever known. Every day we are served fresh wild fowl, golden hare, or some other delicacy. Women often bring a shellful of palm nut purée or wild bee honey.

"*Agatíma gonyã!*" says Chief Pentotí one day. Considerately, he always speaks as clearly and simply as possible. One-eyed Robndó helps me get the meaning by striking a bundle of twigs with a stick. That means fishing with poison.

The men gather timbó vines and crush them with axes into yellow strands. Then the whole tribe marches to a big lake, men carrying the vines, women and children trailing behind with baskets and knives.

At a deeply indented inlet young men erect a screen of boughs and leafy twigs in the water to prevent the fish from escaping.

With shouts of *Hoouuh! Hoouuh!* the men jump into the bay. They beat the shredded timbó vines and swish them in the water until the whitish-blue soaplike sap spreads over the surface. Frightened fish try to escape, but old men waiting at the leafy barrier shoot them with bow and arrow. The lake soon looks as if it is sprinkled with giant snowflakes—the white bellies of dying fish. Women wade in and finish them off with bush knives. Piles of fish, of many species, grow on the bank. Each family fills its baskets—no envy, no haste, plenty for everyone!

A few days later we see how the Suyá make salt from the ashes of burned water hyacinths. Making a funnel of flexible sticks and banana leaves, with a filter-like layer of plant fibers at the bottom, they put in the ashes and let water trickle through to leach out the salt. The water is then boiled until it evaporates, leaving a yellowish-brown powder.

Men, women, and children line up to take tiny pinches. They smack the tongue with pleasure. *Katuyani!* Salt! Very fine! It is bitter and stings my tongue. It is not common salt, sodium chloride, but mostly potash and potassium chloride.

Sweetening also comes from the forest. In late afternoon Pentotí returns from a reconnoitering expedition, his expressive face betraying satisfaction. He gestures to show that he has felled a giant tree with a bees' nest on the trunk.

Two hours of rapid walking the next morning bring us to the tree. In the cool

SUYÁ WOMEN *twist cotton strands to make hammocks; girl feeds a parrot from her mouth with corn chewed to a pulp.*
The author, in traditional body paint, types notes before a fascinated spectator.
Lip disks, for married men only, are cut from light wood and measure 2 to 3 inches in diameter. Plugs of twisted palm leaves whitened with chalk distend the earlobes.

HARALD SCHULTZ

HARALD SCHULTZ

DAILY LIFE *is a quest for daily bread.
The Suyá burn off a patch of forest,
dig holes with pointed sticks (right),
and plant seed corn from a gourd.
To make salt, women gather water
hyacinth leaves (left), burn them,
pour water through ashes and sieve
(far left), and evaporate by boiling.
The bitter, yellowish-brown residue
made the author's tongue sting.*

*Fish are a staple. Proud lads
(below left) lug home a string of
giant traira that their fathers shot
with reed arrows tipped by spines
of freshwater stingrays.*

*For a village-size catch, the Suyá use
poison; a diskless bachelor (below right)
shows how. He flails a golden sheaf
of timbó vine to spread milky sap
on the surface. Small fish suffocate
and float belly-up. Big fellows surge
through the film for a breath,
and are shot, clubbed, or slashed.*

INNOCENT OF CLOTHING *except for beads bestowed by Dr. Schultz, Suyá Indians set out on*

air the bees are still clustered on the nest, which adheres to the trunk like a great tumor. Pentotí's eldest son, Koyosí, approaches it with blazing palm leaves at the end of a pole. Now two daring youths rush forward and knock the nest off with axes. Others join them and carry away chunks, at the same time swatting the bees. Groups form around the chunks, plunge in their hands, and gulp down the precious honey. Today life is sweet.

At nightfall the young men gather and sing to the rhythm of thumping feet and the glasslike tinkle of a pig's hoof rattle.

The songs are simple, low-toned, repetitious. Often the women join in, voices ringing like metal. They grab each other and dance, one step forward, one back.

The rattle is the only instrument I see.

"Don't you have any flutes like other tribes?" I ask Ngeré, my "uncle."

He looks at me and laughs softly, pointing eloquently to his lip disk.

To wash his disk, Ngeré pulls it from his lip and dives into the river. When he comes up, his lower lip hangs like a crumpled worm. He reinserts the disk, then paints it—red on top, white on bottom.

a fishing trip. Chief Pentotí sits amidships, one-eyed Robndó plies the stern paddle.

"Do you not find it beautiful?" he asks.

As soon as a man is married, his lip is pierced and a small disk inserted. Progressively larger ones stretch the hole. Disks are worn always, even during sleep. Some men tilt them up at night so the face is partly hidden and the delicate ornamentation of the underside is visible.

THE RAINS BEGIN, and as the ground softens we know we will have to leave; soon aircraft will no longer be able to land at Diauarum. Our friends are happy with the things we can no longer use: pots, knives, trousers, and bed linen.

Ngeré has carved a cassava cake turner for us. "Now you are leaving us," he says. "The water will rise and flood everything! But when the shore appears again, when the sun becomes hot and beautiful, I shall be waiting for you here."

Men, women, and children follow our boat a while along the bank. "*Suyá betkoomeneene!*" we call. "The Suyá are fine, they are good!"

The answering cry, "*Karaí betkoomeneene!*" comes from every Suyá lip, big and little. "You whites are also fine!"

437

ROCKET PLANE *was sketched by Alexander Graham Bell in 1893.*

Scouting the Wild Sky

SOMEWHERE, SOMETIME in the dim past, man looked up at a soaring bird, then peered down at his own earthbound body. From that moment, he yearned to fly. But, as Confucius said, "The heavens cannot be gone up to by the steps of a chair." For centuries man could only dream—of Daedalus and Icarus soaring on wings of wax and feathers, of magic carpets and flying chariots. Then, in the early 1500's, Leonardo da Vinci sketched a hundred ideas for flying machines and boldly predicted: "There shall be wings. If the accomplishment be not for me, 'tis for some other. The spirit cannot lie...."

That spirit moved the brothers Montgolfier. In 1783 the two Frenchmen filled a great paper-and-linen balloon with hot air, then watched it carry two men in a wicker basket "calmly and majestically into the atmosphere" above Paris. Still, man wanted wings. In the 1890's Otto Lilienthal took to the air in gliders. "He rushed along at race-horse speed," his friend R. W. Wood wrote in *National Geographic*, "60 or 70 feet in the air, the wind playing extraordinary aeolian harp music on steel piano wires with which the framework was trussed." The brilliant German died in the crash of one of his own gliders.

Man's dream of powered flight came true on December 17, 1903, at Kitty

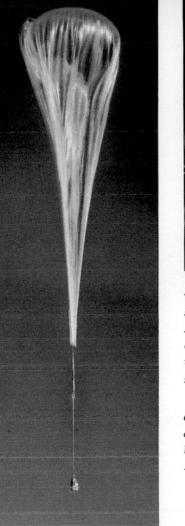

TO THE STRATOSPHERE
*soared balloonists
Anderson, Kepner,
and Stevens (at right)
in the pressurized
gondola of* Explorer I.

GHOSTLY BALLOON
*carries parachutist
Kittinger up for his
102,800-foot jump.*

ROCKET-POWERED *X-15 hitches a ride
beneath a B-52's wing before blasting off
on a research flight to the edge of space.*

Hawk, North Carolina. For 12 seconds Orville Wright flew in the heavier-than-air machine he and his brother Wilbur had created. Only five spectators were on hand and the nation paid little heed. But a few years later, when the brothers tested their Type A *Flyer* for the U.S. Army at Fort Myer, Virginia, large crowds gathered. Among them was 13-year-old Thomas W. McKnew, later Vice President and Secretary of the National Geographic Society and now its Vice Chairman. "There was something akin to magic in the very words 'flying machine,'" he recalled. "Endlessly repeated, the phrase...seemed on the tip of every tongue: 'I would rather be Wright than President.'"

When interest in aviation seemed to sag, Wilbur Wright used the podium at a National Geographic Society banquet to remind America—and President Taft, a fellow guest—that "the leading nations of the earth are taking up the subject, our own nation being the first of all to begin it. Unfortunately there seems to be some hesitation at present."

There was little hesitation among members of the Society. Alexander Graham Bell, its second President, had concluded as early as 1877 that a heavier-than-air machine was feasible, and "should be supported by the revolution of a fan

439

WHIRLING HEELS OVER HEAD, *a test pilot
flies a wind-tunnel mission. Gas jets spin
his chair dizzily to simulate roll, pitch,
and yaw of a space capsule. He counters
with a control stick. National Geographic's
Allan C. Fisher, Jr., rode the wild whirligig
before the astronauts did. His skilled
science reporting has won him top awards.*

wheel or screw." He and his colleagues in the Aerial Experiment Association
put these words into action. In 1909 their *Silver Dart* achieved Canada's first
powered flight. Dr. Bell's prediction of 1914 was even more visionary; "...heav-
ier-than-air machines...of a different construction from anything yet con-
ceived of, will be driven over the earth's surface at enormous velocity, hundreds
of miles an hour, by new methods of propulsion.... Think of the enormous
energy locked up in high explosives! What if we could control that energy and
utilize it in some form of projectile flight!"

Another prophet of the air, Gen. William ("Billy") Mitchell, challenged the
battleship's supremacy. "Compared to an airplane," he wrote in the March,
1921, *Geographic,* "these great vessels are very much like the knights in the
middle ages, encased in heavy armor, in which they could scarcely move." Six
months later his bombers sank a condemned battleship to prove his point.

Mitchell pushed his pilots to new exploits. John A. Macready flew a supercharged biplane to 34,509 feet. "At 20,000 feet," he reported, "a peculiar depression takes possession. The sky looks gray and dreary...faculties are slowed.
The pilot inserts an oxygen tube and the whole world brightens...."

MAKING HISTORY WITH A SPLASH, *Astronaut Alan B. Shepard, Jr., completes the first U. S. space flight, May 5, 1961. National Geographic's Dean Conger recorded the epic on film for* NASA.

FIRST AMERICAN *to orbit the earth, John H. Glenn, Jr., receives the Hubbard Medal from Vice President Lyndon B. Johnson, April 9, 1962. He relived his flight for an audience of 6,000. Right:* NASA's *Hugh L. Dryden, a Society Trustee. Left: Melville Bell Grosvenor.*

WINFIELD PARKS, NATIONAL GEOGRAPHIC PHOTOGRAPHER

But the high sky still belonged to the gas bags. In 1931, Auguste Piccard rose to 51,775 feet over Bavaria. When his airtight aluminum gondola sprang a leak, he told *Geographic* readers, he plugged it with oakum and vaseline. The ascent convinced him that "the stratosphere is the superhighway of the future." Four years later the National Geographic Society's *Explorer II* soared 72,395 feet above South Dakota, a record that stood 21 years. From such a height, wrote Albert W. Stevens, earth seemed "a vast expanse of brown. . . . Sunlight sparkled from rivers and lakes, but we saw no sign of life."

It was a balloon that carried Joseph W. Kittinger, Jr., 20 miles up for the highest parachute jump man had ever made. As he took the great step from his gondola, a National Geographic automatic camera recorded it for history.

By the early 1960's, Dr. Bell's prediction of projectile flight had become a reality. Joseph A. Walker gunned his rocket-powered X-15 to five times the speed of sound—so fast that "wings, nose, and tail glowed red." John Glenn, a National Geographic flag in the cramped cockpit of his space capsule, hurtled around the earth in 97 minutes. Man now sees the planets within reach; step-by-step, *National Geographic* will record his journey to them.

To the Threshold of Space

Capt. Albert W. Stevens plunged to earth, then soared to glory as the National Geographic Society's stratosphere probes hung a 21-year record in the sky. Join him as he explores a new frontier.

To LOOK BACK, we were indeed in a strange predicament. One moment we were comfortably imprisoned in a stout metal shell, hanging from a huge balloon more than 11 miles above the earth. We could talk through our radio to almost anyone in the United States. We were neither hungry nor thirsty, and the prepared air we breathed was surprisingly good. The clatter of scientific instruments all around us was music to our ears.

Then I noticed a great rent in our balloon! We stopped the ascent and soon were descending—bag, gondola, and men.

We had only to open two hatches to be free. But at that height the change of pressure would have meant almost instant unconsciousness. So long as things held together there was hope. But if too many breaks in the fabric developed, the gondola would go hurtling through space and we with it. A strange predicament indeed!

But let us start with our ascent from the Stratobowl near Rapid City, South Dakota, in the largest free balloon ever constructed. For weeks scientists and soldiers had tested and installed equipment in *Explorer I* for the National Geographic Society-U. S. Army Air Corps Stratosphere Flight. No pains had been spared to produce the best possible instruments for this flight, which would gather samples of the upper air, study cosmic rays, and determine ozone concentrations.

Shortly before dawn on July 28, 1934, Capt. Orvil A. Anderson and I entered the gondola, while Maj. William E. Kepner climbed to its rope-enclosed top to direct the takeoff. Then, at 5:45: "Cast off!"

The ground dropped away and we rose rapidly. At 15,000 feet we closed the airtight manholes. As scheduled, we stopped at 40,000 feet to let the instruments go through their cycles of operations. Never before had a stratosphere balloon been halted between the ground and the maximum altitude of a flight. Yet by careful valving of gas, Anderson kept our balloon in equilibrium for almost two hours before resuming the ascent. Nearing 60,000 feet we valved, and the balloon slowed.

A small rope fell from the bag and clattered on top of the gondola. Through the port I looked up, startled, to see the large rip in the balloon's lower surface. It was just past one o'clock.

Minutes crept by. We started to descend. The rent grew larger. There was little talking as we strained to hear the swishing noises that signaled a new or longer rip. Outside it was 80° below zero F.; inside it was 42 above. Ice formed on the gondola.

We passed 40,000 feet. Half an hour later, at 20,000 feet, we forced open the hatches and for the first time I felt free. Kepner and I climbed out on top and took a good look at the balloon. Large waves swept across the lower fabric. With every wave the rents grew bigger. How long would it hold together?

Suddenly the entire bottom of the bag dropped out. I climbed into the gondola and poured out lead dust ballast.

We had snapped on parachutes, and at 10,000 feet we really should have left the balloon. But we did not wish to abandon the scientific apparatus, so we stayed. At 6,000 feet we decided we must leave. The last altimeter reading I transmitted was 3,000 feet above the ground.

EXPLORER II POISES FOR TAKEOFF FROM THE STRATOBOWL NEAR RAPID CITY, SOUTH DAKOTA, NOVEMBER 11, 1935; MAJ. H. LEE WELLS, JR.

GAS BAG SHREDDED, Explorer I *drops
a mile a minute with only 800 feet to go.
Kepner's frantic kick frees the author
as Anderson floats safely to earth in
the distance. Kepner jumped at 300 feet.*

PAINTING BY TOM LOVELL FOR NATIONAL GEOGRAPHIC

445

Anderson, whose parachute had accidentally been sprung open, gathered the folds and sat in a hatch.

Then things happened fast. Anderson disappeared. The balloon exploded. The gondola dropped like a stone. I struggled to get through the hatch. Kepner helped, shoving me with his foot. I broke free and pulled my rip cord.

The silk opened in a large circle—then a portion of the balloon fell on top of my parachute. Luckily it slid out from under and worked itself free.

How about Kepner and Anderson? I spotted two parachutes and knew they were safe. Below, I heard the gondola hit with a tremendous thud. Forty seconds later I hit—fortunately with a much lighter thud. We rolled up our chutes and hurried to the gondola, in a cornfield near Holdrege, Nebraska. Hundreds of people seemed to rise out of the very ground.

We found our beautiful globe flattened, the instruments a heartbreaking mass of wreckage. But two barographs, hanging outside, suffered little damage. They revealed that we had reached 60,613 feet above sea level, just short of the 61,237-foot record set by Comdr. T. G. W. Settle and Maj. C. L. Fordney in 1933. We felt sure another balloon could be built to top that without mishap.

NEARLY 16 MONTHS LATER the largest balloon ever constructed—192 feet across when fully expanded—towered 315 feet over the Stratobowl. Beneath it hung *Explorer II*. This time it would be a two-man flight.

During inflation a pocket of helium in the fabric caused a 17-foot tear. It was hurriedly patched, but Captain Anderson and I felt confident it would hold. At 7:01 A.M., November 11, 1935, Anderson signaled to release the ropes.

We soared upward, cleared the bowl, and were 100 feet above the rim when Anderson shouted through the porthole, "I believe the balloon is leaking!"

We began to settle. Beneath us the crowd of spectators scattered to right and left. There was not a second to lose. We released ballast; one spray of lead sprinkled directly over a man in full retreat.

About 50 feet above the treetops, the balloon suddenly reversed and shot skyward. Apparently we had encountered merely a strong down current of air. Andy valved to check our rapid rise.

At 10:30 we reached pressure height—65,000 feet. Our great balloon was full and overflowing from the bottom.

Anderson methodically tripped sack after sack of lead, sending us higher and higher. Now we had only enough ballast to assure a safe landing. At 11:40 the balloon stopped. We were at the top. From our altimeter we made a rough estimate of our ceiling—73,000 feet!

From nearly 14 miles above sea level, we saw the earth as a vast expanse of brown. Highways and houses were invisible, larger farms appeared as tiny rectangles. Streaks of green vegetation traced streams. Sunlight sparkled from rivers and lakes, but we saw no sign of life. It seemed a foreign and lifeless world.

The horizon was a band of white haze. Above it the sky was light blue; at the highest angle it became black with a suggestion of dark blue.

447

CAPT. ALBERT W. STEVENS. LEFT: UNDERWOOD AND UNDERWOOD

FIRST PHOTOGRAPH *showing the boundary between the dust-laden troposphere — the lower air — and the dark stratosphere was made from* Explorer II *at 72,395 feet, an altitude record that stood for 21 years. Ruled white line points out the curvature of the earth 330 miles from the camera.*

Taking off, the cluttered gondola dangled pear-shaped bags of lead ballast and square battery boxes. Beneath hung a circular bumper to cushion the landing of Stevens and Anderson.

STRATOBOWL

HILLS ● Rapid City

D S

DAKOTA

We remained at our ceiling for an hour and a half, instruments clicking away. Then we started down. I released spore-collecting apparatus and opened and closed air-sample flasks. The radio functioned perfectly—even ten miles up Andy was not beyond his family's voice.

Mrs. Anderson, in a tent at the Stratobowl, asked, "How is everything?"

"Very good, Muddy," Andy replied.

"Where are you?"

"I am up in the air," he said dryly.

I was amused when I overheard an announcer instruct his colleagues: "Don't play up this record business, boys, until we are sure that they have gotten down safely. There is still plenty of chance for them to crash and they have to come down alive to make it a record."

On a special hookup I talked direct to an astonished newspaper reporter in London who thought that the rip in our fabric had occurred in flight.

"What about the rip in your balloon?"

"We fixed it."

"You fixed it?"

"We cemented it. We put a patch on."

"Most extraordinary."

We were now at 16,000 feet, time to crack the manholes. Air hissed out of the gondola. Andy watched our rate of fall while I spilled ballast and released apparatus by parachute. Planes circled. Below, cars converged on our probable landing point near White Lake, South Dakota.

We donned helmets, borrowed from a Rapid City high school football team, and hooked up a linen strap as a grab line.

The balloon, traveling at 12 miles an hour, settled to within a foot or two of the ground. We skimmed across a field. Andy shouted, "Make ready for landing!"

We pulled the rip cord and felt the steel cable tear through the fabric at the top of the balloon, releasing the gas. We grabbed for the linen strap.

The gondola struck, stopped, and rolled on its side. Clothes, tools, cameras, and lead dust filled the air. It was 3:14 P.M.

We had ascended to a record altitude of 72,395 feet and returned to an "eggshell landing." Our load, a ton of scientific instruments, was intact.

Our flight had added to man's store of knowledge of cosmic rays, of living spores at high altitudes, and of the sun's brightness in the stratosphere. And we had made vertical photographs of the earth from a higher altitude than ever before.

ABOVE AND FAR LEFT: M/SGT. G. B. GILBERT AND CAPT. H. K. BAISLEY, LEFT: CAPT. JAMES HAIZLIP AND RICHARD H. STEWART, NATIONAL GEOGRAPHIC STAFF

SOARING LAZILY *over South Dakota's Badlands (far left), the great gas bag rises ever higher on its historic 13.71-mile climb. Eight hours from lift-off and 225 miles away the rip cord is pulled, collapsing the balloon, and* Explorer II *lands as dusty cars converge.*

Congratulated by President Roosevelt, Stevens (shaking hands) and Anderson were awarded the Society's Hubbard Medal.

LOOKING ON ARE GEN. MALIN CRAIG (LEFT), ARMY CHIEF OF STAFF, AND BRIG. GEN. OSCAR WESTOVER, ACTING CHIEF OF THE ARMY AIR CORPS; UNITED PRESS INTERNATIONAL

451

Flight of the *Silver Dart*

A frail contraption wobbles skyward—Canada enters the Air Age!
Fifty years later, Gilbert M. Grosvenor watches history repeat.

IT WAS LATE when I glanced up from my table in the Alexander Graham Bell Museum. Snow blew gently across the Nova Scotia night. Moonlight reflected from iced-over Baddeck Bay, and beyond loomed the peninsula known as Beinn Bhreagh, Gaelic for "beautiful mountain."

The bay must have looked much the same in February, 1909, when Dr. Bell and his companions of the Aerial Experiment Association achieved Canada's first airplane flight with a frail bamboo-and-silk contraption called the *Silver Dart*.

Now a second *Dart* had been built by the Royal Canadian Air Force, and on February 23, 1959—exactly 50 years later—it was to re-create the historic flight.

The documents I had been studying— faded blueprints, photographs, handwritten notes showing the progress of AEA experiments—had been preserved by the National Geographic Society, of which my great-grandfather, Dr. Bell, was second President. Recently they had been turned over to the Bell Museum at Baddeck.

Dr. Bell and four associates had estab-

J. A. D. McCURDY LIFTS THE SILVER DART FROM THE ICE ON THE BRAS D'OR LAKES OF NOVA SCOTIA IN CANADA'S FIRST
AIRPLANE FLIGHT, FEBRUARY 23, 1909; H. M. BENNER. INSET: AVIATION PIONEERS OF THE AERIAL EXPERIMENT
ASSOCIATION—GLENN H. CURTISS, McCURDY, ALEXANDER GRAHAM BELL, F. W. "CASEY" BALDWIN, AND U. S. ARMY
LT. THOMAS E. SELFRIDGE, POWERED FLIGHT'S FIRST CASUALTY, WHO WAS KILLED IN A 1908 CRASH; © BELL FAMILY

453

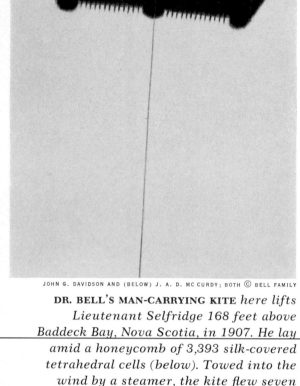

DR. BELL'S MAN-CARRYING KITE *here lifts Lieutenant Selfridge 168 feet above Baddeck Bay, Nova Scotia, in 1907. He lay amid a honeycomb of 3,393 silk-covered tetrahedral cells (below). Towed into the wind by a steamer, the kite flew seven minutes. Bell also experimented with "winged fly-wheels," powered by rockets. Today we'd call them helicopter rotors.*

lished the AEA in 1907 with a simple aim: "To get into the air." Mrs. Bell, whose idea it was, backed them with $35,000. The AEA contributed much to early aeronautical development, and by 1908 had built four successful powered aircraft.

Three of these "aerodromes" (a term Dr. Bell always preferred to "aeroplane"), used hinged-surface, wing-tip ailerons to give lateral stability. These had been used earlier in Europe, but Dr. Bell arrived at a stabilizing system independently. After one of his planes cracked up, he suggested a device to take advantage of a pilot's "instinctive attempt to lean to the left to counterbalance an undesirable tip downwards of the right wing."

"That's just how our *Silver Dart* is controlled," I was told by R.C.A.F. Wing Commander Paul Hartman, who was to make the commemorative flight. "When I lean to either side, my shoulder pushes a yoke which moves a lever that moves the hinged wing tips. That levels the wings."

The snow had stopped when we left the museum. Even the wind had died.

"I hope it's this calm on the 23d," Flight Lt. William Bell said. "We can't fly the *Dart* safely in much over ten knots. Sometimes the AEA waited three weeks for

favorable weather. But we're scheduled to be on television. The AEA didn't have *that* problem."

Early next morning I hurried to the polyethylene-covered shelter where the new *Dart*, still in sections, awaited assembly. Flying Officer Charles Walker treated me as an official member of his crew. "How do you expect us to put the plane together if you waste time taking pictures?" he asked. "Grab that wing tip."

Finally the *Dart* was ready, and huge snow rollers were brought in to smooth the ice runway. But high winds prevented the test flight, and for a week we waited.

At dusk one day we drove across the frozen bay to Beinn Bhreagh and up the snow-covered road to the mountaintop where Dr. Bell and his wife lie at rest. The telephone's inventor would have marveled at the television relay station erected for the flight of *Silver Dart II*. Some 150 townspeople saw the original flight; all Canada would watch this one.

"The old gentleman's going to peer right down my neck when I fly that bucket," Hartman said. "I'd better not prang her."

"What do you mean, 'prang'?" I asked.

Hartman laughed. "That's slang for bending an airplane. A rough landing—

© BELL FAMILY. BELOW: GILBERT M. GROSVENOR, NATIONAL GEOGRAPHIC STAFF

"**I FEEL NAKED**," *said Wing Commander Hartman as he took the pilot's seat of* Silver Dart II *amid a spider's web of wires and bamboo. J. A. D. McCurdy (top), testing controls of* Dart I *fifty years earlier, flew the flimsy craft half a mile to become Canada's first aviator.*

455

but the kind the pilot walks away from."

Saturday the 21st came, still windy. Again we waited. This was the last day the *Dart* could be test-flown in private; on Sunday visitors would be streaming in.

Toward sundown the breeze died. We rolled out the *Dart*. Smoke from red smoke bombs wafted straight up: Conditions were ideal. Hartman revved the engine, then released the brake. The *Dart* moved forward, struggling, for 150 feet. Then she was airborne at about 40 miles an hour, flying straight and true.

"Magnificent," said an elderly man who had arrived during the flight. "All my life I've longed to watch the machine in the air again. I piloted the original *Silver Dart*." It was J. A. D. McCurdy.

McCurdy recalled his flight in vivid detail. "I took off and flew at an altitude of about 60 feet for about half a mile," he said. "Bell seemed the only one to realize it was an historic occasion. He jumped down from his red sleigh, and I shall never forget the pleasure and animation in his face when he said to me, 'My boy, put the machine away. Fly tomorrow, or the next day, but today is almost a sacred day. We'll have nothing to mar it!'"

Wise words, for next day McCurdy barely missed disaster when a wing skidded on the ice in landing. But such mishaps were common in days when "we built our airplanes from curtain rods and bamboo fishing poles." He had his *Dart* flying again in a short time.

MONDAY the 23d dawned beautifully. Chimney smoke hung lazily over a building. But at 9:30, only two hours to flight time, the wind was ripping the smoke into horizontal ribbons. On the ice whirls of snow danced. In the shelter Hartman wore a long face. "We may not get her off the ground today," Flight Lt. Bell groaned.

Near flight time the wind was blowing 8 to 10 knots, gusting to 15.

"Let's get the *Dart* ready anyway," Flying Officer Walker ordered. Slowly the huge plastic shelter slid aside. The crowd cheered and moved in for a better view.

"Warm up the engine," Walker said. The cold machine sputtered to life.

Hartman, in the pilot's seat, glanced at the crowd, then turned to face the breeze. Far up the runway the red smoke swirled in the gusts. "Let's go," Hartman said.

The engine revved up, and slowly the *Silver Dart* began to roll. Gaining speed, the fragile aircraft strained to get into the air. Suddenly a wicked gust kicked up snow, blotting out the plane. But when the snow settled I saw light under the wheels. The *Dart* was airborne.

Flight Lt. Bell, much nearer the *Dart* than I, reported the flight on my tiny tape recorder: "Here she comes...down the runway...laboring, but still moving... *there, she's in the air!*...she's leveled off, flying at about 10 feet...hit a gust... he's leveling out...having a little trouble...*one wing way down*...he's got her back again!

"She's rocking pretty badly...height about 50 feet...*she's climbing very abruptly*...he tries to straighten out... he's almost at 100 feet...has nosed down level now, but is sliding to the left...*she's crabbing almost 20 degrees...he's in trouble...trying to get her down for a landing...he's at 20 feet now...left wing way down...strikes the ground with his wing tip...aircraft down, damaged.*"

I ran to the plane. Hartman climbed out, unhurt. We carefully surveyed the damage: a crumpled wing tip and collapsed landing gear. It was minor.

But Hartman was dejected. He looked toward Beinn Bhreagh's mountaintop and said, "What would that old gentleman up there say today if he could see this mess?" He stood silent a moment, then: "Gil, I take my hat off to McCurdy and his like. I wonder what made them go on."

I thought of something McCurdy had said before the flight: "Remember that in those days we were looking into darkness. That gave us a sense of romance and a spirit of adventure. Without those, life loses its full meaning."

FLYING OUT OF THE PAST, Silver Dart II *soars over Nova Scotia to give the author a 1959 color record of a 1909 spectacle. The pilot is not going backward: What seems to be the tail is really the nose of this 65-horsepower re-creation.*

GILBERT M. GROSVENOR, NATIONAL GEOGRAPHIC STAFF

"Lord, Take Care of Me Now"

On a lonely mission for science Joseph W. Kittinger, Jr., pauses to pray, then takes a 20-mile step

OVERHEAD my onion-shaped balloon spreads its 200-foot diameter against a black daytime sky. Nearly 20 miles below lies the cloud-hidden New Mexico desert to which I will parachute.

My earphones crackle. Ground control at Holloman Air Force Base informs me: "Three minutes till jump, Joe."

I am ready to go. For about one hour I have been exposed in my open gondola to an environment that would kill me within two minutes if my equipment failed.

My job up here on the threshold of space is to test a new type of parachute for high altitude escape. Consider the plight of an airman or spaceman who has to bail out above 20,000 feet. Should he open his chute immediately after leaving a speeding craft, he risks death from his canopy's opening shock, from lack of oxygen, or severe cold. If he falls free to lower, livable altitudes, his body may whirl like a runaway propeller, in a fatal flat spin.

We think this new parachute holds the answer. To find out, I will take what we call "the highest step in the world."

It is seven o'clock in the morning of August 16, 1960, and I have reached float altitude at 102,800 feet. A mixed feeling of awe and remoteness builds up in me; man has never achieved such a height

before without the protection of a sealed cabin. I radio ground control: "Man will never conquer space. He may live in it, but he will never conquer it. The sky above is void and very black and very hostile."

I turn my gaze to the earth below. I should be able to sweep a 780-mile-wide circle, but haze curtains the horizon and clouds blot out much of the landscape.

Burdened by heavy clothes and gear, I begin to pay the physical toll for my altitude. Every move demands a high cost in energy. My eyes smart from the fierce glare of the sun. On one side, I feel the effect of radiation and begin to sweat. On the shaded side, heat from my garments steams. One pressure glove is not working; the hand is swollen and painful.

A 30-knot wind is speeding me west; ground control decides I should step out over the target zone despite the thick cloud cover. Activity comes as a welcome relief to the surge of emotions. The big drop ahead of me is the only way home.

At X-minus-70-seconds I drop the trailing antenna, cutting communications with the ground. I begin my countdown and start the cameras in the gondola. Their clicking makes me abruptly aware of how silent my stay in space has been. At zero count I stand in the door of the gondola

and breathe a prayer: "Lord, take care of me now." Then I step into space. No wind whistles or billows my clothing. I have absolutely no sensation of the increasing speed with which I fall.

When the six-foot stabilization canopy pops out, I have already dropped to about 96,000 feet. I am delighted to find myself perfectly anchored against the dreaded flat spin. I turn with ease by sticking out an arm and leg.

The clouds, seconds before motionless and remote, now rush up at me. I have to persuade myself that they are mere vapor and not solid earth. The thick blanket envelops me at 21,000 feet. Some 3,500 feet lower, and 4 minutes, 38 seconds after my fall began, my main canopy pops open.

I escape the clouds at 15,000 feet and behold a beautiful sight—two helicopters circling attentively. I know that recovery trucks are speeding toward my landing site. I detach the seat kit except for a single line; my swollen right hand lacks the strength to unfasten it. I will have to land with the heavy box dangling at my side.

The landing is as hard as any I have ever made. But I am on the ground—and in one piece. I am surrounded by sand, salt grass, and sage. No Garden of Eden could look more beautiful.

*"**THANK YOU, LORD,**" the author breathed when his main chute opened at 17,500 feet, after he had fallen 16 miles in 4¹/₂ minutes.*

He swings over a New Mexico desert (left) dotted with ponds from recent rain. The stabilization chute that kept him from a fatal spin lies atop the main canopy.

On landing, Captain Kittinger gets fast care for his right hand, swollen by the failure of a pressure glove.

I Fly the X-15

*Test pilot Joseph A. Walker
rides a winged bullet into space
and returns at blistering speed*

THE TIME HAD COME. "Launch now!"
I said and flicked a switch. Shackles
released the X-15 from its cradle
under the wing of the huge B-52 mother
plane cruising at 45,500 feet.

For a second we fell like a bomb, my
black bird and I. Then I had her under
control in a glide toward the glaring rock
and sand of the Nevada desert. We "got
a light," or engine start, and the X-15's
liquid rocket cut in with explosive force.
Under full throttle it began a surge to the
power of 548,000 raging horses.

"I'm on my way!" I radioed exultantly.
On this April day in 1962, if all went well,
I would pilot this half plane, half missile
to 250,000 feet, a new record for a winged
vehicle. Our research program, a partner-
ship of the Air Force, Navy, and National
Aeronautics and Space Administration,
called for a step-by-step buildup in altitude and speed. It was my job to explore
speeds faster than a high-powered bullet
and the problems of controlled re-entry
into the atmosphere.

Earlier that morning at Edwards Air
Force Base in California, specialists had
shoehorned me into a pressure suit after
plastering my body with electrodes. These
would record my heartbeat, respiration,
and temperature, just as scores of little
sensors in the X-15's skin would pick up
information on air flow, pressures, and
heating. The long countdown check of
intricate systems had been a test pilot's
dream, trouble free and no sweat.

Now the acceleration pinned me back

463

SPEWING A LONG CONTRAIL, *the X-15 thunders into a speed run five times as fast as sound.*

in my seat with a force of two g's, twice the force of gravity, thus twice my weight of 164 pounds. Pulling back the control stick, I increased my climb angle.

Three g's ... four g's ... the force built up rapidly. My bullet would have to be slowed to follow the carefully planned flight path. After 40 seconds of power, I popped out the speed brakes.

Ground control began the countdown for engine shutoff. We had planned on 81 seconds of engine-burning time—and that meant 81 on the nose. Extra seconds would propel me above the intended altitude and stretch my arc. Coming back for a dead-stick landing, I might find myself beyond gliding range of the hard, dry floor of Rogers Lake at Edwards. That could be a fatal embarrassment.

At 79 seconds I reached for the throttle with my left hand—and grasped nothing. Glancing down, I saw my gloved fingers a good two inches from the handle. G-forces had driven me so far back in the seat that

I couldn't reach it. But I *had* to. Bracing right elbow and shoulder, I lunged forward with all my strength. That did it. I yanked the throttle back a second late.

WHEN I SHUT DOWN the engine, I was going 3,443 miles an hour at an altitude of 142,800 feet. I became weightless, a welcome relief. Checklist pages on my clipboard rose eerily, and dirt particles drifted from the floor.

Upward the X-15 soared. It had become, in effect, a cannon shell in space, following the inexorable laws of physics. I could not alter course until I fell back into denser air and regained aerodynamic control.

But I *could* change my craft's attitude. I could dip the wings and move the nose up and down or from side to side with jet-powered controls.

My lunge for the throttle had bobbed the nose down. I blasted it up and smoothed out other small movements. Seconds later I coasted up to the peak of my arc. My

464

The rocket plane arcs upward through a sunlit sky diffracted by the chase plane's canopy.

instruments showed exactly 250,000 feet (later corrected to 246,700 – 46.7 miles above the earth). I took a quick look around from the top of the hill: on my left the Gulf of California, on my right Monterey Bay. Way out in front the horizon curved like a scimitar. As the nose tipped down I could see the white glare of Rogers Lake.

Now I had to think about the most critical part of the flight – re-entry. You have to do this maneuver right, or buddy, you've "bought the farm," as pilots say. If I slashed into the atmosphere with the nose straight down, g-forces would break up the X-15 when I tried to pull her out. What's more, she couldn't survive the heat of sudden re-entry.

So, using jets, I pushed the nose up to an 18-degree angle of attack and dropped "belly buster" into the atmosphere. At 100,000 feet the g-forces began mounting rapidly, soon reaching 5½ g's. I could feel bladders in my suit puffing up to grip me tightly and dam the downward flow of blood. The heat built up to 1,000° F. Leading edges of wings, nose, and tail glowed red. Through the faceplate of my helmet I felt a little radiation heat from the metal windshield frame, but the air-conditioned cabin and suit kept me comfortable.

Below 100,000 feet I no longer needed the jets, and at 65,000 feet the X-15 pulled out in gliding flight. A chase plane soon closed in, its pilot ready to give advice and instrument readings in an emergency, and to make sure I jettisoned the lower tail fin instead of trying to land on it.

The fin went off O.K. I touched the X-15's steel skids down on Rogers Lake at more than 200 miles an hour. The nose wheel came down hard – *whomp!* and we slid a mile and a quarter.

We had shown that a winged vehicle could fly into space, return through the atmosphere at blistering speed, and land at a predetermined spot.

"Well," I said to ground control, "there's that one for today."

465

Two minutes and 40 seconds after launch, the pilot reaches 246,700 feet, topping 99.996 percent of the atmosphere. He can see from Monterey Bay to the Gulf of California

Speeding at 3,000 miles an hour, Walker points X-15 into re-entry attitude. Faulty angle would cause plane to break apart

At re-entry, 150,000 feet above the earth, 1,000° F. temperatures redden the plane's wings, tail, and nose. Pilot returns to his atmospheric controls below 100,000 feet

G-stresses at leveling-off point—65,000 feet— swell Walker's 164 pounds to over 900. He slows plane and lands at more than 200 m.p.h. Total flight time: 9 minutes 46 seconds

Monterey

Cracked right windshield confronts Major White after pull-out. Speed brakes control rate of deceleration

Sierra Nevada

Approaching Edwards AFB, plane begins landing maneuver at 40,000 feet. Flight time: 9 minutes 31 seconds

Los Angeles

Dry lake beds beneath flight path provide emergency landing strips

Ballarat Lake

Rosamond Lake

Edwards Air Force Base

Rogers Lake

Cuddeback Lake

CALIFOR

Death Valley

Mojave Desert

N

TEST PILOTS *like Walker and his teammate, Air Force Major Robert M. White, memorize their flight plans and follow them carefully, for the X-15 allows no mistakes. Launching from a mother ship to save fuel, she burns 9.4 tons of liquid oxygen-ammonia in less than two minutes. She coasts up to her planned altitude, then glides toward Rogers Lake at about 350 miles an hour. With no power, the pilot must put this 50-foot bullet down, tail skids first, often at better than 200 miles an hour. It takes a mile or more to stop.*

Observers rush out to unstrap the pilot (right). One carries an air conditioner to cool the space suit. Canopy up and helmet removed (left), the author grins in elation.

ACTUAL FLIGHT PATH

PLANNED FLIGHT PATH

In space, the X-15 behaves like a Mercury capsule, using small jets in nose and wing tips to control pitch, roll, and yaw

On pilot Walker's record altitude run of April 30, 1962, he cuts rockets off at 142,800 feet, 82 seconds after ignition. Space flight begins. Pilot becomes weightless

San Francisco

PLANNED FLIGHT PATH

ACTUAL FLIGHT PATH

On Major White's record speed run of November 9, 1961, the X-15 attains 4,093 miles an hour at burnout, 87 seconds after ignition

Cradled under a B-52's wing, the X-15 is carried to 45,500 feet over Mud Lake, Nevada

After a drop of 1,450 feet, the rocket engines roar into action as the X-15 starts its climb

Tonopah

Grapevine Lake

Mud Lake

NIA

Beatty ground station

Beatty and Edwards ground stations monitor the X-15 flights with radar and receive telemetered data on the plane's performance

NEVADA

Staff artist *A. Barrett*

Research by Eugene M. Scheel

© National Geographic Society

America's First Orbital Space Flight

On February 20, 1962, John Glenn rode Friendship 7 *into history. He reports his voyage here, before a National Geographic audience.*

I**T WAS A NOVEL EXPERIENCE** to sit on top of the 70-foot Atlas vehicle after the gantry had been pulled back. Through my periscope I could see much of Cape Canaveral. If I moved back and forth in my seat I could feel the whole vehicle move slightly under me. While the tank was being filled with liquid oxygen the spacecraft shuddered as the metal skin flexed; through my window I could see the white plume of lox venting around the top of the capsule.

As with every countdown, problems arose. But after three years of waiting we weren't unduly concerned by a few delays. When the count finally reached zero I could feel the engines fire. The whole craft shook very solidly. I thought lift-off would be gentle, since acceleration is low as you leave the pad. But there's an immediate surge that lets you know you're on the way.

I had preset the rear-vision mirror and could see the horizon turning as the vehicle rolled to the correct azimuth. In the capsule I could hear a muffled roar—the sound of the booster engines. As acceleration built up, vibration smoothed out.

Before the flight my backup, Scott Carpenter, said he thought it would feel good

WITH FINAL PREPARATIONS; GLEAMING 14-STORY GANTRY HOLDS STAGE CENTER AMID TITAN AND ATLAS MISSILE SERVICE TOWERS. JAMES M. GODDOLD

THE SPACECRAFT HE NAMED FRIENDSHIP; THE 7 REFERS TO AMERICA'S FIRST SEVEN SPACEMEN. TIME: 6:03 A.M.—3 HOURS, 44 MINUTES TO LIFT-OFF. BILL TAUB, NASA

to accelerate in a straight line rather than just in a circle as we were used to doing on the centrifuge. It did feel good. This time I knew it was for a purpose.

The rest of the powered flight phase—the cutoff of the booster engines, the jettison of the escape tower—functioned normally. When the fuel and liquid oxygen tanks are getting empty the Atlas apparently becomes considerably more limber than normal. You have the sensation of being out on the end of a springboard, as if the nose of the vehicle were waving back and forth. The noise also increased near the end of powered flight.

Then the sustainer engine cut off and acceleration dropped. I had a slight sensation of tumbling forward. As the spacecraft came around to its normal backward-facing attitude I could see the Atlas booster through the window. I kept it in sight for six or seven minutes while it traveled across the Atlantic. The last time I reported seeing it, the Atlas was approximately two miles behind and one mile below my spacecraft—a dark object against the bright background of earth. Earlier, it had been bright against a black background of space.

WEIGHTLESSNESS was pleasant. I felt fine as soon as the spacecraft separated from the Atlas. Every 30 minutes I went through a series of exercises to determine whether weightlessness was affecting me, to see if head movements produced nausea or vertigo. I felt no ill effects at all. I pulled on a bungee cord once a second for 30 seconds. It had the same effect on me that it has on the ground. It made me tired.

It seemed natural to take advantage of the weightless condition. One time I left a camera floating in midair while I at-

ATOP THE ROARING ROCKET *Glenn surges skyward from Cape Canaveral as watchers (opposite) push him up with their hearts. Space capsule is the dark cone; escape tower, not yet jettisoned, juts ahead. Though flame thunders below, the silver body of the Atlas remains frosted like a julep cup from super-cold liquid oxygen.*

tended to something else. I just parked it and went about my business and came back to it and it was still there.

I had brought along a number of instruments, stowed in a ditty bag by my right arm. Each piece of equipment had a three-foot line attached to it. By the time I started using the equipment, the lines had become tangled and got in the way.

Still, it was important to have some way of securing the loose gear, as I found out when I tried to change film. The film canisters weren't tied down. I left one floating in midair while I was working on the camera, and when I reached for it I accidentally hit it and it floated out of sight behind the instrument panel.

I ate in orbit to see whether there was any problem in consuming and digesting food in a weightless state. I took a xylose tablet over Africa, probably just about in the area where the National Geographic Society was investigating some of the oldest remnants of man (page 210). The tablet contained radioactive sugar which showed whether my body could digest food at zero g. Later I ate a tube of applesauce.

We joked before the flight about throwing all this stuff out and taking along a ham sandwich. I think we should try it.

CLOUDS COVERED much of the Atlantic, but western Africa was clear. In the Sahara I could plainly see dust storms and brush fires. Just off the east coast of Africa were two large storm areas. Weather Bureau scientists had wondered whether lightning could be seen on the night side. It certainly can. Within thunderheads it looks like flashing light bulbs surrounded by cotton.

Western Australia was clear. The lights of the city of Perth were on and I could see them very well—like flying at high altitude over a small town.

Coming out of night on the first orbit, I was checking instruments as the first glint of sunlight touched the capsule. When I glanced out the window I thought the capsule had tumbled. I could see nothing but stars.

I soon realized that I was in normal attitude and the capsule was surrounded by luminous particles, light yellowish-green

471

in color. It was like moving through a field of fireflies. They appeared to vary in size from a pinhead to possibly three-eighths of an inch, and they seemed to be about eight to ten feet apart.

I observed these particles for approximately four minutes each time the sun came up.

MOST OF THE AREA across Mexico and nearly to New Orleans was covered with high cirrus clouds. Across the United States I could see New Orleans, Charleston, and Savannah very clearly. I could also see rivers and lakes. The best view of any land area during the flight was the clear desert region around El Paso. I could see the irrigated area north of it. Off the east coast I could see across Florida and far back along the Gulf Coast.

Over the Atlantic I saw what I assume was the Gulf Stream. Different colors of the water were clearly visible. Over the recovery area I looked down at the water and saw a little V — probably the wake of a ship.

Sunsets were always slightly to my left, and I moved the spacecraft to get a better view. A black shadow moves across the earth until the whole surface is dark except for a bright band at the horizon. When the sun has gone down to the level of this bright band it seems to spread to each side of the point where it is setting.

I had expected that once the sun set, the light would close in immediately, but this was not the case. The band is extremely bright as the sun sets, but as time passes, the bottom layer becomes bright orange and fades to reds and finally off into blues and blacks.

Because of a malfunction at the end of the first orbit, I controlled the capsule manually for the last two orbits. And there was uncertainty as to whether the landing bag which fits between the heat shield and the basic spacecraft had been extended.

[EDITOR'S NOTE: *If the heat shield had come free, Glenn faced incineration in the heat of re-entry.*]

After dawn on the last orbit I prepared to fire the retrorockets. My attitude indicators were still in error, but I maneuvered the spacecraft to the right attitude by checking through the window and periscope. I received a countdown from the ground, and the rockets

SUNSET GILDS GLENN'S FACE *as he soars above the Indian Ocean near the midpoint of his 83,450-mile odyssey in space. An automatic camera photographed the astronaut every 12 seconds in orbit and 6 times a second during his climb and re-entry. The clock at right pegs each picture to the time in flight. The looping tube carries oxygen under pressure to inflate the visor seal.*

NASA

were fired on schedule off the California coast. I could hear each one fire and feel the surge as they slowed the capsule. Coming out of the zero-g condition produced the sensation of being accelerated back toward Hawaii.

Following retrofire, the decision was made to have me re-enter with the retropackage still on. I would have to perform manually a number of operations which are normally automatic during re-entry, but this was no problem. It was what we had trained to do. I brought the capsule to the proper attitude and retracted the periscope by pumping the lever.

As deceleration built up I could hear a noise like small particles brushing against the capsule. Then one of the straps that holds the retropackage on swung up in front of the window. I think that the explosive bolt which holds the straps together fired at that time.

It was no trouble to control the capsule manually through the high deceleration of re-entry. We've operated on the centrifuge at a 16-g level, and re-entry was a little less than 8 g's.

Communication was lost because of ionization due to heat. The fireball was very intense. Large flaming pieces of the retropackage broke off and flew past the window. This was of some concern, to put it mildly, because I wasn't real sure what they were. I had assumed that the retro-

474

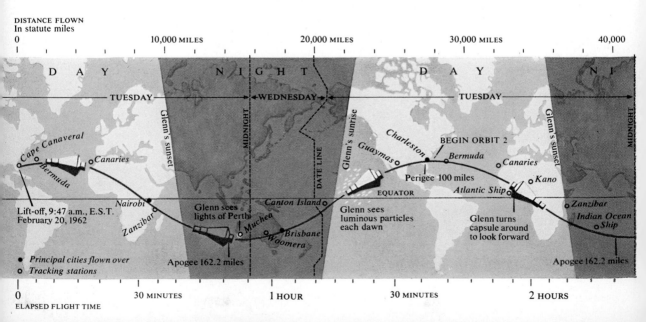

DISTANCE FLOWN
In statute miles

0   10,000 MILES   20,000 MILES   30,000 MILES   40,000

D A Y   N I G H T   D A Y   N I

TUESDAY   WEDNESDAY   TUESDAY

Glenn's sunset   MIDNIGHT   DATE LINE   Glenn's sunrise   Glenn's sunset   MIDNIGHT

Cape Canaveral   Charleston   BEGIN ORBIT 2
Bermuda   Guaymas   Bermuda
Canaries   Perigee 100 miles   Canaries
          Atlantic Ship   Kano
Lift-off, 9:47 a.m., E.S.T.   EQUATOR
February 20, 1962   Nairobi   Glenn sees   Canton Island   Glenn sees   Glenn turns   Zanzibar
          Zanzibar   lights of Perth   Muchea   luminous particles   capsule around   Indian Ocean
                    Brisbane   each dawn   to look forward   Ship
                    Woomera
• Principal cities flown over
○ Tracking stations   Apogee 162.2 miles   Apogee 162.2 miles

0   30 MINUTES   1 HOUR   30 MINUTES   2 HOURS
ELAPSED FLIGHT TIME

JOHN H. GLENN, JR., NASA. DIAGRAM BY IRVIN E. ALLEMAN AND ISAAC ORTIZ, BOTH NATIONAL GEOGRAPHIC STAFF

"A BEAUTIFUL, BEAUTIFUL SIGHT!" *Glenn exclaims, watching an orbital sunset (opposite) with brilliant colors and strange distortions. By day, he saw the Spanish Sahara (top) and the coast of Florida (lower) unreel beneath him. His flight took him three times from winter to summer (below) and shuttled him between Tuesday and Wednesday.*

Daylight areas of map are wider because Glenn's 900-mile view ahead and behind enabled him to see light on earth before sunrise and after sunset. Dark areas expand above equator, where winter makes nights longer than days.

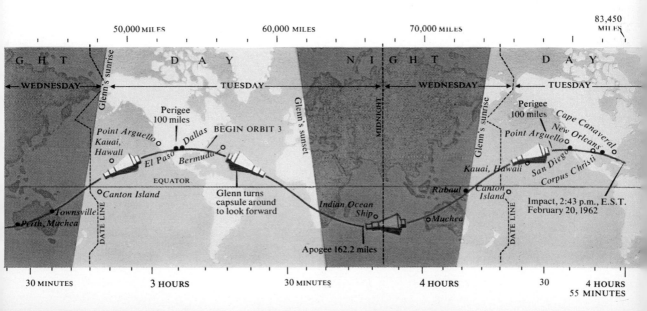

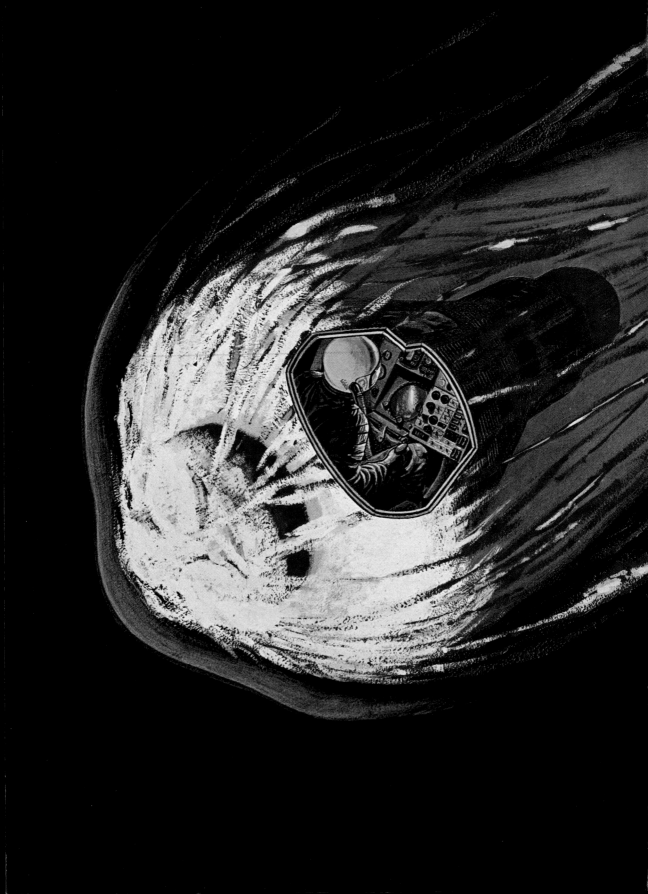

*Re-entry at 15,000 miles an
hour puts Glenn in a fireball.
Atmospheric shock wave glows
at 50,000° F., nearly five times as hot
as the sun's face. If the heat shield slips,
the astronaut will incinerate in seconds,
so his retropack is kept strapped on.
On-board tapes record the crucial moments:*

**Astronaut Wally Schirra from
California:** *John.... Leave your
retropack on through your
pass over Texas....*
Glenn: *Roger....*
Schirra: *Five, four, three, two,
one, fire!*
Glenn: *Retros are firing....
It feels like I'm going back
toward Hawaii!*
Schirra: *Don't do that! You
want to go to the East Coast....*
Texas Communicator: *We are
recommending that you leave
the retropackage on through
the entire re-entry....*
Glenn: *What is the reason for
this? Do you have any reason?*
Texas: *...This is the judgment
of Cape Flight....*
Alan Shepard, Cape Canaveral:
*....Recommend you go to
re-entry attitude....We are
not sure whether or not your*
*landing bag has deployed. We
feel it is possible to re-enter
with the retropackage on....*
Glenn: *Roger. Understand....*
Shepard: *We recommend that
you....* [*Shepard's voice fades;
a communications blackout
begins.*]
Glenn: *This is Friendship 7.
I think the pack just let go.
This is Friendship 7. A real
fireball outside.
Hello Cape. Friendship 7. Over.
Hello Cape. Friendship 7. Over.
Hello Cape. Friendship 7. Do
you receive? Over.*
Shepard: *....Loud and clear.
How are you doing?*
Glenn: *Oh, pretty good....
That was a real fireball, boy....
Drogue is out.... The drogue
looks good.... Chute is out...
beautiful chute. Chute looks
good.... Chute looks very good!*   477

pack had gone when I saw the strap in front of the window. So I thought these flaming chunks could be parts of the heat shield breaking off.

There was no doubt when the heat of re-entry occurred—at the same time as the fireball. But the heat didn't reach me for some time. I didn't feel particularly hot until I was getting down to about 80,000 feet. From there on down I was uncomfortably warm.

I was reaching for the switch to deploy the drogue parachute early in order to reduce the re-entry oscillations, when it deployed automatically and rapidly stabilized the spacecraft.

At 10,800 feet I could see the main parachute stream out behind me and fill partially. Then, as the reefing line cutters were actuated, it filled completely. The opening of the chute caused a jolt.

By the time I reached the water I was sweating profusely. I lay quietly in the spacecraft trying to keep as cool as possible. The temperature inside didn't seem to diminish, and it combined with the high humidity of the air being drawn in.

Once the destroyer Noa was alongside, the spacecraft was pulled part way out of the water to let the landing bag drain. During pickup, I received one good bump as the spacecraft swung against the side of the ship. It was the most solid jolt of the whole trip.

In orbit, I had actually hated to see the mission end. But it was very good to be on the deck of the Noa.

As a human experience, the mission defies description. No adjectives that I can think of are adequate to convey the feeling of all these things that I was able to see. All my life I've been what I guess you would call a sunset bug. I remember them as some folks do beautiful paintings. February 20, 1962, was a good day because I was permitted the luxury of four sunsets —the last one aboard ship.

Thanks to a team of thousands, it has been my privilege to take part in a historic adventure. I am extremely proud to accept this Hubbard Medal tonight (page 441), not only for myself but as a representative of all those others. I think I might liken myself to the visible part of an iceberg— it takes an awful lot that's out of sight to keep that little bit up on top showing.

HOME SAFE, *the capsule bobs in the Atlantic. Glenn's periscope peers from its door; a round dye marker stains the ocean.*

By now re-entry heat has turned the craft into a steam bath; the astronaut suffers his one period of discomfort.

A cable secures Friendship 7 *to the* Noa, *one of more than 20 recovery ships. Hauled aboard, Glenn blows his hatch off and eases out. An engineer salvages the ditty bag with Glenn's camera and other gear (opposite).*

Into the Future

*Man has scaled the highest peaks,
plumbed the ocean depths, orbited
in space; but challenges remain
on land, in the sea, and in the sky*

Now this book is ended. The deeds that lived again in its pages return once more to those treasured shelves where history stores her grandest memories. But the story of man's quest for knowledge and adventure has no foreseeable end. Truly, as Gardiner Greene Hubbard observed at the birth of the National Geographic Society, "the horizon of the unknown advances with us and surrounds us wherever we go."

We have scraped the patina of age that crusts the earth, revealing here and there the gold of history—the history of life—hidden within. Could we peel the world layer by layer like an onion, what lodes of precious knowledge would we mine!

We have dipped a tentative toe in the sea, that alien world that laps forever at our feet. But is it forever alien? Or will we learn someday to range its dark depths as boldly as we explore the most isolated reaches on earth.

We have poked a hesitant finger into the infinite fabric of space. Now, through the tiny rent, we can see what vast and endless journeys stretch beyond.

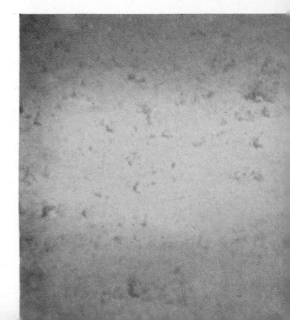

Land, sea, and sky—the brown, the green, and the blue of the National Geographic flag. Each element has yielded secrets to man's unremitting search for knowledge. Each element challenges man to unlock further mysteries. He will accept that challenge. In the words of the poet Robert Browning, "... a man's reach should exceed his grasp, or what's a heaven for?"

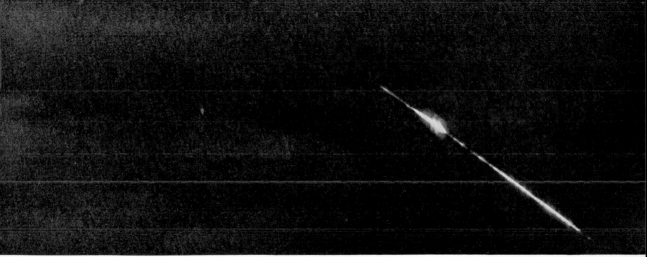

BLAZING ROCKET FROM CAPE CANAVERAL STREAKS ANTIGUA'S SKY; LUIS MARDEN, NATIONAL GEOGRAPHIC STAFF

AGELESS SENTINELS STAND WATCH ON A RIDGE OF CASTLE VALLEY, UTAH; BARRY C. BISHOP, NATIONAL GEOGRAPHIC STAFF

PRICKLY SEA URCHIN AND SPINDLY STARFISH 3,280 FEET DOWN IN THE PACIFIC OFF JAPAN; GEORGES S. HOUOT

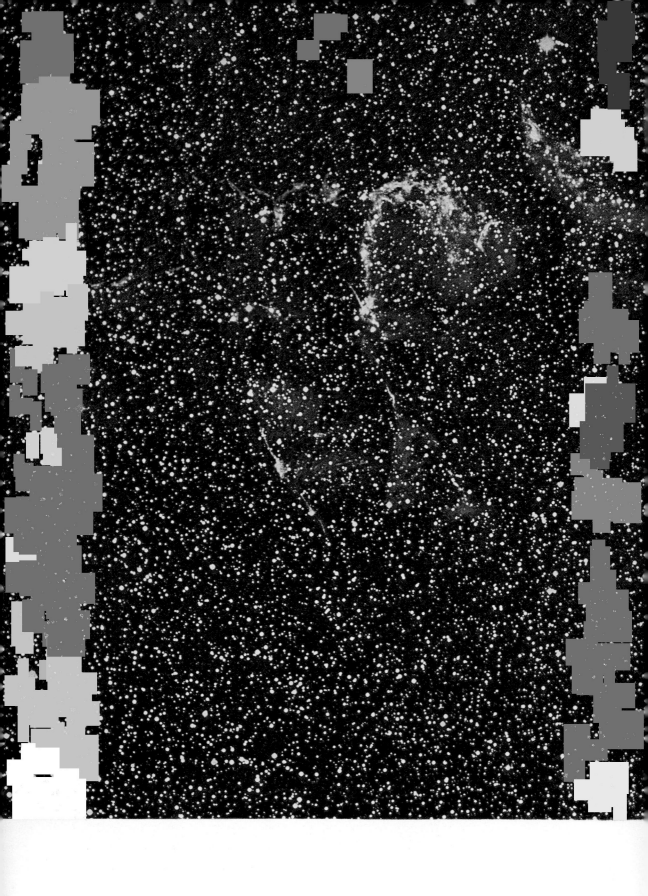

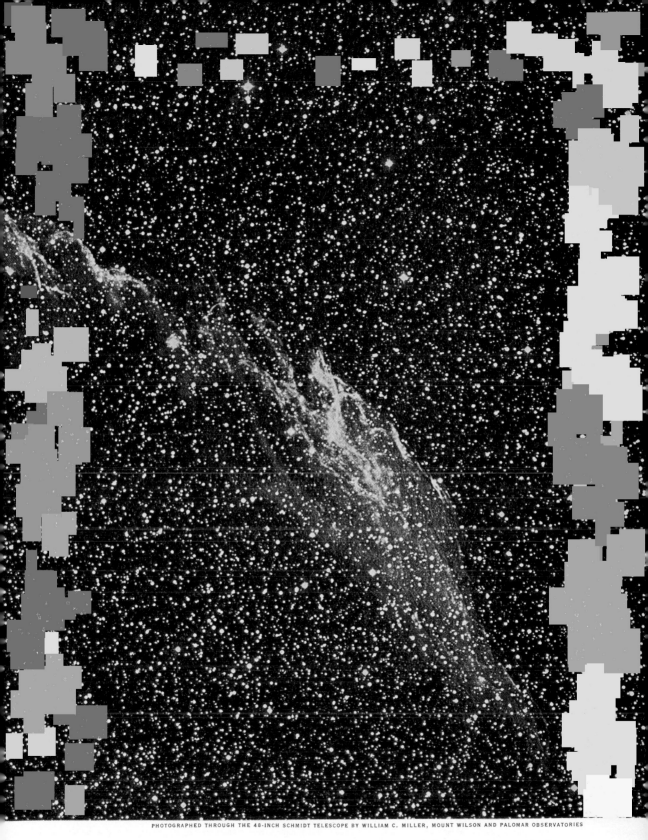

PHOTOGRAPHED THROUGH THE 48-INCH SCHMIDT TELESCOPE BY WILLIAM C. MILLER, MOUNT WILSON AND PALOMAR OBSERVATORIES

HEAVEN'S BLACK VAULT *reveals new splendors. Here, in one of the first natural color photographs of the night skies, the Veil Nebula in Cygnus, the Swan, tickles the face of the Milky Way with faint brush strokes of blue and red. The limitless horizon of the universe stirs man's unconquerable urge to explore and to understand.*

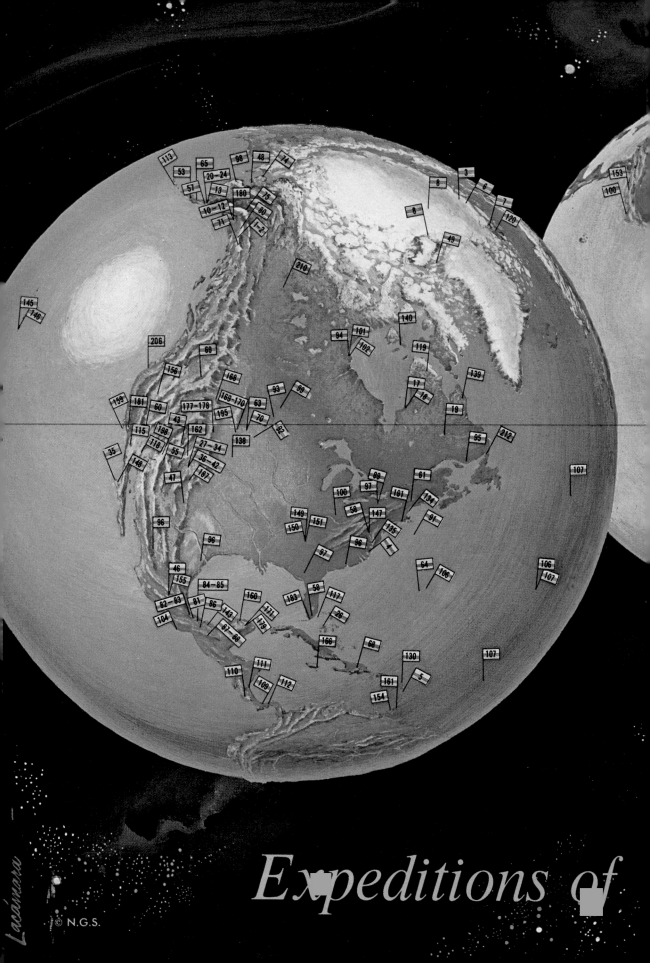

Expeditions of

Chronology of adventure and discovery

A key to the map of National Geographic expeditions and scientific researches

1 **2** In 1890, with U. S. Geological Survey, mapped Mt. St. Elias region, Alaska; discovered Mt. Logan, Canada's highest peak. Further exploration, 1891.

3 Aided the Walter Wellman Polar Expedition, 1898-9, which mapped Franz Josef Land and discovered new Arctic islands.

4 Society members sailed from Washington to Norfolk, Va., for solar eclipse, May 28, 1900.

5 Investigated the eruptions of Mont Pelée on Martinique and Soufrière on St. Vincent, 1902.

6 Directed scientific work of Ziegler Polar Expedition, 1903-5.

7 Provided chief scientist for Walter Wellman's effort to reach North Pole by dirigible, 1906-7.

8 Gave $1,000 to 1908-9 expedition of Robert E. Peary, first to reach North Pole, April 6, 1909.

9 Observed the effects of earthquake at Messina, Sicily, 1909.

10 – **12** Studied glaciers in Alaska, 1909, '10, '11, resulting in classic Tarr-Martin report.

13 With U. S. Geological Survey, scouted Mt. Katmai area, Alaska, after 1912 volcanic eruption.

14 – **16** With Yale University, supported excavation, in 1912, of lost city of Machu Picchu discovered by Dr. Hiram Bingham in Peruvian Andes; also his further explorations in Inca land, 1914, 1915.

17 – **19** Biological studies by Dr. W. E. Clyde Todd of Carnegie Museum, Pittsburgh, on Hudson Bay, 1912, '14; in Labrador, '17.

20 – **24** Discovered, named, and explored Valley of Ten Thousand Smokes, in Mt. Katmai region of Alaska, 1915-9; these expeditions, led by Dr. Robert F. Griggs, resulted in establishment of Katmai National Monument.

25 Assisted biological work of Dr. Frank M. Chapman, American Museum of Natural History, in Urubamba Valley, Peru, 1916.

26 Flamingos photographed by John Oliver La Gorce and Louis Agassiz Fuertes, Bahamas, 1920.

27 – **34** Acting on report of 1920 reconnaissance party to Pueblo Bonito in Chaco Canyon National Monument, N. M., sent expeditions led by Neil M. Judd of Smithsonian to excavate its communal dwellings, 1921-7. In 1963 backed publication of his final report.

35 Shared study of seals and other fauna of Baja California islands, 1922; two isles later set aside as wildlife reservations.

36 – **42** Tree ring studies under Prof. A. E. Douglass, University of Arizona, revealed age of Pueblo Bonito and other ruins, 1923-9.

43 Neil M. Judd explored prehistoric ruins of Utah between Colorado and San Juan Rivers, 1923.

44 Yünnan-Szechwan Expedition, 1923-4, led by Dr. Joseph F. Rock, explored river gorges and mountains of China.

45 Central China Expedition, led by Frederick R. Wulsin, collected plant and animal specimens, Inner Mongolia, 1923-4.

46 Ruins of Cuicuilco, Mexico, preserved by lava flows, studied 1924-5 by Dr. Byron Cummings.

47 Willis T. Lee, in 1924, mapped Carlsbad Caverns, N. M., leading to preservation as a national park.

48 Explored Alaskan coast in 1924, prior to proposed polar flight of dirigible *Shenandoah*.

49 MacMillan Arctic Expedition with U. S. Navy unit under Lt. Comdr. Richard E. Byrd made first extensive use of planes in Arctic exploration, 1925.

50 Helped Dr. C. G. Abbot of Smithsonian erect solar radiation observatory on Mt. Brukkaros, South-West Africa, 1925-9.

51 Dr. Joseph F. Rock explored holy mountains in the Tibetan borderlands of China, 1927-30.

52 Encouraged and helped finance Byrd Antarctic Expedition, 1928-30, which achieved man's first flight over South Pole and mapped by aerial photography 160,000 square miles of Antarctica.

53 Pavlof Volcano area, Alaska, explored by Dr. T. A. Jaggar, Jr., 1928, in amphibious vehicle.

54 Sponsored birdlife study in Venezuela, 1929-30, by Ernest G. Holt of Carnegie Museum.

55 Neil M. Judd excavated at Chavez Pass and three sites within Hopi reservation, Ariz., in 1929, seeking fragments to close gap in tree ring chronology.

56 Ernest G. Holt, with Brazilian-Venezuelan Boundary Survey, collected jungle creatures of South America, 1929-31.

57 Dr. Robert F. Griggs, 1930, studied revegetation of lands desolated by Katmai eruption.

58 Capt. A. W. Stevens made the first aerial survey of Latin American air routes, Washington-Buenos Aires-Chile, 1930.

59 Granted funds and the services of Dr. Maynard Owen Williams to Citroën-Haardt Trans-Asiatic Expedition, 1931-2, which blazed a 7,370-mile motor trail across Asia.

60 Scientific investigation in Death Valley, Calif., under Dr. Frederick V. Coville, 1931.

61 With U. S. Army, in 1932, photographed eclipse of sun and observed cosmic rays from an airplane five miles above Maine.

62 In 1933-5, supported the second Byrd Antarctic Expedition, which enlarged knowledge of topography of Ross Sea area.

63 National Geographic-U. S. Army Air Corps stratosphere balloon *Explorer I* in 1934 carried Maj. W. E. Kepner, Capt. Albert W. Stevens, and Capt. Orvil A. Anderson to 60,613 feet. Flight from South

166 Explored drowned city of Port Royal, Jamaica, submerged by a 1692 earthquake. Inventor Edwin A. Link led National Geographic-Smithsonian expedition, 1959.

167 With National Science Foundation, in 1959, helped Jocelyn Crane, N. Y. Zoological Society, continue study of fiddler crabs.

168 Cosponsored grizzly bear research of wildlife biologists Frank and John Craighead in Yellowstone National Park with Montana Cooperative Wildlife Research Unit since 1959.

169 170 With University of Wyoming and Smithsonian, carbon-dated early Indian artifacts at Agate Basin, Wyo., 1959 and '61.

171 Ceremonial chambers in Balankanche Cave, Mexico, yielded to Dr. E. Wyllys Andrews of Tulane University, in 1959, artifacts from A.D. 1100.

172 - 175 Supported, since 1959, the work of Dr. and Mrs. Louis S. B. Leakey, who had discovered *Zinjanthropus*, the tool-maker of 1,750,000 years ago, at Olduvai Gorge, Tanganyika. Continuing expeditions have found parts of an even older manlike creature, and at Fort Ternan, Kenya, remains of a primate of 14,000,000 years ago.

176 Backed the scientific researches of Barry C. Bishop, with Sir Edmund Hillary's Himalayan expedition, 1960-1.

177 178 Helped recover skeleton of a 5-ton mammoth found near Rawlins, Wyoming, in 1960-1, with tools and weapons of men who trapped it 11,000 years ago.

179 Maya Well of Sacrifice at Chichén Itzá, Mexico, explored in collaboration with Mexican Government and others, 1960-1.

180 In 1961 cosponsored Dr. Maynard M. Miller of Michigan State University remeasuring southeast Alaska glaciers surveyed in 1909-11 by Tarr and Martin.

181 Photographer - naturalist Frederick Kent Truslow studied rare California condor in 1961.

182 Dr. Edward S. Ross of Calif. Academy of Sciences collected insects in Pakistan, India, Southeast Asia, and Australia, 1961-2.

183 With the University of Miami Marine Laboratory, studying life among coral reefs near Key Largo, Florida, in program begun in 1961.

184 Recorded, 1961, life of cock-of-the-rock in British Guiana. Cosponsored with American Museum of Natural History this research by E. Thomas Gilliard.

185 186 Supported George Bass, Univ. of Pennsylvania Museum, in sea-bottom study, 1961-3, of a Byzantine ship wrecked 1,300 years ago off Yassi Ada, Turkey.

187 In re-evaluation of Sandia Cave, New Mexico, 1961-2, by Dr. George A. Agogino of University of Wyoming, carbon-14 dating confirmed human occupancy in Glacial Age.

188 Joined in survey by S. Frederick Starr of Persian Royal Road and other ancient routes in Anatolia, Turkey, 1961.

189 Assisted Jane Goodall in study of chimpanzees near Lake Tanganyika, Africa, 1961-3.

190 Enabled Dr. Harald Schultz of São Paulo State Museum to make ethnological expedition to Canoeiro Indians in Brazil, 1962.

191 Supported Roger Tory Peterson's experiments with artificial nesting sites in an effort to counter depletion of osprey in Connecticut River area, 1962.

192 Salvaged "knocked-down" Byzantine altar in Greek ship sunk off Syracuse, Sicily, in 6th century A.D. Edwin A. Link made 1962 recovery.

193 In special aluminum cylinder, Edwin A. Link and teammates, in "Man-in-Sea" project, 1962, spent up to 24 hours at depths to 200 feet in Mediterranean. Society aided project development, 1963.

194 Helped Dr. Kathleen M. Kenyon excavate, 1962-3, for earliest walls in Jerusalem.

195 Found early Indian artifacts at Hell Gap, Wyo., with Peabody Museum of Harvard, 1962-3.

196 Recorded Neolithic culture of Dani tribe, West New Guinea, with Peabody Museum, 1962.

197 Aided observations of rare hummingbirds in State of Espírito Santo, Brazil, by naturalist Dr. Augusto Ruschi, 1962.

198 Backed, in 1962, publication by Lowell Observatory of photographic survey of brighter planets, to be edited by Dr. E. C. Slipher.

199 With American Research Center in Egypt, excavated in 1963, ancient fortress and cemetery of Gebel Adda to be inundated by Aswan High Dam.

200 Aided American Museum of Natural History in collection and study, 1963, of meteorites and tektites in Australia.

201 As principal sponsor, backed glaciological and solar radiation programs of American Mount Everest Expedition which, in 1963, pioneered a West Ridge route and made the first traverse of the summit. Staff man Barry C. Bishop was one of six men who battled to Everest's crown.

202 In 1963 supported Woods Hole Oceanographic Institution research cruise in study of distribution and biology of tunas and other large pelagic fishes of central North Atlantic.

203 Richard D. Estes of Cornell studied the behavior of hoofed mammals in Africa, 1963.

204 Dr. Edwin Gould of Yale studied, 1963, echolocation in Madagascar's shrewlike tenrecs.

205 Helped Dr. Robert F. Heizer, Univ. of California, in archeological research in Andes, 1963.

206 Sponsored, in 1963, National Park Service ecological survey and conservation of California's giant coast redwoods.

207 Thomas P. Monath of Harvard studied herpetological specimens in French Guiana, 1963.

208 Cosponsored with N. Y. Zoological Society, 1963, exploration of northwestern extremity of Peru's Cordillera Vilcabamba.

209 Aided Cynthia Booth's study of primates in East Africa, 1963.

210 Joined with Douglas Aircraft Co. to make airborne observations of solar eclipse, July 20, 1963, over Canada.

211 Supported electronic search for tomb of Antiochus I of Commagene on Nemrud Dagh, Turkey, by Dr. Theresa Goell, 1963.

212 Helge Ingstad investigated archeological site of possible Norse origin at Lance aux Meadows, Newfoundland, 1963.

490

Medals Awarded by the Society

SINCE THEODORE ROOSEVELT presented the first National Geographic Society medal in 1906, eight other United States Presidents have similarly honored the Society. The Hubbard Medal, named for Gardiner Greene Hubbard, first President of the Society, is awarded for research, exploration, and discovery; the Gold Medal for achievement; the Grosvenor Medal for outstanding service to geography. The Jane Smith Award Medal accompanies life membership in the Society, given for contributions to geographic knowledge.

Comdr. Robert E. Peary – Hubbard Medal: Arctic explorations; Farthest North, 87° 06'. Presented by President Theodore Roosevelt, Dec. 15, 1906.

Capt. Roald Amundsen – Hubbard Medal: First traverse of Northwest Passage in a vessel; location of North Magnetic Pole. Presented by Vice President Charles W. Fairbanks, Dec. 14, 1907.

Comdr. Robert E. Peary – Special Medal of Honor: Discovery of the North Pole, April 6, 1909. Presented by Dr. Willis L. Moore, President, National Geographic Society, Dec. 15, 1909.

Capt. Robert A. Bartlett – Hubbard Medal: Attaining Farthest North, 87° 48', with Peary's 1909 expedition. Presented by James Bryce, Ambassador of Great Britain, Dec. 15, 1909.

Grove Karl Gilbert – Hubbard Medal: Thirty years of investigations and achievements in physiographic research. Dec. 15, 1909.

Sir Ernest H. Shackleton – Hubbard Medal: Explorations in Antarctic and Farthest South, 88° 23'. Presented by President William Howard Taft, March 26, 1910.

Capt. Roald Amundsen – Gold Medal: Discovery of the South Pole, Dec. 14, 1911. Presented by Rear Adm. Robert E. Peary, Jan. 11, 1913.

Col. George W. Goethals – Gold Medal: Directing completion of Panama Canal. Presented by President Woodrow Wilson, March 3, 1914.

Vilhjalmur Stefansson – Hubbard Medal: Discoveries in Canadian Arctic. Presented by Maj. Gen. Adolphus W. Greely, Jan. 10, 1919.

Lt. Comdr. Richard E. Byrd, Jr. – Hubbard Medal: First to reach North Pole by airplane. Presented by President Calvin Coolidge, June 23, 1926.

Floyd Bennett, Aviation Pilot, USN – Gold Medal: Flight to North Pole with Byrd. Presented by President Calvin Coolidge, June 23, 1926.

Col. Charles A. Lindbergh – Hubbard Medal: Solo flight from New York to Paris. Presented by President Calvin Coolidge, Nov. 14, 1927.

Hugo Eckener – Special Medal of Honor: First around-the-world navigation of an airship. Presented by Dr. Gilbert Grosvenor, President, National Geographic Society, March 27, 1930.

Rear Adm. Richard E. Byrd – Special Medal of Honor: Adding to knowledge of Antarctica; first attainment of South Pole by air. Presented by President Herbert Hoover, June 20, 1930.

Roy Chapman Andrews – Hubbard Medal: Geographic discoveries in Central Asia. Presented by Dr. Gilbert Grosvenor, March 13, 1931.

Amelia Earhart – Gold Medal: First solo transatlantic flight by a woman. Presented by President Herbert Hoover, June 21, 1932.

Anne Morrow Lindbergh – Hubbard Medal: Notable flights, as copilot, on the Charles A. Lindbergh aerial surveys. Presented by Dr. Gilbert Grosvenor, March 31, 1934.

Capts. Albert W. Stevens and Orvil A. Anderson – Hubbard Medals: Research achieved while gaining world altitude record of 72,395 feet in *Explorer II*, National Geographic Society-U. S. Army Air Corps Stratosphere Expedition. Presented by Gen. John J. Pershing, Dec. 11, 1935.

Lincoln Ellsworth – Hubbard Medal: Heroic and extraordinary achievements in Arctic and Antarctic exploration. Presented by President Franklin D. Roosevelt, April 15, 1936.

Dr. Thomas C. Poulter – Gold Medal: Achievements on Byrd Antarctic Expedition. Presented by Dr. Gilbert Grosvenor, April 27, 1937.

NORTH POLE DISCOVERER *Robert E. Peary presents the Society's Gold Medal to South Pole discoverer Roald Amundsen. Behind Peary stand British Ambassador James Bryce and Society President Henry Gannett. Hiram Bingham looks on from far left, French Ambassador J. J. Jusserand from right.*

Gen. H. H. Arnold—Hubbard Medal: Contributions to science of aviation. Presented by President Harry S Truman, Nov. 16, 1945.

Gilbert Grosvenor—Grosvenor Medal: Outstanding service to geography as editor of the *National Geographic,* 1899-1949. Presented by Dr. Charles F. Kettering, May 19, 1949.

Comdr. Donald B. MacMillan—Hubbard Medal: Arctic explorations, 1908-52. Presented by Dr. Gilbert Grosvenor, Jan. 9, 1953.

British Everest Expedition—Hubbard Medal: Conquest of earth's highest mountain. Sir John Hunt, leader. Sir Edmund Hillary and Tenzing Norkey reached the top. Presented by President Dwight D. Eisenhower, Feb. 11, 1954.

Mrs. Robert E. Peary—Gold Medal: Contributions to Admiral Peary's expeditions to North Greenland and Canadian Arctic, 1891-1909. Presented by Dr. Gilbert Grosvenor to her daughter, Marie Peary Stafford, May 6, 1955.

John Oliver La Gorce—Grosvenor Medal: Outstanding service to the increase and diffusion of geographic knowledge, 1905-55. Presented by Dr. Gilbert Grosvenor, Nov. 17, 1955.

Prince Philip, Duke of Edinburgh—Gold Medal: Promoting science and fostering better understanding among world's peoples. Presented by President Dwight D. Eisenhower, Oct. 18, 1957.

Dr. Paul A. Siple—Hubbard Medal: Scientific leadership of first group to winter at the South Pole; in recognition of 30 years of Antarctic explorations. Presented by Chief Justice of the United States Earl Warren, March 28, 1958.

U. S. Navy Antarctic Expeditions, 1955-9—Hubbard Medal: Exploring South Polar regions; establishing stations for International Geophysical Year. Presented by President Dwight D. Eisenhower to Secretary of the Navy Thomas S. Gates, Jr., Feb. 4, 1959.

Sir Vivian Fuchs—Hubbard Medal: Leadership of British Trans-Antarctic Expedition; contributions to geographic knowledge. Presented by President Dwight D. Eisenhower, Feb. 4, 1959.

Capt. Jacques-Yves Cousteau—Gold Medal: Giving to earthbound man the key to undersea exploration. Presented by President John F. Kennedy, April 19, 1961.

Dr. and Mrs. Louis S. B. Leakey—Hubbard Medal: Unearthing fossil bones of earliest man and giant animals in East Africa. Presented by Chief Justice Earl Warren, March 23, 1962.

Lt. Col. John H. Glenn, Jr.—Hubbard Medal: Contributions to scientific knowledge of the world and beyond as a pioneer in exploring the ocean of space. Presented by Vice President Lyndon B. Johnson, April 6, 1962.

Lyndon B. Johnson—Jane Smith Award Medal: Contributions to world understanding. Presented by Dr. Melville Bell Grosvenor, President, National Geographic Society, June 8, 1962.

American Mount Everest Expedition—Hubbard Medal: Contributions to geography through high-altitude research; conquest of earth's highest peak; pioneering a West Ridge route and making the first summit traverse. Norman G. Dyhrenfurth, leader. Presented by President John F. Kennedy, July 8, 1963.

WOODROW WILSON (*right*) *presented the Society's Gold Medal to Col. George Goethals in 1914 for completing the Panama Canal. The President characterized the National Geographic Society as a "custodian of the globe... about to honor a gentleman who has had the audacity to change the globe."*

WILLIAM McKINLEY (*below left*) *gave the young National Geographic Society presidential recognition in 1898 when he attended its reception in honor of Capt. Charles Sigsbee, commander of the ill-fated battleship* Maine. *Later that year the Society elected the Chief Executive to honorary membership.*

WILLIAM HOWARD TAFT (*left*), *former President of the United States and steadfast friend of the Society, served on its Board of Trustees from 1917 to 1930. One other Chief Executive joined the Board—Calvin Coolidge. He served from 1929 to 1933.*

PRESIDENT HARRY S TRUMAN *presents the Hubbard Medal to H. H. Arnold, first five-star General of the Air Force and a Trustee of the Society, for 34 years of service to the science of aviation.*

PARTICIPATING IN THE 1945 WHITE HOUSE CEREMONY ARE (FROM RIGHT) THOMAS W. McKNEW, ROBERT V. FLEMING, GILBERT GROSVENOR, AND (FAR LEFT) JOHN OLIVER LA GORCE; WIDE WORLD. ABOVE LEFT: LIBRARY OF CONGRESS. CENTER, TOP RIGHT, AND OPPOSITE: HARRIS & EWING

American Mount

WHITTAKER

HORNBEIN

UNSOELD

GOMBU

For nearly seven hours they battled upward, kicking steps, flirting with treacherous snow cornices, until at last they gained the summit. There, Whittaker planted Old Glory.

Triumph nearly turned into disaster on the descent. As the two climbers felt their way along a heavy cornice, a huge chunk broke away between them. "There I was," Whittaker reported, "looking between my legs at Tibet, 10,000 feet below." They crept down and stumbled into Camp VI, exhausted.

Now the expedition pushed a twin assault. William Unsoeld of Corvallis, Oregon, and Thomas Hornbein of San Diego, California, would tackle the untrodden West Ridge. National Geographic glaciologist Barry Bishop of Bethesda, Maryland, and Luther Jerstad of Eugene, Oregon, would follow Whittaker's trail. On May 22 the teams set out to rendezvous at the summit.

Bishop and Jerstad found the going rough. Once Bishop slipped off a sloping ledge—a diving catch by Jerstad saved him. On they slogged, through hours of tortured breathing. Finally, at 3:30 P.M., they sighted Whittaker's flag whipping in the wind. Unsoeld and Hornbein were nowhere in view. For 45 minutes the men made scientific observations and photographs atop the peak, then started back.

Unsoeld and Hornbein, meanwhile, had fought up a couloir, past rotten, downsloping slab rock to the West Ridge. They struggled to the top at 6:15 P.M. and 15 minutes later started down, making a historic first traverse of the summit. Following Bishop's and Jerstad's steps, they hurried in the deepening dusk, then lost the tracks among rocks. Their flashlight faded rapidly. They began to shout.

Some 400 feet below, Bishop and Jerstad heard the shouts. The temperature fell, and both felt their toes go numb. Still they waited two hours, shouting to guide the others down. At 9:30 Unsoeld and Hornbein emerged from the curtain of night.

Weakened by fatigue and lack of oxygen, the quartet groped down the knife ridge toward Camp VI. At 12:30 A.M. they dared go no far-

O N MAY 1, 1963, Big Jim Whittaker of Redmond, Washington, tied the National Geographic Society flag to his ice ax at 29,028 feet and held it aloft. For the first time an American stood on the crest of Mount Everest. For the first time the Society's banner fluttered atop the highest point on earth.

Whittaker's salute paid tribute to the Society for its vital support of the American Mount Everest Expedition. With 20 members, 37 Sherpas, and 909 porters, who packed in 27 tons of supplies and scientific equipment from Katmandu, Nepal, it was the largest expedition ever to challenge the mountain.

Under the leadership of Norman Dyhrenfurth of Santa Monica, California, the expedition early in 1963 moved up the Khumbu Glacier and established Base Camp at 17,800 feet. Scientific work shifted into high gear: studies of the glacier, the weather, and the bodies, minds, and behavior of men under stress.

Preparations for the assault continued. Sherpas and mountaineers leapfrogged supplies through camps placed a day's climb apart up the traditional South Col route. But not without a tragic note. Traversing the Khumbu Icefall, John Breitenbach of Jackson, Wyoming, died when an ice wall collapsed on him.

"The expedition was stunned," said Dyhrenfurth. "But there was no thought of giving up."

By the end of April, Camp VI was set up at 27,450 feet, and the first assault team made ready. On May 1, in 20°-below-zero temperature and 60-mile-an-hour winds, Whittaker and Sherpa Nawang Gombu struck out for the top.

Everest Expedition

JERSTAD

BISHOP

DYHRENFURTH

ther in the blackness. Oxygen cylinders long since emptied, they huddled on a sloping rock outcropping at 28,000 feet. With no shelter, they risked death from the elements.

Miraculously, the wind died. The calm lasted the night, but exposure to subzero cold in the highest bivouac in history took its toll. Bishop's, Unsoeld's, and Jerstad's toes froze.

In morning light, the men reeled down to Camp VI, fresh oxygen tanks, and safety.

In a hospital in Katmandu, Bishop pondered the lessons they had learned: "Everest is a harsh and hostile immensity. Whoever challenges it declares war. And when the battle finally ends, there are no victors and no vanquished. There are only survivors."

PRESIDENT JOHN F. KENNEDY *presents the National Geographic Society's Hubbard Medal to the American Mount Everest Expedition. Leader Norman G. Dyhrenfurth accepts on behalf of the triumphant climbers. Joining in the 1963 White House ceremony are (at left) Melville Bell Grosvenor, President of the Society, and Melvin M. Payne, Executive Vice President and Secretary.*

GEORGE F. MOBLEY (BELOW) AND BARRY C. BISHOP, BOTH NATIONAL GEOGRAPHIC STAFF

502